THE TAFT MUSEUM
Its History and Collections

THE TAFT MUSEUM

European and American Paintings

HUDSON HILLS PRESS · NEW YORK

First Edition
© 1995 by Taft Museum Publications, Inc.
All rights reserved. No part of this book may be reproduced or transmitted in any form or by any means, electronic or mechanical, including photocopying, recording, or any information storage and retrieval system, without permission in writing from Taft Museum Publications, Inc.

Published in the United States by Hudson Hills Press, Inc.,
Suite 1308, 230 Fifth Avenue, New York, NY 10001-7704.

Distributed in the United States, its territories and possessions, Canada, Mexico, and Central and South America by National Book Network.
Distributed in the United Kingdom and Eire
by Art Books International Ltd.
Exclusive representation in Asia, Australia, and New Zealand
by EM International.

For Hudson Hills Press

Editor and Publisher: Paul Anbinder

Copy Editor: Fronia W. Simpson

Proofreader: Lydia Edwards

Indexer: Karla J. Knight

Designer: Howard I. Gralla

Composition: U.S. Lithograph, typographers

Manufactured in Japan by Dai Nippon Printing Company

For the Taft Museum

Editor: Dr. Edward J. Sullivan

General Editor: Dr. Ruth Krueger Meyer, Director of the Taft Museum 1983–1993

Associate Editor: David Torbet Johnson,
Assistant Director / Curator of Collections, Taft Museum

Copy Editor: Catherine L. O'Hara, Publications / Press Officer,
Taft Museum

Photographers: Tony Walsh, Cincinnati, Ohio, and Anthony Lauro, Columbus, Ohio

The preparation of the manuscript for this publication
was supported in part by:
Two grants from the National Endowment for the Arts,
a federal agency;
The Corbett Foundation, Cincinnati, Ohio;
The Getty Grant Program, Santa Monica, California;
The Thomas J. Emery Memorial, Cincinnati, Ohio.

The paperbound edition of this publication was made possible with grants from The Procter & Gamble Fund and the National Endowment for the Humanities, a federal agency.

Library of Congress Cataloguing-in-Publication Data

The Taft Museum : its history and collections
Edward J. Sullivan, Ruth Krueger Meyer.—1st ed.
p.   cm.
Includes bibliographical references and indexes.
Contents: v. 1. Preface—v. 1, A. An introduction to the art collection of Charles Phelps and Anna Sinton Taft—v. 1, B. Introduction to the collection of European and American paintings in the Taft Museum—v. 2, C. European decorative arts at the Taft Museum—v. 2, D. The Taft collection of Chinese porcelains.
ISBN 1-55595-107-4 [v. 1, B].
1. Taft Museum—History. 2. Taft, Charles P. (Charles Phelps), 1843–1929—Art collections—Catalogues. 3. Taft, Anna Sinton, d. 1931—Art collections—Catalogues. 4. Art—Private collections—Ohio—Cincinnati—Catalogues. 5. Taft Museum—Catalogues. I. Sullivan, Edward J. II. Meyer, Ruth Ann Krueger. III. Taft Museum.
N550.5.T34   1994
708.171'78—dc20   94-16313 CIP

Contents

Director's Foreword

WORLD-CLASS ART, monumental architecture, social history, a domestic atmosphere—the variety that is the Taft Museum is reflected in the essays and illustrations that follow. Whether it is the history of domestic architecture and interior design from the Federal period through the 1920s; the story of a philanthropic couple who devoted their lives to art, music, and public education; the history of art from medieval Europe and the great dynasties of China through painting and sculpture of the early twentieth century—each area provides the reader and museum visitor with an exceptional experience that could not be had elsewhere.

This same variety of experience, which makes the Taft Museum a must for visitors to the city as well as a hometown favorite, brought me to the Taft, first as a member of the Taft Museum Committee and now as director. I am delighted that these volumes will permit even more people to share our love of this unique institution and am grateful to the many people who have made them possible.

The preparation of the manuscript for this catalogue was supported in part by two grants from the National Endowment for the Arts, a federal agency, which were matched by grants from the Corbett Foundation, Cincinnati, and the Getty Grant Program, Santa Monica, California. In addition, the Thomas J. Emery Memorial in Cincinnati provided a generous grant in support of color photography of the permanent collections.

During the ten-year period that the Taft Museum's staff has worked to compile this catalogue of the collections, the museum's administrative staff and advisory committee rose to the challenge of raising the necessary funds to publish these books. The hardbound edition has been made possible with generous grants from local philanthropic and corporate foundations, including the Louise Taft Semple Foundation; the Eleanora C.U. Alms Trust, Fifth Third Bank, Trustee; the Greater Cincinnati Foundation; the Robert and Adele Schiff Foundation; and the Ohio Valley Foundation. In addition, the Getty Grant Program, which had previously funded the preparation of the manuscript, continued to support this project by providing a second grant to help offset publication costs.

Members of the extended Taft family were instrumental in securing grants and contributed personally to this project. The management of the Taft Museum and the Cincinnati Institute of Fine Arts acknowledges the generous gifts made by Mr. and Mrs. John T. Lawrence, Jr., Mr. and Mrs. John T. Lawrence III, Mrs. Margo Tytus, Mr. and Mrs. Robert A. Taft II, and Mr. Seth C. Taft.

Two longtime members of the Taft Museum Committee and devoted patrons of the Taft Museum provided much needed advice and funding for this project: Dr. Martin and Dr. Carol M. Macht and Mr. and Mrs. John W. Warrington.

A separate fund-raising campaign was initiated to produce an economically accessible softcover edition of this research for the Cincinnati public. The paperbound edition of this catalogue was made possible with grants from the Procter & Gamble Fund and the National Endowment for the Humanities, a federal agency. We are grateful to both of these supporters for understanding and endorsing our desire to have these books readily available to our local audiences.

Phillip C. Long, DIRECTOR

Preface

For sixty years the Taft Museum has welcomed its visitors to the display of an international collection of fine arts objects housed in a landmark building. The people of Cincinnati, to whom by its charter the museum was given, as well as regional visitors and travelers from all over the world, have found here the personal collection of a local couple, Anna Sinton and Charles Phelps Taft, whose dedication to public enjoyment of the arts was manifested not only through the museum that bears their name but also through their many other philanthropies.

As the museum approached its sixtieth anniversary, the museum administration recognized the need for a comprehensive publication that would document not only the artistic treasures of the collection but also the motivations of our founders in creating an art museum. We felt that two perspectives on that activity would be required. To that end, we have endeavored to write a history of our museum that both the general audience and the scholar can use. We know that this publication, like all our public programs, must reach out to those in our potential audience who have either not yet visited us or not known of the museum's existence.

This catalogue supersedes a handbook published in the early years of our public history and subsequently reissued with slight revisions. Our goal has been to make a record of new expert opinions, informed by international research standards and presented in a style that our public can enjoy. From the outset we have planned to publish the catalogue in both hard- and paperbound editions. The latter edition is available in four separate volumes that give readers the opportunity to purchase them as their interests dictate. The first volume of this series tells the story of the successive residents of the Baum-Taft House and how it became a museum open to many visitors, even in the Tafts' lifetimes. This volume is followed by three more that focus on the separate fields of the collection—the paintings, the decorative arts, and the Chinese ceramics. Each is introduced by an essay that explains why the Tafts selected these rare and beautiful objects to decorate their home and enrich their lives.

To assist us in telling the story of the Taft Museum, we have selected a team of specialists who could verify the excellent quality of the majority of our holdings. Being truthful, they had also to tell us that certain paintings, porcelains, and pieces of jewelry, for example, must now be acknowledged as deliberate fakes, while others are genuine but only the product of a workshop and not from a master's hand. Glancing over the catalogue entries on every object we learn that the Tafts were, on the whole, fortunate in their purchases and that their mistakes were no greater or more frequent than the errors of judgment made by other collectors of their time (and since). The usefulness of such entries to the contemporary reader is that they may stimulate more careful investigation in personal collecting, while they should encourage the taking of an occasional risk on an unsigned but perfectly convincing work of art.

Furthermore, we asked our catalogue authors to explain to current audiences the significance of our collection within the context of the art-collecting practices of Americans in the first quarter of this century. The Tafts were by no means the only wealthy couple who could buy valuable things and endow public museums through their generosity, nor were they the richest. But occasionally they did make a purchase that earned them the envy of other great collectors.

In preparing this publication, we have also considered the growing public interest in historic preservation of both architecture and interior design. Thus, to the list of specialists in the fields of European old-master paintings, decorative arts, and Chinese ceramics we have added contributions from those who have studied the history of American architecture, furniture, and domestic decoration. The Taft Museum is rare for its combination of features: early-nineteenth-century American domestic architecture; examples of European and American interior furnishings and decoration, including unique mural paintings from the mid-nineteenth century; and the display of a world-famous collection of art works dating from about 1250 to 1906. The thoughtful integration of this ensemble has earned the Taft Museum its international reputation.

The research phase of the preparation of this publication has already prompted us to make many changes in the presentation and interpretation of our collections and our house to attract the new audiences that await us. Reevaluation of two fields, the Chinese porcelains and the European ornamented wares and watches, has led to displays that focus the viewer's attention more on aspects of their manufacture and decoration than was previously the case. The paintings will be reordered in the galleries to highlight some often overlooked masterpieces and to create chronological and stylistic groupings. And gallery renovations already underway are designed to enhance the federal-period atmosphere of the Baum-Taft house.

This publication is therefore more than an accumulation of scholarly detail—the factual matters of attribution and authenticity—although it certainly affirms the regard our professional colleagues have long shown our collections. The Taft Museum has always embodied the wisdom, vision, and capacity for enjoyment of the arts that our founders possessed. Their love of the arts and their further commitment to sharing the collection with the public has become the modern Taft Museum's mission, exemplified by these volumes. More than just a set of books, this catalogue offers us the opportunity to renew our faithfulness to Charles and Anna Taft's commitment to art and its role in public education.

Ruth Krueger Meyer, DIRECTOR

Acknowledgments

Over the course of more than a decade, many friends and colleagues have given unstintingly of their advice and encouragement toward the making of this publication. As in any attempt to express thanks for a project of this magnitude, some names will inadvertently be omitted, but it is hoped that everyone who participated in even the smallest way will feel recompensed by seeing the work accomplished.

For myself, the organization of the publication was done in payment of the debt one owes one's mentor for the inspiration that shapes and guides one's career. Professor Fred Licht, Boston University, was among the first to hear of my appointment as director of the Taft Museum in 1983. During our subsequent phone conversation, we discussed the need for a new catalogue of the museum's collections, and he signed on as editor. Although Licht was later forced to withdraw from his editorial role, his appointed successor, Dr. Edward J. Sullivan, professor of art history at New York University, carried through with dedication and enthusiasm.

Of singular importance to the success of our publication has been the participation of Paul Anbinder, president of Hudson Hills Press, New York. As our publisher, Anbinder endorsed our decision to set the highest standards for the project, and he steadfastly retained and reinforced that commitment. He brought to the publication the sensitive editorial skills of Fronia W. Simpson, whose challenges to our scholars burnished their entries and resolved many issues of documentation.

Through the participation of our team of scholars, the significance of this publication for the museum was greatly magnified. Their visits to Cincinnati for research and public lectures afforded our staff opportunities to examine objects in the collection with them, hear their musings, and thereby profit from their experience. Many of them have since provided consultation on a variety of topics ranging from conservation to exhibitions and interpretation. Collectively, they have helped to reshape our education program and gallery installations.

Several museum colleagues and independent scholars deserve special recognition for their assistance in identifying writers for the European decorative arts. Olga Raggio, chair of the department of European sculpture and decorative arts at the Metropolitan Museum of Art, New York, sagely guided our selection of members of her department to write various entries in this difficult area of connoisseurship. Winthrop Kelly Edy, New York, identified his colleague Jonathan Snellenburg as the appropriate expert for the Taft Museum's collection of watches.

Special praise and gratitude must be expressed for the efforts of the Taft Museum staff and members of the Taft Museum Committee who have been involved in this catalogue. Assistant Director/Curator of Collections David Torbet Johnson seconded the project in every conceivable way, from fund-raising through endless research in support of scholars. He took up recalcitrant objects that would not disclose the secrets of their manufacture and matured his own scholarship in the process. With the death of Anthony Derham, Johnson, working in collaboration with Anthony du Boulay, completed the section of this catalogue devoted to Chinese ceramics and works of art. These tasks were done while Johnson simultaneously served as registrar and participated in every facet of curatorial and administrative work at the museum.

Catherine L. O'Hara joined the museum staff primarily to copyedit the scholars' manuscripts. She has remained as publications editor and press officer and has written essays for other museum publications. O'Hara has been relentless in her determination to deliver a perfect manuscript, and the reader will greatly benefit from her sensitivity and attention to detail. Abby S. Schwartz assisted with the laborious process of searching for and identifying all the photographic illustrations and preparing their captions while meeting her responsibilities as curator of education. Tony Walsh joined the museum's staff as photographer during the preparation of this catalogue. He has photographed with a sensitive eye nearly every object in the collection as well as most installations. Anthony Lauro, Columbus, Ohio, also provided photographs for this catalogue, including the Duncanson murals.

Among the members of the Taft Museum Committee who showed constant concern for the welfare of the catalogue, I must thank Dr. Carol M. Macht, curator emerita of the Cincinnati Art Museum; Anne Lawrence, great-granddaughter of the museum's founders; Phillip C. Long, my successor as director of the Taft Museum; Robert Stautberg, chairman of the committee; and Sallie Wadsworth, secretary/treasurer.

Because this publication is divided into four sections representing the history of the museum and its collections, special recognition must be given to outside readers and other consultants for each field. Section one, *The History of the Collections and the Baum-Taft House*, benefited from consultation with Heather Hallenberg, former curator of education at the Taft Museum; William Seale, Washington, D.C.; Elizabeth Tuttle and Walter Langsam, Cincinnati; Dr. Zane Miller, professor of history at the University of Cincinnati; Kenneth Trapp, curator of crafts and decorative arts, The Oakland Museum, California; Jayne Merkel, New York; and Colin Streeter, New York.

Section two, *European and American Paintings:* Dr. John H. Wilson, curator of paintings and sculpture, Cincinnati Art Museum; Dr. Gabriel Weisberg, department of art history, University of Minnesota, Minneapolis; Dr. Robert L. Herbert, department of art history, Yale University, New Haven, Connecticut; Madeleine Fidell-Beaufort and Robert Hellebranth, Paris; and Dr. Martha Wolff, curator of European painting before 1750, The Art Institute of Chicago.

Section three, *European Decorative Arts:* Yvonne Hackenbroch, London; Dr. James Draper and Clare Le Corbeiller, curators of European sculpture and decorative arts, The Metropolitan Museum of Art; Hugh Tait, keeper, Waddesdon Bequest, British Museum, London; Anna Somers Cocks, editor-in-chief, *Art Papers*, London; Charles Truman, Christie's, London; Madeleine Marcheix, director emerita, Musée Municipal de l'Evêché, Limoges; Véronique Notin, director, Musée Municipal de l'Evêché; Doreen Stoneham, Research Laboratory for Archaeology and the History of Art, Oxford, England; and Otto C. Thieme, curator of costume and textiles, Cincinnati Art Museum.

Section four, *Chinese Ceramics and Works of Art.* Sheila Keppel, Oakland; Dr. Stephen Little, curator, Asian art, Honolulu Academy of Arts; Dr. Julia B. Curtis, Williamsburg, Virginia; Terese Tse Bartholomew, curator of Indian art, Asian Art Museum of San Francisco; Suzanne Valenstein, research curator of Asian art, The Metropolitan Museum of Art; and Ellen Avril, associate curator of Far Eastern art, Cincinnati Art Museum.

Ruth Krueger Meyer

Editor's Introduction

AT A TIME when art exhibitions have taken the form of media events, and great attention is paid to the enormous prices paid for pictures, some scholars and the public often seem to neglect the permanent collections of museums. Among the basic tasks of the art historian are the study, interpretation, and categorization of works of art so that others can carry out further analytical research. Catalogues of the permanent collections of museums are indispensable for both experts and members of the interested general public. For historians to do their work, they must know not only the location of works of art but also such empirical facts as to their size, media, date, and provenance. The bringing together of such material and extending its significance with historical interpretation should result in a catalogue that serves as a point of departure for a broader historical network of ideas.

Now, when the emphasis of art-historical publication appears to be weighted toward the explication of theoretical aspects of art, the essential labor of cataloguing is not given the credit it deserves. The rewards of such projects, however, are obvious. This catalogue of the Taft Museum is the result of over six years of intensive work on the part of thirty authors and additional experts who have served as consultants. Virtually every aspect of the museum is covered in its pages, from the history of the house and the acquisition habits of the Taft family to an examination of the myriad paintings, sculptures, and decorative-arts objects in the collections.

The Taft Museum, one of the outstanding small museums in the United States, possesses a collection that, in many areas, rivals those of the great artistic institutions both in this country and abroad. As with all significant personal collections such as those of Henry Clay Frick, Isabella Stewart Gardner, or Archer Milton Huntington, specific patterns of acquisition have lent a definite personality to the Taft collection. The Tafts, for instance, had a special fondness for Dutch and Flemish old-master paintings, nineteenth-century French landscapes, and Chinese porcelains. Their affection does not mean they neglected other areas. A strength of the Taft Museum is its eclecticism (typical of collections formed by nineteenth- and early-twentieth-century buyers of art), which provides the visitor (and the reader of these volumes) with a wealth of visual material concerning many periods of time, numerous nations, and a wide variety of manifestations of artistic sensibility.

In its earlier years, the Taft Museum benefited from the care and intelligence of Walter Siple, who served as the institution's first director. Under his aegis, an initial catalogue was published in 1939. In 1958 it was updated with information on provenance and exhibitions provided by Katherine Hanna, the museum's second director. This handbook provided a useful guide for visitors to the Taft for many years. In 1983 Ruth Krueger Meyer, the third director, envisioned an ambitious cataloguing project with full scholarly apparatus for every object in the museum. I was honored to be invited to be the editor of this catalogue and have learned a great deal about the collection in the process. But, more importantly, working with the material and consulting with the authors have expanded my understanding of many facets of the history of art. The all-embracing scope of the catalogue will certainly have a similar effect on its readers. We hope that the catalogue, through its wide-ranging discussions of numerous artistic phenomena, will not only serve to deepen the public's knowledge of what is contained within the walls of the Taft Museum but also stimulate thought and curiosity about the very nature of artistic expression.

Edward J. Sullivan
New York University

THE TAFT MUSEUM

EUROPEAN
AND AMERICAN
PAINTINGS

Introduction to the Collection of European and American Paintings in the Taft Museum

Edward J. Sullivan

The European and American paintings in the Taft Museum cannot be called a comprehensive collection, yet they do represent consistent standards of connoisseurship. This fairly large grouping of works by both major masters and lesser-known figures reflects the taste of a large proportion of American collectors during the late nineteenth and early twentieth centuries.

The Tafts chose paintings with secular subjects, predominantly landscape and portraiture. They did not buy paintings with mythological, historical, or religious subjects, nor did they buy many examples from either countries or periods in which such themes predominated. This was a common practice in the United States in the nineteenth century. Most of the great collectors were Protestants and thus not emotionally in sympathy with the subject matter of the Catholic countries as it had developed in the Renaissance and baroque periods. The collectors' conservative aesthetic also accounts for their preference for Barbizon and Hague School pictures. These were predominantly landscapes and did not display the types of subjects (for example, mythological themes that were likely to depict nude figures) that were more common in the works of the academic masters. Thus, there is virtually no Italian painting in the collection; Renaissance and baroque art of France, Flanders, and Spain are also absent. Seventeenth-century Dutch painting, however, forms a concentration, and the Tafts were able to assemble an impressive group of pictures that attests to the wide variety of subjects cultivated by the painters of baroque Holland. The eighteenth century is represented principally by a group of English portraits. In their purchases of more modern art, the Tafts tended to eschew the avant-garde, preferring images that reflect timeless values, such as the harmony between humanity and nature. This preference is seen, for example, in their choice of nineteenth-century pictures. Among French masters, the more conservative members of the Barbizon School were favored over the impressionists. The Hague School was composed of artists active during the last decades of the century in Holland who displayed strong affinities with both their French Barbizon contemporaries and the Dutch baroque masters of land- and seascape. Although the inherent drama of Spanish painting would appear inimical to the collecting impulses of the Tafts, they did purchase two portraits by followers of Goya and commissioned several others by fashionable Spanish artists of their own day. This introduction will attempt to offer a general overview of the various categories of paintings in the collection and will highlight some of the outstanding works.

Dutch painters of the seventeenth century were, for the most part, specialists in a single subject — portraiture, landscape, marine painting, cityscape, still life, or scenes of peasant life. Rembrandt was one of the few artists of his generation successfully to bridge the gaps among many of these themes, always imbuing his subjects with his special stamp of genius. There is often a surprising element in Rembrandt's paintings, as is the case with the Taft Museum's splendid *Portrait of a Man Rising from His Chair* (see 1931.409, p. 153), a work that is dated 1633. The subject, exuding an air of wealth and success, does not merely stand and face the viewer but is caught in a moment of action. He rises and gestures across space to direct the viewer's attention to the companion picture of his wife (New York, The Metropolitan Museum of Art). Scholars have cited the Taft picture as one of the most important Rembrandt portraits of its period.

The 1630s was also a time of great productivity for another of Holland's most outstanding portraitists, Frans Hals. The Taft Museum possesses three paintings by Hals: *Portrait of a Seated Man Holding a Hat* (see 1931.451, p. 143); its pendant, *Portrait of a Seated Woman Holding a Fan* (see 1931.455, p. 145); and the earlier *Portrait of a Man* (see 1931.450, p. 141), which is the most significant of the three. The subject of this last portrait (which can be dated to the mid-1630s) was previously thought to be Michiel de Wael, one of the men portrayed in Hals's group portrait of the Saint George Militia Company (1627; Haarlem, Frans Halsmuseum). We can no longer be certain of the subject's identity, but his high social status is indisputable. In this three-quarter-length view, he stands, one hand on his hip and the other holding a glove. The nonchalant elegance of this work might remind the viewer of portraits by Anthony van Dyck, yet the characteristic thick, spontaneous brushwork of Hals marks this, a major monument of his career from the 1630s, as a product of his distinct artistic personality.

Along with Jan Vermeer, Pieter de Hooch ranks as one of the most important Dutch genre painters of the seventeenth century. His *Woman with a Cittern and a Singing Couple at a Table* (see 1931.395, p. 175), which can be dated to the late 1660s, offers a glimpse of contemporary upper-class surroundings with their restrained yet richly appointed furnishings. The harmony of this classicizing interior is underlined by the musical harmonies produced by the three figures in the painting. Other Dutch genre paintings in the collection include scenes of people on a more modest rung of the social ladder, such as the figures in two works by Adriaen van Ostade (*Interior of an Inn with Three Men and a Boy* [see 1931.400, p. 148] and *An Old Toper* [see 1931.420, p. 149]), as well as those in one of the many representations in Dutch art of the doctor's visit (see 1931.396, p. 172), this one by Jan Steen.

Jacob van Ruisdael is judged by many scholars to be the foremost Dutch baroque landscapist. He executed a wide variety of evocative country and seaside scenes and is represented in the Taft collection by *Farmhouses on a High Road* (see 1931.391, p. 164). One of Van Ruisdael's most gifted pupils, Meyndert Hobbema, a painter from Amsterdam, specialized in woodland scenes. The museum's *Farmland with a Pond and Trees* (see 1931.407, p. 166) is an outstanding example of the contribution of this painter. Dated to the mid-1660s, it presents a screen of trees to the left and farm buildings to the right, with several herdsmen and a woman in the center and to the left of the composition. These figures and the animals may have been painted by Adriaen van de Velde.

Most of the major masters of eighteenth-century British portraiture are represented in the Taft collection; among them are Thomas Gainsborough, Joshua Reynolds, John Hoppner, and Henry Raeburn. Their works provide a representative cross section of the various trends of portraiture during this period. Thomas Gainsborough, who began his career by studying with the French rococo graphic artist Hubert Gravelot, had established himself as an independent portraitist by 1750, first at Sudbury and later at Ipswich, Bath, and London. He was a founding member of the Royal Academy, where he exhibited until disputes with other members arose over the hanging of his pictures. He was always interested in landscape and was especially influenced by Dutch baroque painting (particularly the works of Jacob van Ruisdael and Jan Wynants). Later in his life he executed picturesque seascapes and genre paintings (or "fancy pictures," as they are usually called) in the manner of Murillo. The Taft's portrait, *Edward and William Tomkinson* (ca. 1784; see 1931.412, p. 182) is a particularly important example of the artist's late work and one that evidences his extraordinary expertise in integrating figures into a seemingly untamed landscape setting. There is, in addition, a sense of sweetness and fraternal devotion present that makes this work exceptionally appealing. This painting was probably among those that figured in Gainsborough's final dispute with the Royal Academy in 1784, when he removed all his submissions before the opening and never exhibited there again. Another painting by Gainsborough, the bust-length portrait of *Maria Walpole, Countess Waldegrave, Duchess of Gloucester* (see 1931.406, p. 181), may have been cut down from a full-length portrait. It has darkened with age, possibly owing to the artist's use of bitumen in emulation of the chiaroscuro technique of Sir Joshua Reynolds.

Reynolds, unlike Gainsborough, flourished in the atmosphere of the academy; he became the first president of the Royal Academy in 1768 and, from 1769 until 1790, delivered yearly discourses on art, which had great theoretical and practical impact on the artists of his day. He spoke enthusiastically of the achievements of the masters of the Renaissance and the baroque past, although in his own art he rarely strayed beyond the confines of portraiture. Among the many innovations he introduced to the usually staid portrait is the extremely convincing and naturalistic portrayal of children, which is especially well observed in the Taft Museum's portrait *Mrs. John Weyland and Her Son John* of 1776 (see 1931.491, p. 184), in which the boy squirms and bounces with a freedom and delight rarely seen in earlier art. It is this aspect of Reynolds's art that connects him with some of his Continental contemporaries, such as Boucher, Greuze, or Carle van Loo.

One of the many artists who emulated the ideals of Reynolds's style was John Hoppner; he was trained at the Royal Academy and first exhibited there in 1780. He became full academician in 1795 and was appointed portrait painter to the Prince of Wales in 1792, thus assuring his financial security and fashionable reputation. In the end, however, he was not as appreciated as his rival Sir Thomas Lawrence, who was appointed Painter to the King, also in 1792. The museum's portrait *Catherine Horneck Bunbury* of about 1780 (see 1931.403, p. 188) represents one of the celebrated beauties of London of her day. Catherine and her sister, Mary, frequented literary and artistic circles and are affectionately referred to in some of the verses of Oliver Goldsmith. This painting has an air of decorous informality, which is characteristic of many of Hoppner's portraits of women; yet the artist's setting of the subject against a broad sky also hints at monumentality.

A similar monumentality is evident in the work of another British artist who fell under the influence of Reynolds, Henry Raeburn, one of the great names of Scottish eighteenth-century portraiture. His works, especially those from the later portion of his career, exhibit a great sense of sculptural stability and even severity, coinciding with the neoclassical sentiments of the times. Such a work is the portrait *Jane Fraser Tytler* of about 1810 (see 1931.424, p. 195). Done in Raeburn's soft style, the painting has little precise detail except for the solidly drawn head placed close to the picture plane. Little is known of the sitter except that she was the daughter of a well-known professor of history at the University of Edinburgh who published several important accounts of his travels to the Himalayas and other exotic locales.

The principal treasures of nineteenth-century British painting in the Taft Museum are two oil paintings and numerous watercolors by the greatest of all English romantic artists, J. M. W. Turner. The two oils, *The Trout Stream* of 1809 (see 1931.459, p. 197) and *Europa and the Bull* of 1840–50 (see 1931.442, p. 199), are major monuments from both the early and the late phases of Turner's career. The former portrays the flow of the River Dee in Wales and evidences, with its dark colors and use of the seventeenth-century landscape formula of coulisses receding along a river into the distance, the artist's admiration for baroque painting. One of Turner's most ambitious oils, it has figured in many important exhibitions, including the 1857 *Manchester Art Treasures* show, a large exhibition of works of art from private and public collections. *Europa and the Bull* is one of a series of eleven related canvases by Turner. Based on a mezzotint engraving from the artist's *Liber Studiorum* of 1806–19, it depicts the moment when Europa, daughter of the king of Tyre, is abducted by Zeus, who has turned himself into a white bull. Possibly following Reynolds's dictum that history painting was the noblest form of art, Turner (in the manner of Richard Wilson) dignified the landscape setting with a classical subject.

Victorian Renaissance painters also regularly employed classical themes. For example, Lawrence Alma-Tadema, a Dutch artist who acquired British citizenship, was absorbed by a desire to reconstruct the archaeological past in his art. The Taft Museum's late work by him, *A World of Their Own* (1905; see. 1931.392, p. 220) depicts a pair of lovers in a classical Mediterranean genre scene. Although this mildly erotic dalliance takes place in an ancient setting, the models are recognizably of their own time, that is, Victorian and English.

Returning to the eighteenth century in other countries, we see that it was a period of great internationalism in art, as painters and sculptors traveled more widely than ever before and knowledge of stylistic developments spread from one country to another with great rapidity. Spain, for example, witnessed dramatic artistic changes. The baroque severity of Diego Velzáquez, Francisco Zurbarán, and others was replaced by styles based on the contributions of Italian, French, and German artists like Giovanni Battista Tiepolo, Corrado Giaquinto, Louis Michel van Loo, Jean Ranc, and Anton Raphael Mengs, all of whom worked at the court in Madrid during the eighteenth century. Spain's greatest master of this period was Francisco de Goya. Although his early work presents an amalgam of the reigning rococo styles, he developed, especially after the early 1790s, a manner of unmistakable singularity. Goya was well known for his genre, religious, historical, and mythological paintings and for his numerous prints, but his portraits assured his fame in his own time. He was portraitist to three Spanish monarchs and their families and created many unforgettable images of political and intellectual leaders of his own country as well as of France and England. Portraits of his friends from all levels of society evidence an intimacy and psychological penetration not often present in his official commissions. Goya's portraiture had a strong impact on contemporary Spanish and non-Spanish painters.

The Taft Museum collection contains two works by anonymous followers of Goya portraying subjects that the master himself had painted on several occasions. In 1800 Goya began work on the famous portrait of *The Family of King Charles IV* by making sketches of the king, Queen María Luisa, and their children. Many of these sketches are lost, but some survive in what are certainly excellent copies. The Taft Museum's portrait *Queen María Luisa* (see 1931.446, p. 223) very likely represents either a replica of a lost Goya sketch or possibly a painting done after the group portrait was finished. Although the painting is not by Goya himself, the lively personality of the sitter, brilliantly evinced by Goya in the group portrait, is amply reflected by the anonymous creator of this work. Goya, a great aficionado of the bullfight and maybe even while still a young man a participant in amateur *corridas*, produced a number of bullfighting scenes in his paintings and prints as well as several important portraits of bullfighters. One of these was of Pedro Joaquín Rodríguez, called Costillares (see 1931.393, p. 226). Goya's original portrait of him may be lost, but its popularity is affirmed by the numerous copies in public and private collections in Spain and elsewhere. Although the Taft portrait of Costillares does not have the high quality of a Goya likeness, it is nonetheless a pleasing portrait and an important historical document of the esteem in which Goya's depictions of popular heroes were held.

Spanish portraiture from the eighteenth century to the present owes an inevitable debt to the great masters of the baroque age, especially to Diego Velázquez. In the Taft collection, three examples of Spanish portraiture from the early twentieth century continue the tradition of this great master. Joaquín Sorolla's portrait of William Howard Taft (1909; see 2.1931, p. 232) captures the open, engaging personality of Charles Phelps Taft's half-brother, who was painted in the White House while he was president of the United States. The deep, rich colors and the stately bearing of the sitter make this work a link in the chain of Spanish master portraits stretching back to the baroque period and earlier. Charles Phelps and Anna Sinton Taft were painted by another Spaniard whose fame as a portraitist reached well beyond the confines of his native country (see 3.1931, 4.1931, pp. 230 and 231). Raimundo de Madrazo was known as a portrayer of Spanish, French, and American high society of the late nineteenth and early twentieth centuries. His pictures are brilliant combinations of tour-de-force brushwork and a pleasing informality that nonetheless perfectly suggest the social, literary, or political station of the sitter.

Several of the most important artistic movements of nineteenth-century France are represented in the Taft Museum collection. The neoclassical phase of French painting is embodied by the portrait *Mademoiselle Jeanne Gonin* painted by J.-A.-D. Ingres in 1821 (see 1931.414, p. 235). Having spent both time in the studio of Jacques-Louis David and many years in Italy, Ingres's narrative paintings reflect the archaeological accuracy that audiences in the age of neoclassicism craved. From his early pencil drawings to his mature portrait canvases, Ingres's likenesses of well-known members of fashionable society and political circles were in great demand. Mlle Gonin is represented in a somewhat severe image compared with other paintings by Ingres, in which a wealth of jewelry and elegant clothing is often displayed. The demureness of the subject's dress may reflect her Swiss Calvinist background.

One of the many manifestations of the romantic spirit among artists in France and throughout the Continent was the desire to evoke earlier historical moments as well as exotic (often oriental) settings. Romantic artists continued the neoclassical interest in situating their subjects in historical surroundings. However, instead of depicting the antique past, the romantics were more interested in the medieval and Renaissance periods. The Taft Museum contains several important examples of both historical genre and orientalist scenes by nineteenth-century artists. Jean-Louis-Ernest Meissonier was known for his pictures of military life and for small, highly detailed historical genre pictures based on the seventeenth-century Dutch "little masters" such as Gerard Dou and Gerard ter Borch. To the latter category belongs the Taft Museum's *Les Trois Amis* (*The Three Friends*) (see 1931.399, p. 236). This modestly sized painting — showing three men wearing Louis XVI costumes, smoking clay pipes, and talking in an inn — was highly praised for its photographic accuracy of detail when it was exhibited at the 1848 Salon. The picture was later purchased by Queen Victoria as a gift for Prince Albert.

A somewhat less specific historical time is suggested in *The Communicants* (1872; see 1931.417, p. 244) by Louis-Gabriel-Eugène Isabey, who was as well known for his landscapes (especially the coastal scenes that influenced both Eugène Boudin and Jehan Barthold

Jongkind) and for his depictions of church interiors that often recall, in true romantic fashion, the Gothic age. In 1830 Isabey had accompanied French expeditionary forces to North Africa and there painted scenes of the Moroccan landscape. He did not, however, develop the genre of orientalist painting to the extent that some of his contemporaries did, such as Eugène Delacroix. Although the Taft Museum possesses no paintings by Delacroix, significant works by two other contemporaries of Isabey represent that element of romanticism. Alexandre-Gabriel Decamp's *Albanians (Albanais se reposant sur les ruines)* of 1849 (see 1931.432, p. 238) depicts two Arnauts, Greek or Albanian conscripts in the Ottoman army, before a dramatic red-orange sunset that serves as a perfect foil for the exotic pair. *An Arab Guard* (1863; see 1931.430, p. 229) was not painted by a French orientalist but rather by a Spanish painter who was both well known and active in Paris. Mariano Fortuny i Marsal made several trips to North Africa and became enamored of the color and light of Morocco. Throughout his career he continued to paint, draw, and etch scenes of everyday life set in that part of the world. The Taft painting, which was actually done in Fortuny's studio in Rome, represents a model who often appears in his orientalist pictures, a man named Farragi.

The middle years of the nineteenth century witnessed a growing interest on the part of French painters, as well as those from other nations, in subjects drawn from the lives of ordinary people engaged in ordinary activities (which nonetheless were often charged with political and social meaning) and in scenes of the fields, forests, and mountains of rural locales. Jean-François Millet was one such painter who bridged the gap between realistic figure and landscape compositions, evident in the Taft's *Mother and Child* (1846–48; see 1931.422, p. 264). The museum possesses another extraordinary example of his work in *Maternité: A Young Mother Cradling Her Baby* of 1872–73 (see 1931.448, p. 265). In this poignant scene of maternal love, the young woman has a sorrowful expression on her face, similar to that worn by the Virgin Mary in many traditional Pietà scenes. Indeed, the presence of a crucifix on the back wall leads us to consider the possibility that this image mirrors the painful reality of a sorrowful mother grieving the loss of her child.

The history of nineteenth-century realistic landscape painting in France is dominated by the personality of Jean-Baptiste-Camille Corot. Corot is often cited as bringing a new freshness and spontaneity to nature painting, which had previously looked for inspiration to patterns established by baroque artists like Poussin and Claude Lorrain. Direct contact with nature was deemed necessary to evoke a convincing depiction of the land, and artists like Corot himself, Charles-François Daubigny, and Pierre-Etienne-Théodore Rousseau left Paris for the Forest of Fontainebleau and other regions to experience the plenitude of nature firsthand. The Taft collection includes numerous examples of the work of these Barbizon artists, whose plein-air paintings later inspired the impressionists. Corot's *Evening: The Festival of Pan* (ca. 1855–60; see 1931.449, p. 247) combines the direct approach to nature with figures drawn from classical mythology. Daubigny's *A River Scene: The Ferryboat at Bonnières* (1861; see 1931.463, p. 267) and Rousseau's *Pond at Dagneau (Forest of Fontainebleau: On the Plateau of Belle-Croix)* (1858–60; see 1931.413, p. 262) are both the sort of nature scenes, unencumbered by historical or mythological references, that characterize the achievements of the Barbizon School.

Another artist associated with the Barbizon group, Narcisse Virgil Diaz de la Peña, is represented in the Taft collection by a landscape scene of the Fontainebleau area and by *Oriental Children* (1840s; see 1931.434, p. 253). The latter represents a group of five children in vaguely oriental dress, which is more an approximation of the look of the Near East or North Africa than the exact representations by artists like Decamps or Fortuny. Diaz, who was better known for his landscapes and scenes of gypsy life, never traveled to these exotic countries. Nevertheless, this picture, which can be characterized as a fusion of eighteenth-century love of detail with the later orientalism of Delacroix and others, is an appealing work of the sort that found great appreciation among contemporary collectors in France.

France was not the only country, of course, where artists were cultivating an unmediated approach to landscape painting. A similar phenomenon occurred in the later nineteenth century in the Netherlands. Artists constituting the Hague School — Anton Mauve, Jacob Maris, Jozef Israëls, and others — were reviving the spirit of the Dutch masters of the Golden Age, such as Jacob van Ruisdael and Meyndert Hobbema, and infusing it with a new, simplified approach. The Taft collection offers the viewer ample opportunity to gauge the achievements of these artists with several splendid examples of their work. Outstanding among the Hague School landscapes in the museum are *Changing Pastures* (ca. 1887) by Mauve (see 1931.457, p. 276), *The Quay: A Dutch Town* (1880–90) by Jacob Maris (see 1931.456, p. 280), and *Cattle in Meadows* (before 1905) by Jacob's brother Willem Maris (see 1931.453, p. 285). Equally representative of the Hague School are scenes of peasant life, and one of the Taft's treasures of nineteenth-century art is Jozef Israëls's 1881 *Sewing School at Katwijk* (see 1931.460, p. 273), which shows eight young girls and their teacher at work in a cottage interior. Israëls's painting reflects a spirit of respect for the time-honored customs and traditions of these people, similar to that observed in the early work of Vincent van Gogh of roughly the same time.

The collection of nineteenth-century American paintings in the Taft Museum is particularly strong in the work of artists who were themselves of European background, lived for long periods of their lives on the Continent, or were greatly influenced by European modes of art. A perfect case of such varied artistic identity is James McNeill Whistler, a native of Lowell, Massachusetts, who spent most of his life in London, Paris, and elsewhere in Europe. Although Whistler is categorized in this catalogue with the British artists, he retained important links to the art world in the United States and may be as easily discussed in that context. One of Whistler's early masterpieces, the beautiful *At the Piano* of 1858–59 (see 1962.7, p. 218), entered the museum collection in 1962. Whistler was in close contact with such French artists as Gustave Courbet, Henri Fantin-Latour, Théodule Ribot, and others, and this work echoes elements of the styles of each of these masters. It portrays the artist's half-sister, Deborah Delano Haden, and her daughter, Annie Harriet Haden, in a planar composition that looks forward to such famous works as *Arrangement in Grey and Black: Portrait of the Painter's Mother* (1871; Paris, Musée d'Orsay). The limited palette of the Taft work is reminiscent of Whistler's admiration for Velázquez. It was shown successfully at the Royal Academy in London and purchased by the English painter John Phillip, who was famous for his adaptations of Spanish techniques and compositions. Equally Spanish in its color and intensity is John Singer Sargent's portrait of Robert Louis Stevenson (1887; see 1931.472, p. 295), one of several likenesses of the writer by Sargent. It was painted while Sargent was visiting Stevenson and his wife, Fanny, at Bournemouth; the painting had been commissioned by Sargent's friend Charles Fairchild of Boston, whose wife, a literary hostess, was a great admirer of the writer.

The engaging picture *The Cobbler's Apprentice* (1877; see 1931.415, p. 292) was painted by the Cincinnati artist Frank Duveneck, who, like many Americans in the last quarter of the nineteenth century, studied in Munich. Contemporary German art vied for Americans' attention with Dutch and Flemish genre painting (the future cobbler could almost have stepped from a work by Adriaen Brouwer) as well as the sobriety of Velázquez. This is the second of three similar pictures executed by Duveneck; the others date to 1872 and 1878, and all three resemble *Boy Smoking (The Apprentice)* of 1875 (Hartford, Wadsworth Atheneum) by Duveneck's friend William Merritt Chase.

Another American artist with European ties, Henry F. Farny, was born in Alsace but lived most of his life in Cincinnati. Like Duveneck, he also studied in Germany, especially in Düsseldorf on his way to Munich. Farny is well known for his paintings and illustrations of native North Americans. One of his masterpieces (along with a study for it) is owned by the Taft Museum: *The Song of the Talking Wire* (1904; see 1931.466, p. 299), a poignant image showing a man in Sioux dress in a snowy landscape. Pressing his ear to a telegraph pole, he expresses a combination of bewilderment and resentment in the face of "progress" and "civilization." This work became famous during the artist's lifetime. Farny selected it for inclusion in an exhibition of American paintings held at Berlin in 1910, after which time photographic reproductions of it were widely circulated. Although his art had fallen out of critical favor, it is now undergoing reassessment, and Farny is again appreciated for the many visual subtleties of his work.

From this brief overview it is obvious that the collection of European and American paintings in the Taft Museum does not represent the achievements of all the important artists in their respective times and nations. Rather it is a collection that is outstanding for the depth of the schools it does encompass. We sense in this selection the intelligence and sensitivity of collectors who assembled for themselves — and for posterity — a group of paintings that instructs us in the nuances of a few important movements in Western art of the post-Renaissance period.

Early Renaissance Italian Panel Paintings

Rona Goffen

1962.11

❧

Anonymous Italian Master

Crucifixion

Mid-fourteenth century?
Tempera on panel, 42.2 x 23.2 cm (16⅝ x 9⅛ in.), including frame
Inscribed on plaque above the cross: *hic. est.* ɪхе / *Nazzarenus* / *rex. yudeor[um]*

Christ on the cross is isolated against a gold ground in the upper part of the picture. Two angels catch the blood from his hands in chalices such as those used during the celebration of the Mass. As in many other depictions of the Crucifixion, Mary Magdalene kneels at the foot of the Cross, embracing it and looking up toward her Lord. To their right Saint John the Evangelist and two of the holy women support the swooning figure of the Virgin Mary. This, too, is a traditional motif. More unusual is the depiction of several saintly figures to the Savior's left, where one expects to see his enemies and the soldier-saint Longinus, who was converted to the faith only after piercing Christ's side with a lance. Although the man standing closest to the cross and pointing toward Christ recalls the traditional gesture and position of Longinus, he is not dressed as a soldier and remains anonymous. The bearded old man next to him may be either Joseph of Arimathea, who gave his tomb to Christ, or Nicodemus, who helped remove the body from the cross. The identity of the third saint in the group cannot be determined. Accompanying these saints are two men without halos, anonymous supernumeraries who witness the Crucifixion. The back of the panel is painted in imitation of porphyry or dark marble.

The contours of the frame are repeated by tooling in the gold ground of the panel itself, and the halos are also tooled, as one would expect in a fourteenth-century painting. The outlines of the halos of the holy women seem to have been drawn with a compass, but those of the men appear to have been drawn freehand. The figures do not have incised outlines, as one might expect, and the gold ground looks comparatively new or repainted. The paint surface is abraded, and there are scattered losses throughout the composition.

In addition to these problems of conservation and technique, there is the problem of quality. It must be said that the *Crucifixion* is an inferior painting, clearly unworthy of Bernardo Daddi, the great Florentine master to whom it had previously been attributed.[1] The faces, for example, are crude in both formal conception and expression, and the execution of the work is clumsy. The composition resembles that of a *Crucifixion* by Daddi in the Thyssen Collection (Lugano) and seems to have been copied after that work, as Everett Fahy has suggested.[2] The question then becomes a matter of when the copy was made, and one cannot discount the possibility, as Fahy has also noted, that the panel is a modern work.

1. Raimond van Marle, *The Development of the Italian Schools of Painting,* vol. ɪɪɪ, The Hague, 1924, p. 382.
2. Letter from Everett Fahy to Dr. Ruth K. Meyer, Aug. 18, 1984, Taft Museum files.

Provenance Cavalier Bellini, Florence; Annesley Gore, London (until 1931); Mr. and Mrs. Albert S. Ingalls, Cleveland (Dec. 1931); Jane Taft Ingalls bequest, 1962.

Exhibitions Cincinnati, Taft Museum, *Italian Panel Paintings from the Permanent Collection,* Dec. 2, 1989–May 30, 1990; Cincinnati, Taft Museum, *In Praise and in Prayer: Jewish and Christian Devotional Objects,* Nov. 21, 1991–Jan. 10, 1992.

Literature Raimond van Marle, *The Development of the Italian Schools of Painting,* vol. ɪɪɪ, The Hague, 1924, p. 382.

1962.11

1962.9

᠃

Attributed to the Panzano Master/Master of the Richardson Tabernacle

Triptych with the Madonna and Child Enthroned with John the Baptist, Mary Magdalene, and Two Male Saints (Anthony Abbot and Anthony of Padua?)

Siena, ca. 1390
Tempera on panel: central panel, 45.7 x 20 cm (18 x 7⅞ in.); wings (each), 40.6 x 9.8 cm (16 x 3⅞ in.)
Inscribed on the scroll of John the Baptist: *Ecce Agnu[s Dei]*

The Virgin and Child are enthroned on the central panel, their identity as Queen and King of Heaven emphasized by the gold brocade cloth suspended over the back of the throne and by the brocade, of a different pattern, worn by the Infant. This taste for richness, color, and varied design is typical of the Sienese school. The object that Christ holds, now much damaged, is a bird, a common symbolic device alluding to his sacrifice on the cross.

Two saints stand on either side of the throne. Saint John the Baptist (on the right hand of the Virgin and Child) holds his scroll with the traditional Latin inscription, which in translation reads "Behold the Lamb of God." On the other side, Mary Magdalene holds her attribute, the jar of ointment with which she bathed Christ's feet. In the pinnacle above the Madonna and Child, Christ is shown in half-length as the adult Savior; he looks directly out of the picture and blesses the viewer.

Two full-length, standing figures are represented on the wings. The identity of the older, bearded saint in the left wing is unknown, although the type recalls Anthony Abbot. The saint in the right wing may be Anthony of Padua, whose habit features the Franciscan knotted cord. The backs of the wings are painted in imitation of stone, black with a red grain. The hinges and holes for clasps, now missing, indicate that the triptych was designed as a portable devotional image that could be closed for easy transport.

There are scattered losses throughout the three panels, the most serious being in the Christ Child's symbolic bird and in the head of the older saint in the left wing. Some contours are incised into the panel. The edges and halos are embellished with tooling, and certain details are built up in gesso and gilded, notably the colonnettes and arches enclosing the figures and the floral patterns decorating the unpainted areas.

The Taft triptych closely resembles one that depicts the Madonna with saints published by Berenson with an attribution to the Panzano Master, a painter active in Siena during the last quarter of the fourteenth century. Recalling the Taft work are the figure types and such revealing details as the punch designs of the halos, the floral motifs built up in gesso, and the moldings of the frames.[1] Furthermore, the Taft triptych formerly had a base much like that of Berenson's "homeless painting."[2] More recently, Everett Fahy has reconstructed the oeuvre of this Sienese painter, whom he calls the Master of the Richardson Tabernacle, so named after the work ascribed to him in the Fogg Art Museum at Harvard. Fahy ascribes the Taft triptych, which was evidently unknown to Berenson, to the same artist, although it should be noted that this triptych is of lesser quality than other works associated with this painter.[3] In any case, the artist was clearly influenced by the Sienese master Paolo di Giovanni Fei (act. 1372–1410).

1. Bernard Berenson, *Homeless Paintings of the Renaissance*, ed. Hanna Kiel, Bloomington, Ind., and London, 1970, pp. 43–47, for the oeuvre of the Master of Panzano with an illustration of the lost triptych on p. 47, fig. 67. Berenson notes that the master is very close to Cola di Petrucciolo. See also Berenson, *Italian Pictures of the Renaissance, Central Italian and North Italian Schools*, rev. ed., vol. I, New York, 1968, pp. 254–55, for the Master of the Panzano Triptych, so-called for a painting in the Pieve di S. Leolino in Panzano.

2. I owe this information to Everett Fahy. In a letter of Aug. 18, 1984, to Ruth K. Meyer, Fahy refers to a photograph of the Taft triptych in the collection of William Salomon, New York (American Art Galleries, New York, Apr. 5, 1923, no. 345).

3. Fahy to Meyer, Aug. 18, 1984. See also Fahy's forthcoming catalogue of the Italian paintings in the Fogg Art Museum. The author also ascribes a triptych in the possession of Piero Corsini to the same master, but Corsini himself, following the suggestion of Richard Offner, attributes

this picture to Gregorio di Cecco di Luca; see Piero Corsini, *Italian Old Master Paintings: Fourteenth to Eighteenth Century*, New York, 1984, pp. 14–15. See also Berenson 1968, p. 201. The Taft picture seems to me more closely related to Berenson's homeless triptych (cited in note 1) and to other works associated with the Master of Panzano/Master of the Richardson Tabernacle than to Corsini's painting.

Provenance Annesley Gore, London; Mr. and Mrs. Albert S. Ingalls, Cleveland (Dec. 1936); Jane Taft Ingalls bequest, 1962.

Exhibition Cincinnati, Taft Museum, *Italian Panel Paintings from the Permanent Collection*, Dec. 2, 1989–May 30, 1990.

1962.9

Anonymous Master (Carlo da Camerino?)

Triptych with the Madonna and Nursing Child with Saints

Early fifteenth century
Tempera on panel: central panel, 45.7 x 32.4 cm (18 x 12¾ in.); wings (each), 45.7 x 16.5 cm (18 x 6½ in.), including frame
Inscribed on the frame: *Ave Gratia Plena*

The Virgin and Child are enthroned in the central panel of the triptych. The throne is a monumental stone structure draped

1962.10

with a gold brocade cloth decorated with birds and flowers stamped into the surface. Despite these conspicuous reminders of their royalty — Christ and Mary are the King and Queen of Heaven — they are shown in a completely human and informal situation: the Infant has been nursing but pauses to turn toward the viewer. Mary likewise welcomes the spectator with her gaze. Examination of the painting under black light reveals damage in the Infant's flesh and in the Madonna's face, as well as scattered losses in her garment.

The frame below the throne is inscribed in Latin, which in translation reads "Hail, Full of Grace," the words with which the Archangel Gabriel greeted Mary at the Annunciation. The Annunciation itself is depicted in the spaces between the rectangular border of the central panel, decorated with tooling in the gold ground, and the trilobate frame, built up in gesso, which encloses the figures of the Madonna and Child. The archangel kneels at the left and addresses the Virgin, who is seated at the right and points to herself to acknowledge the angel's tidings, as she replies to Gabriel, "Ecce ancilla dei" (Behold the handmaid of the Lord).

The wings of the triptych are also subdivided by raised gesso forming arched frames within the rectangular panels. Each wing is divided horizontally into two sections containing paired figures of saints standing in arches created by gesso and tooling in the gold ground. Saint Paul with his sword and Saint Peter holding the keys to heaven occupy the upper part of the left wing. Below them are Saint Bartholomew, grasping the knife with which he was martyred, and Saint Christopher, carrying the Christ Child on his back. In the right wing Saint James and a figure who may be Saint Anthony Abbot appear above Saint Catherine of Alexandria, with the wheel of her martyrdom, and an unidentified female saint. Three of these four pairs of saints appear with half-length figures of angels set above them, while a bust of Saint John the Baptist is depicted above saints James and Anthony.

The triptych is hinged, like the earlier triptych in the Taft collection, and like that work, this too was designed as a portable devotional image that could be closed for ease of transport. The backs of the wings, which become the cover of the triptych when closed, are decorated with the coat of arms of the owner: gold keys are crossed on a red shield with a star-shaped flower set at the top between the two keys.

This triptych is a good example of fourteenth- and early-fifteenth-century Italian painting techniques. The borders of the three panels, the edges of Mary's gown, details of the brocade cloth, and the halos of Christ and of the saints are all embellished with punched designs in the picture surface. Other designs, notably the pattern of the Virgin's mantle, are merely painted on the surface. The outlines of the figures and other major forms are incised into the panel and provided a drawing of the composition to guide the painter's application of color.

Everett Fahy has tentatively ascribed this panel to Carlo da Camerino, or Carlo da Macerata, about whom little is known except that he was active in his native region of the Marches at the turn of the fifteenth century.[1] In 1396 he signed and dated a crucifix that is now in the church of San Michele Arcangelo outside Macerata. Other works associated with Carlo include the *Madonna and Child with Saints Francis and Louis and a Donor* in the Pinacoteca Comunale Podesti of Ancona, the *Madonna and Child with Two Donors* in the Palazzo Municipale of Mondavio, and the *Stigmatization of Saint Francis* in the office of the mayor of Falerone in the Palazzo Municipale of that city. At any rate, it is clear that the painting in the Taft Museum, previously considered to be an anonymous work of the Florentine school, is rather to be associated with the Marches. The soft modeling, choice of colors, and decorative embellishment of the image all suggest the Marchigian tradition rather than the more austere style of Florence.

1. Letter from Everett Fahy to Ruth K. Meyer, Aug. 18, 1984, Taft Museum files. Camerino is to the south of Urbino and to the southwest of Macerata.

Provenance Lord Darnley (before 1936); Annesley Gore, London (in 1936); Mr. and Mrs. Albert S. Ingalls, Cleveland (Dec. 1936); Jane Taft Ingalls bequest, 1962.

Exhibition Cincinnati, Taft Museum, *Italian Panel Paintings from the Permanent Collection*, Dec. 2, 1989–May 30, 1990.

1962.10

Sixteenth-Century French Panel Paintings

Guy Bauman

Corneille de Lyon
(also called Corneille de La Haye)
The Hague ca. 1500–1575 Lyon

Corneille was born at the Hague, Holland, probably about 1500. Sometime before 1533 he moved to Lyon, then a major city on the trade route between Italy and Flanders. In all contemporary archival sources he is referred to as Corneille de La Haye (Cornelius from the Hague); only in the nineteenth century did he become known as Corneille de Lyon, because he was active in that town for over forty years and because his proper surname was not recorded. In 1534 Corneille was described as Painter to the Queen to Eleanor of Austria, second wife of King Francis I and sister of Emperor Charles V. In 1541 he was named Painter to the Dauphin to the future Henry II, and he became a naturalized French citizen in 1547 (when the Hague was recorded as his birthplace). In 1551 Corneille was recorded as Painter to the

King, and documents of 1557 and 1574 attest to his position as Painter to the King and Servant of the King's Bedchamber, the most honored post then attainable by a French painter. He was buried in Lyon on November 8, 1575.

All the paintings attributed to Corneille de Lyon are small, half- or bust-length portraits on panel, usually with green or blue-green backgrounds, a format he appears to have introduced to France. These display the influence of Netherlandish portrait traditions — especially of portraits by Joos van Cleve, who was active at the court of Francis I about 1530. Most of the surviving portraits depict the nobility, although more portraits of a bourgeois clientele than were hitherto supposed to have existed may have perished owing to their less stable circumstances of preservation. To judge by the numerous — approximately two hundred — pictures that survive, often in several versions, Corneille was immensely successful and widely imitated. Their varied styles and degrees of quality indicate that many must be by workshop assistants (among whom are presumably to be included his son and daughter, both of whom were painters) or by contemporary imitators of his style.

It is difficult to attribute works to Corneille de Lyon with assurance and even more so to assign them a chronology. He seems never to have signed his portraits, and few are dated. A small number of portraits, which were considered to be originals by Corneille when in the renowned collection of Roger de Gaignières (1642–1715), form the fragile traditional basis for assigning works to the artist. Among these, however, are portraits of mediocre quality that would appear to be shop works. Louis Dimier, who at the beginning of the twentieth century was the preeminent scholar of sixteenth-century French portraiture, attempted on stylistic grounds to define the oeuvres of individual hands within the Corneille de Lyon group of portraits.[1] Among the putative masters he isolated and named were the Master of the Benson Portraits (L'Anonyme Benson), the Master of Brissac (Peintre de Brissac), and the Master of Rieux-Châteauneuf (Peintre de Rieux-Châteauneuf), whose name Dimier took from the Taft portrait of Jean d'Albon (see 1962.5, p. 135), which at the time was thought to depict Jean de Rieux, sire de Châteauneuf.

The discovery in 1962 of the portrait of Pierre Aymeric, now in the Louvre, Paris, has required a revision of Dimier's view of Corneille de Lyon.[2] An inscription in Aymeric's own hand on the verso of the painting identifies the painter as Corneille de La Haye and dates it 1534. It is now considered to be the only surely documented work by Corneille and the point of departure for further attributions. It is evident from the style of that painting that many of the works attributed by Dimier to the Master of the Benson Portraits must now be regarded as paintings by Corneille himself. Dimier's so-called Master of Rieux-Châteauneuf is an artistic personality that also has not found general acceptance in recent scholarship.

1. Louis Dimier, *Histoire de la peinture de portrait en France au XVIe siècle*, pt. 2, Paris, 1925, pp. 73–82.

2. P. Roudié, "Sur un portrait de Corneille de Lyon," *Gazette des beaux-arts*, 6th per., vol. LX (1962), pp. 481–86; see also Sylvie Béguin and Anne de Groër, "A Propos d'un nouveau Corneille: Le Portrait de Pierre Aymeric," *La Revue du Louvre*, vol. XXVIII (1978), pp. 28–42.

1962.5

𝕰

Style of Corneille de Lyon

Jean d'Albon de Saint-André

ca. 1535
Oil on panel, 16.2 x 13 cm (6⅜ x 5⅛ in.)
Inscribed on reverse: JEAN SIRE DE RIEUX . . . *Holbein f[ec]it*

The sitter, a clean-shaven, fleshy-faced man who appears to be in his mid-to-late fifties, is portrayed against a green background shadowed at the top and left as if by the frame. He is depicted bust length and nearly full face, turned slightly to the viewer's right. His blue eyes engage the viewer's, and his graying brown hair falls just over his ears. His head is covered by a flat, black felt toque inclined to the left. The cap is fastened at the back with a narrow strap and ornamented with a gilt medal. He wears a black doublet over a white chemise, of which only part of the collar with an arabesque border trimmed with black-edged ruche is visible. His dark brown, damask-patterned coat is open to reveal the insignia of the order of Saint Michael suspended from a gold chain. The coat has wide ermine lapels and is lined with the same fur, visible in patches through its horizontally slashed sleeves fastened with small ties fitted at the ends with cylindrical gilt tips.

The Taft painting is one of at least nine versions of the portrait that have survived. It is appropriate here to list the eight others with their dimensions and histories of ownership, because hitherto not all of them have been identified: changes of ownership have created some confusion about which was which, and the issues of determining the portrait's date and the sitter's identity involve discussion of several of the others.

1. England, Chatsworth, duke of Devonshire Collection, inv. no. 107
   15.2 x 12.1 cm (6 x 4¾ in.)
   There at least since the eighteenth century
2. New York, The Metropolitan Museum of Art, inv. no. 32.100.103
   17.5 x 14.6 cm (6⅞ x 5¾ in.)
   Provenance: Comte G. de Montbrison, Château de Saint-Roch, Auvillar, Tarn-et-Garonne (until about 1908); Leopold Hirsh, London; [F. Kleinberger, Paris, 1924]; Michael Friedsam, New York (1924–31)
3. England, Waddesdon Manor, James A. de Rothschild Collection, inv. no. w1/129/1
   17.8 x 14.6 cm (7 x 5¾ in.)
   Provenance: Hollingworth Magniac, Colworth, Bedford (sale, Christie's, London, July 2ff., 1892, no. 56, as by Holbein, bought C. J. Wertheimer)
4. Richmond, Virginia Museum of Fine Arts, inv. no. 50–3–2
   16.8 x 14.6 cm (6⅝ x 5¾ in.)
   Provenance: Graf Géza Brunsvik, Schloss Sommerau near Spital am Semmering (sale, Vienna, Nov. 25ff., 1902, no. 130, as French master, bought M. Hamburger); Leo Lanczi, Budapest?; [Newhouse Gallery, New York (until 1950)]; Adolph D. Williams, Richmond, Va. (1950)
5. Paris, Musée du Louvre, R.F. 342
   16.8 x 13.7 cm (6⅝ x 5⅜ in.)
   Provenance: Charles Timbal, Paris (until 1882)
   Inscribed: MONSIEVR DE SAINCT-ANDRE
6. France, Clermont-Ferrand, Musée Municipal, inv. no. 116h-3235
   16.8 x 13.7 cm (6⅝ x 5⅜ in.)
   Provenance: Besse-Beauregard family, Château de Beauregard (until at least about 1830–40, when the Clermont-Ferrand museum was founded)
   Inscribed on reverse: MONSIEVR DE SAINCT-ANDRE; dated on reverse of frame: MDLII
7. The Art Institute of Chicago, inv. no. 40.1144
   20 x 15.9 cm (7⅞ x 6¼ in.) with added strips; 16.5 x 13.3 cm (6½ x 5¼ in.) original panel
   Provenance: Hollingworth Magniac, Colworth, Bedford (sale, Christie's, London, July 2ff., 1892, no. 55, as by Holbein); James P. Labey, London (in 1931); [Dowdeswell and Dowdeswell, London]; Francis T. Haskell, Chicago (until 1935)
8. Present location unknown
   Provenance: Mme Pelouze, Chenonceaux; Louis Monery, Roanne (by 1897–after 1925)
   Said to be inscribed and dated: MONSIEVR DE SAINCT-ANDRE 1548

The Taft painting was long considered to be the finest of the known versions and may still perhaps be regarded as the prototype (if the prototype is by a painter other than Corneille de Lyon). However, Anne Dubois de Groër has recently suggested that the Chatsworth version, which was first published by Waterhouse (1967),[1] is an original portrait by Corneille of which all the others would be copies (see note 16 and below). The versions in New York and at Waddesdon Manor are nearly on a par with the Taft portrait; that in Richmond, slightly less so. The version in Paris is weaker yet, and those in Clermont-Ferrand and Chicago are notably inferior.[2] Although there is no photographic record of the version formerly in the Pelouze and Monery collections, Dimier considered it to be inferior to the Taft painting.[3] The authorship of these portraits, the identity of the sitter, and the date of the prototype have all been subject to debate. It is in this order that the three questions will be discussed.

Of the nine versions of the portrait, the Taft painting was the first to be published. It was described by De Laborde (1855) when in the collection of Andrew Fountaine IV. De Laborde observed that the picture was there attributed erroneously to Hans Holbein the Younger and asserted that it was actually by Corneille de Lyon.[4] When the version in the Louvre was acquired in 1882, it was attributed with question to the school of Clouet.[5] At that time there was still much confusion about the attribution of such portraits and little evidence for determining which should be assigned to Corneille and which to members of the Clouet family of portraitists. Dimier (1902, 1904), who rediscovered the Taft painting when it was in the Butler collection, then considered it as possibly a work by Corneille de Lyon.[6] However, subsequently Dimier isolated it on stylistic grounds and grouped around it a number of other portraits of similar style. Because he believed the Taft portrait to depict Jean de Rieux, sire de Châteauneuf, Dimier assigned this body of work to a painter he named the Master of the Rieux-Châteauneuf. He considered this artist to be a better painter than Corneille de Lyon, and he regarded the Taft painting to be the best of the surviving versions (numbers 5, 6, and 8 were the others known to him) and hence the artist's masterpiece and his eponymous work.[7]

In 1924 Brière catalogued the Louvre version as the work of an unknown sixteenth-century French painter, citing the Taft painting as its probable original.[8] Two years later Réau reproduced the New York portrait as a work attributed to Corneille de Lyon but argued that there was insufficient evidence for determining whether it or the other versions, including the Taft painting, were by Corneille or by the so-called Master of Rieux-Châteauneuf.[9] Lemoisne, in 1929, attributed the Louvre portrait to Corneille and cited the Taft picture as a superior version, possibly the original.[10] Burroughs and Wehle (1932) considered the New York and Taft paintings to be of equal quality and assigned both to the Master of Rieux-Châteauneuf.[11] In 1955 Sterling adhered to this view,[12] but later he and Adhémar rejected this rubric and assigned the Louvre version to the workshop of Corneille de Lyon.[13] A decade later the compilers of the Virginia Museum of Fine Arts catalogue designated the Richmond portrait as being in the manner of Corneille de Lyon, listing five other versions, including the Taft picture.[14] Waterhouse, citing eight versions including the one in Cincinnati, adopted the same rubric for the version at Waddesdon Manor. Before the portrait in the duke of Devonshire's collection came to her attention, De Groër (1974, 1978) considered all the versions to be replicas — the implication being that none of them is by Corneille himself, but that they all descend from an archetype by him.[15] She now considers the Chatsworth version to be possibly autograph, pending further study.[16] Style of Corneille de Lyon is the current designation for the New York version.[17]

Because of the inscription on its reverse, De Laborde described the Taft painting as a portrait of "Jean, sire de Rieux." When the Louvre version was acquired, it was catalogued as a portrait of "Monsieur de Saint-André" because of its inscription. The identity of the sitter in these and the other versions has been debated ever since. The compiler of the Timbal catalogue asserted that the monsieur de Saint-André in question was Jean d'Albon de Saint-André (1472–1549).[18] In 1897 Jeannez and Déchelette drew attention to a documented portrait of Jean d'Albon in a stained-glass window, which can be dated on external evidence to about 1535.[19] The sitter in the window, although depicted in a different medium and in three-quarter profile, does appear to be the same as the one in the painted portraits, perhaps slightly older. Jeannez and Déchelette cited the Louvre, Clermont-Ferrand, and Pelouze/Monery versions (all of which are inscribed on the obverse or reverse MONSIEVR DE SAINCT-ANDRÉ).

Nevertheless, Dimier found evidence for identifying the sitter in the Taft version as a member of the Rieux family. An engraving after one of the versions appears in a book published in 1756.[20] The sitter is there identified as "Le maréchal de Rieux tuteur de la reine Anne de Bretagne." The print also carries the following inscriptions: *Hallé invenit. A. Loir sculpsit. Tiré du cabinet de M. le comte de Rieux* (Painted by Hallé. Engraved by A. Loir. After a painting in the collection of the count of Rieux). This print is undoubtedly the source of the old inscription on the reverse of the Taft panel. Dimier suggested that the Taft painting itself was the picture that belonged to the comte de Rieux in 1756. He noted that the apparent date of the Taft painting, evident from the sitter's costume, precludes the possibility of its depicting Jean IV de Rieux (1447–1518), who was Anne of Brittany's tutor. He concluded that it must instead portray his son, Jean V de Rieux, sire de Châteauneuf (1507–1563), who was the father of "la belle Châteauneuf," the mistress of the future Henry III.[21]

The Louvre version has steadfastly been catalogued as a portrait of Jean d'Albon, but writers on the other versions have wavered. In 1926 Réau identified the sitter as Jean d'Albon or Jean de Rieux, but in the 1927 Kleinberger exhibition he opted for Jean d'Albon. Burroughs and Wehle cited both possibilities, but Sterling settled on Jean de Rieux with question. The compilers of the Virginia Museum of Fine Arts catalogue again cited both possibilities, but Waterhouse settled on Jean de Rieux.

In 1974 De Groër put forward the strongest evidence for rejecting the identification of the sitter as Jean de Rieux in favor of Jean d'Albon. She argued that the numerous versions of the portrait indicate that the sitter was of considerable importance. This Jean V de Rieux was not, whereas Jean d'Albon was. As De Groër noted, no Jean de Rieux was ever governor of Lyon, con-

trary to what has been written.[22] Jean d'Albon, on the other hand, was governor of the Roannais and chamberlain of Anne of Brittany in 1502, chamberlain of Louis XII in 1512, and governor of the duc d'Orléans (the future Henry II) in 1530. In 1534 he was named seneschal of Lyon; in 1539, governor of Lyon and the Lyonnais.[23] Most important, Jean d'Albon became a knight of the order of Saint Michael in 1530, whereas Jean V de Rieux never did. It might be added that the identification as Jean d'Albon is more in keeping with the sitter's apparent age in the portrait, taking into account its evident date. In about 1535 Jean d'Albon would have been sixty-three years old, whereas Jean V de Rieux would have been only twenty-eight.[24]

Thus, since the sitter in the Taft painting wears the order of Saint Michael, he cannot be Jean V de Rieux and must therefore be Jean d'Albon. Indeed, the granting of the order in 1530 may have occasioned the original portrait's commission.

When attempts have been made to date the Taft painting and its variants, the tendency has been to rely on the date 1548 said to be inscribed on the version formerly in the Pelouze and Monery collections. Dimier first proposed a date of about 1547 for the Taft portrait in 1924–25. Sterling and Adhémar dated the Louvre portrait about 1548. Waterhouse dated the Waddesdon portrait to the 1540s, and the New York version has been dated about 1545.[25] However, as Sterling noted in 1955, the inscriptions on the Pelouze/Monery and Louvre versions are not necessarily reliable, especially not the date. Dimier, his adoption of the date notwithstanding, considered both inscriptions to be later additions and false.[26]

Besides the apparent age of a sitter whose life dates are known, the style of a sitter's costume provides the soundest basis for dating portraits in the Corneille de Lyon group, which are rarely if ever dated by the artist. By comparing the sitter's dress here to that in dated portraits by other artists, in 1974 De Groër demonstrated convincingly that the prototype, which she then believed to be the Taft painting, must have been painted during the first half of the 1530s. She suggested that the date of 1548 on the Pelouze/Monery version, if it is genuine, records the year in which that replica was executed. The same may be true of the date 1552 on the reverse of the frame of the Clermont-Ferrand version.

Since the discovery of the only documented work by Corneille de Lyon, the *Portrait of Pierre Aymeric* dated 1534 (see Biography), the Taft painting cannot, on stylistic grounds, be attributed to that artist, particularly since it or its prototype and the *Portrait of Pierre Aymeric* must be of almost exactly the same date. In light of the current state of knowledge about Corneille, the most prudent designation for the Taft painting is style of Corneille de Lyon, by which it is understood that it may be the work of a very gifted follower in his shop or the work of an independent painter in Lyon who imitated his style — one of the many who are documented as having lived and worked in the same neighborhood as the artist.

1. Ellis Waterhouse, *The James A. de Rothschild Collection at Waddesdon Manor: Paintings*, London, 1967, p. 228.

2. Versions of the portrait other than those in Cincinnati, Chicago, New York, and Paris are known to the author only through good black-and-

white photographs. The author thanks the following people for exchanging photographs with him and for answering his queries: Peter Day, keeper of the Devonshire collections, Chatsworth; Pinkney Near, curator, Virginia Museum of Fine Arts; G. Tisserand, curator, Musées d'Art de Clermont-Ferrand; and Martha Wolff, curator of European painting before 1750, The Art Institute of Chicago.

3. Louis Dimier, *Histoire de la peinture de portrait en France au XVIe siècle*, pt. 1, Paris, 1924, p. 40, pl. 12; pt. 2, 1925, pp. 73, 75–76, no. 295.

4. Léon Emmanuel Simon Joseph de Laborde, *La Renaissance des arts à la cour de France*, pt. 2, vol. I, Paris, 1855, p. 634.

5. Musées nationaux, *Catalogue de la collection Timbal*, Paris, 1882, pp. 20–23, no. 4.

6. Louis Dimier, "Une Oeuvre inconnue de Corneille de Lyon," *La Revue de l'art ancienne et moderne*, vol. XII (1902), pp. 5–8, ill. opp. p. 6; Louis Dimier, *French Painting in the Sixteenth Century*, London, 1904, pp. 136–37.

7. Louis Dimier, in Thieme-Becker, vol. VII (1912), p. 423; Dimier 1924–25; Louis Dimier, *Histoire de la peinture française des origines au retour de Vouet*, Paris, 1925, p. 70, pl. XLVIII-1; and Louis Dimier, *La Peinture française au XVIe siècle*, Marseille, 1942, p. 15, pl. 22a.

8. Gaston Brière, *Musée national du Louvre: Catalogue des peintures, I: Ecole française*, Paris, 1924, p. 281.

9. Louis Réau, "Une Collection de primitifs français en Amérique," *Gazette des beaux-arts*, 5th per., vol. XIII (1926), pp. 13, 15.

10. Paul-André Lemoisne, *La Peinture au musée du Louvre, I: Ecole française, XIVe, XVe, XVIe siècles*, Paris, 1929, pp. 50–51.

11. Bryson Burroughs and Harry B. Wehle, "The Michael Friedsam Collection," *Bulletin of the Metropolitan Museum of Art*, vol. XXVII, no. 11 (Nov. 1932), sec. II, p. 14.

12. Charles Sterling, *The Metropolitan Museum of Art: A Catalogue of French Paintings, Fifteenth–Eighteenth Centuries*, Cambridge, Mass., 1955, pp. 40–41.

13. Charles Sterling and Hélène Adhémar, *Musée national du Louvre: Ecoles françaises, XIVe, XVe et XVIe siècles*, Paris, 1965, p. 31.

14. *European Art in the Virginia Museum of Fine Arts: A Catalogue*, Richmond, Va., 1966, p. 36, says the Richmond version is said to be identical with that formerly in the Pelouze and Monery collections, of which no photograph or reproduction is now known. Careful comparison of the Richmond painting with the reproduction in the catalogue of the Géza Brunsvik sale (Vienna, Nov. 25ff., 1902, no. 130) reveals that the Richmond version is identical with that formerly in the Brunsvik collection.

15. Anne de Groër, "Corneille de la Haye, peintre de Lyon," Ph.D. diss., Paris, Ecole de Chartes, 1974, pp. 244–51bis; Anne de Groër, "Nouvelles Recherches sur Corneille, à la lumière du *Portrait de Pierre Aymeric*," *La Revue du Louvre*, vol. XXVIII (1978), p. 42, note 12.

16. In a letter of June 1, 1987, to the author, Anne Dubois de Groër writes, "I did consider all the versions of the *Portrait of Jean d'Albon de Saint-André* to be replicas until I received a photograph of the Chatsworth version, which looks to me like the original." The author is especially grateful to Mrs. Dubois de Groër for sharing with him these recent observations.

17. Katharine Baetjer, *European Paintings in the Metropolitan Museum: A Summary Catalogue*, New York, 1980, pp. 30–31.

18. When the Timbal catalogue was published, Jean d'Albon's life dates were thought to be 1475–1550.

19. Edouard Jeannez and Joseph Déchelette, "Les Vitraux de Saint-André d'Apchon," *Bulletin de la Diana*, vol. IX (1896–97), 1898, pp. 148–67, pl. IV, reproducing the stained-glass portrait of Jean d'Albon in detail.

20. See Dimier 1902. Pierre-Hyacinthe Morice, *Histoire ecclésiastique et civile de Bretagne*, vol. II, Paris, 1756, engraving opp. p. 249.

21. Since the identification of the sitter as Jean IV de Rieux in the 1756 publication is blatantly false, rather than to substitute his son it would have been better to discount it altogether. It is easy to imagine how the erroneous identification was made. Since the painting reproduced by the print then belonged to the comte de Rieux, it was probably presumed to be a portrait of his illustrious forebear.

22. Sterling 1955 and Waterhouse 1967, for instance. A list of the governors of Lyon during the sixteenth century is found in Claude Brosette, *Eloge historique ou histoire abrégée de la ville de Lyon, ancienne et moderne*, Lyon, 1711, pp. 132–36.

23. For Jean d'Albon, see the biography of his more renowned son by Lucien Romier, *La Carrière d'un favori: Jacques d'Albon de Saint-André, maréchal de France, 1512–1562*, Paris, 1909.

24. Those claiming the sitter to be Jean de Rieux believed the portrait to date about 1548 (when Jean de Rieux would have been about forty-one).

25. Baetjer 1980.

26. Dimier 1924–25.

Provenance Sir Andrew Fountaine, Narford Hall, King's Lynn, Norfolk, England (d. 1753); his sister Elizabeth Fountaine Clent (from 1753); her daughter Elizabeth Clent Price; her son Brigg Price, later Brigg Fountaine (d. 1825); his son Andrew Fountaine III (1825–35); his son Andrew Fountaine IV (1835–73); his daughter Mary Fountaine, Narford Hall (1873–94; sale, Christie's, London, July 7, 1894, no. 14, as by Holbein); Charles Butler, London (1902); J. Pierpont Morgan, New York (by 1911–13); his son J. P. Morgan, New York (1913–43); [M. Knoedler, New York, 1943]; Mrs. Albert S. Ingalls, Cleveland (from 1943); Jane Taft Ingalls bequest, 1962.

Exhibitions New York, The Metropolitan Museum of Art, 1911–14, on extended loan from J. Pierpont Morgan (cat. by Bryson Burroughs, p. 48, no. C8–4); New York, M. Knoedler, *Collection of J. P. Morgan*, Nov. 23–Dec. 11, 1943 (cat., p. 9, no. 7).

Literature Léon Emmanuel Simon Joseph de Laborde, *La Renaissance des arts à la cour de France*, pt. 2, vol. I, Paris, 1855, p. 634; Natalis Rondot, *Les Peintres de Lyon du quatorzième au dix-huitième siècle*, Paris, 1888, p. 101; Louis Dimier, "Une Oeuvre inconnue de Corneille de Lyon," *La Revue de l'art ancienne et moderne*, vol. XII (1902), pp. 5–8, ill. opp. p. 6; Louis Dimier, *French Painting in the Sixteenth Century*, London, 1904, pp. 136–37; Louis Dimier, in Thieme-Becker, vol. VII, p. 423; Gaston Brière, *Musée national du Louvre: Catalogue des peintures, I: Ecole française*, Paris, 1924, p. 281; Louis Dimier, *Histoire de la peinture de portrait en France au XVIe siècle*, pt. 1, Paris, 1924, p. 40, pl. 12; pt. 2, 1925, pp. 73, 75–76, no. 295; Louis Dimier, *Histoire de la peinture française des origines au retour de Vouet*, Paris, 1925, p. 70, pl. XLVIII-1; Louis Réau, "Une Collection de primitifs français en Amérique," *Gazette des beaux-arts*, 5th per., vol. XIII (1926), pp. 13, 15; E. M. Sperling, *Catalogue of a Loan Exhibition of French Primitives*, F. Kleinberger Galleries, New York, 1927, p. 144; Paul-André Lemoisne, *La Peinture au musée du Louvre, I: Ecole française, XIVe, XVe, XVIe siècles*, Paris, 1929, pp. 50–51; Bryson Burroughs and Harry B. Wehle, "The Michael Friedsam Collection," *Bulletin of the Metropolitan Museum of Art*, vol. XXVII, no. 11 (Nov. 1932), sec. II, p. 14; Louis Dimier, *La Peinture française au XVIe siècle*, Marseille, 1942, p. 15, pl. 22a; Charles Sterling, *The Metropolitan Museum of Art: A Catalogue of French Paintings, Fifteenth–Eighteenth Centuries*, Cambridge, Mass., 1955, pp. 40–41; *European Art in the Virginia Museum of Fine Arts: A Catalogue*, Richmond, Va., 1966, p. 36; Ellis Waterhouse, *The James A. de Rothschild Collection at Waddesdon Manor: Paintings*, London, 1967, p. 228; Anne de Groër, "Corneille de La Haye, peintre de Lyon," Ph.D. diss., Ecole de Chartes, 1974, pp. 244–51bis; Anne de Groër, "Nouvelles Recherches sur Corneille, à la lumière du *Portrait de Pierre Aymeric*," *La Revue du Louvre*, vol. XXVIII (1978), p. 42, note 12.

1962.5

1962.4

❧

Style of Corneille de Lyon

Portrait of a Gentleman

ca. 1535–45
Oil on panel, 12.7 x 10.8 cm (5 x 4¼ in.)

The sitter, a young man about thirty years old, is depicted bust length against a teal blue background. Seen nearly full face, turned slightly to the viewer's right, he has brown eyes and a brown forked beard and mustache. His head is covered by a black velvet cap inclined to the left and ornamented on the right with a white feather. He wears a high-collared black doublet closed at both sides of the neck with five round gilt buttons. The collar and the shoulders of the sleeveless doublet are gathered with small ties fitted at the ends with cylindrical gilt ornaments. Four tasseled strings hang from his neck. Part of a white collar trimmed with black-edged ruche is visible at the neck, and the sleeves of an olive green undergarment with a brocade pattern highlighted in white emerge from beneath the doublet.

The aristocratic attire of the sitter suggests that he was a member of the nobility rather than of the bourgeoisie. The style of the costume indicates a date of about 1535–45.

Excepting its exhibition in 1911–14 and 1943, this fine portrait is unpublished. Although of significant quality, it cannot, on stylistic grounds, be attributed to Corneille de Lyon. The porcelain-like finish of the flesh tones and the completely unmodulated background are not in keeping with portraits currently attributed to Corneille — works that have a stronger sense of atmosphere and that are more highly modeled in light and shadow.

A label with the following text was once attached to the reverse of the panel:

Corneille de Lyon. From the Fountaine Collection. This portrait decorated a cabinet that belonged more than 160 years ago to Sir Andrew Fountaine of Narford, the great connoisseur and has been in the possession of the family ever since. I bought the cabinet from Mrs. Fountaine of Narford. R. L. D.

R. L. D. is the monogram of Robert Langton Douglas, a dealer who had the picture around the turn of the century. A photograph preserved in the Frick Art Reference Library, New York, which was a gift of Douglas's widow, records the cabinet installation — obviously a nineteenth-century fabrication (fig. 1).

Provenance Sir Andrew Fountaine, Narford Hall, King's Lynn, Norfolk, England (d. 1753); his sister Elizabeth Fountaine Clent (from 1753); her daughter Elizabeth Clent Price; her son Brigg Price, later Brigg Fountaine (d. 1825); his son Andrew Fountaine III (1825–35); his son Andrew Fountaine IV (1835–73); his daughter Mary Fountaine, Narford Hall (from 1873, sold to Douglas); [Robert Langton Douglas, London and Dublin, sold to Morgan]; J. Pierpont Morgan, New York (by 1911–13); his son J. P. Morgan, New York (1913–43); [M. Knoedler, New York, 1943]; Mr. and Mrs. Albert S. Ingalls, Cleveland (from 1943); Jane Taft Ingalls bequest, 1962.

Exhibitions New York, The Metropolitan Museum of Art, 1911–14, on extended loan from J. Pierpont Morgan (cat. by Bryson Burroughs, p. 47 or 48, no. c8–1 or c8–3, the descriptions and dimensions of which appear to be interchanged); New York, M. Knoedler, *Collection of J. P. Morgan*, Nov. 23–Dec. 11, 1943 (cat., pp. 8–9, no. 6).

1962.4

Fig. 1 Nineteenth-century cabinet installation with Style of Corneille de Lyon *Portrait of a Gentleman,* top center. Photograph courtesy of the Frick Art Reference Library, New York, gift of Mrs. Robert Langton Douglas.

Seventeenth-Century Dutch and Flemish Paintings

Walter A. Liedtke

Frans Hals

Probably Antwerp ca. 1582–1666 Haarlem

Frans Hals's family was among the many driven out of the Southern Netherlands after the duke of Parma took Antwerp in 1585. Hals is cited as a native of Antwerp in documents dating from 1611 to 1628, although his father, Franchoys Hals, was a clothworker from Mechelen (Malines). The family had settled in Haarlem (as did many other Flemings about this time) by 1591 when the artist's brother, the genre painter Dirck Hals, was born. Evidently, Hals was in Antwerp in the summer of 1616 but otherwise rarely left Haarlem. Despite prolific work as a portraitist and some prestigious commissions (including "shooting pieces," or group portraits of civic-guard companies, dating from 1616, 1627, 1633, 1634–37, and 1639), Hals had financial problems early and especially late in his career and probably at many other times during his long life. His first wife died in 1615, leaving him with two children. With Lysbeth Reyniers, whom Hals married in February 1617, he had at least eight more children (five of Hals's sons are recorded as artists). Only a few Dutch portraitists were well paid for their works, and after 1650, when Hals's sober (if seemingly spontaneous) style was out of fashion, he suffered lean years, accepting aid from the town council from 1662 on. Hals painted group portraits of the regents and regentesses of the Haarlem almshouse in 1664 (Haarlem, Frans Halsmuseum). He was buried in Saint Bavo's, the city's Great Church, on September 1, 1666, at the age — according to the contemporary note of an acquaintance — of eighty-five or eighty-six.[1]

For little reason other than his stature, the painter is often mentioned in the same breath as Rembrandt and Vermeer and has long been a partly legendary character. The biographer Arnold Houbraken was the first of many critics who imagined Hals as drunk every night and as put to bed by his pupils.[2] It is clear from the large group portraits and from single, pendant, and family portraits of prominent citizens that Hals was well respected in the community, as he must have been by his students Adriaen Brouwer, Adriaen van Ostade (see 1931.400 and 1931.420, pp. 148 and 149), Philips Wouwerman, and Dirck Hals. Judith Leyster and Jan Miense Molenaer also may have been students of Hals.

There is likewise poetic license in the concept of Hals the impressionist, although he influenced Manet and profoundly impressed Van Gogh. Eugène Fromentin, following his tour of the Lowlands in 1875, wrote of Hals's renewed reputation at a time when nature was studied "with some clamor and no little excess. His method serves as a programme to certain doctrines by virtue of which the most word-for-word exactness is wrongly taken for truth, and the most perfectly indifferent execution taken for the last word of knowledge and taste."[3] It is now clear that Hals's compositions and, when present, his iconographic programs are carefully considered[4] and that his open brushwork and tonal palette, while suggesting the fluid properties of light and atmosphere or the movement of an eye or a hand, never fail to convey impressions of substance and surface, of solid, weighty, textured forms in convincing if often featureless space. In Hals's best portraits these visual qualities are complemented by his perception, or at least presentation, of character, which, even more than his technique, has no parallel in portraits by other Haarlem artists, such as the uniformly engaging examples by Johannes Verspronck.

1. For more on Hals's life, see Seymour Slive, *Frans Hals*, vol. 1, London, 1970, chap. 1; and the long list of references assembled by Cynthia von Bogendorf-Rupprath in Peter C. Sutton et al., *Masters of Seventeenth-Century Dutch Genre Painting*, exh. cat., Philadelphia Museum of Art, 1984, pp. 208–9.

2. For Houbraken's life of Hals, 1718, trans. by Michael Hoyle, see Seymour Slive, ed., *Frans Hals*, exh. cat., National Gallery of Art, Washington, D.C., 1989, pp. 17–18.

3. Eugène Fromentin, *The Old Masters of Belgium and Holland*, New York, 1963 (*Les Maîtres d'autrefois*, 1876), p. 225.

4. On Hals and iconography see, for example, E. de Jongh and P. J. Vinken, "Frans Hals als voortzetter van een emblematische traditie," *Oud Holland*, vol. LXXVIII (1961), pp. 117–52; and David Smith, "Courtesy and Its Discontents: Frans Hals's *Portrait of Isaac Massa and Beatrix van der Laen*," *Oud Holland*, vol. C (1986), pp. 2–34.

Frans Hals

Portrait of a Man

ca. 1632–34
Oil on canvas, 121 x 95.8 cm (47⅝ x 37¾ in.)

This is a three-quarter-length portrait of a bearded gentleman standing with his left arm akimbo and his right hand holding a glove. His wide-brimmed hat, the cape over his left shoulder, and his black suit with large lace collar and cuffs were fashionable attire in about 1633–34. A shadow to the right suggests a wall immediately behind the subject, who regards the viewer with a spontaneously friendly expression.

The traditional identification of the model as Michiel de Wael, a Haarlem brewer and captain of the Saint George Militia Company, which Hals portrayed in 1627 and in 1639, was rightly rejected by Seymour Slive.[1] Valentiner's perception of some resemblance between the subject and Tieleman Roosterman — whose portrait by Hals, dated 1634, is in the Kunsthistorisches Museum, Vienna — reveals how subjective such judgments can be.[2] Indeed, the superficial similarity to De Wael in the 1627 group portrait is mostly a matter of mustache and beard, strong lighting from the left, and especially expression. The man in the Taft picture is evidently taller, or at least longer in face, with stronger jawline, cheekbones, chin, and brow, and a much higher break in the line of his sharp nose.

These details may warrant review since the present writer sees some resemblance between the subject here and the supposed portrait of Jacob Hofland, the ensign to the far left in Hals's *Officers and Sergeants of the Saint Hadrian Civic Guard Company* of about 1633 (Haarlem, Frans Halsmuseum).[3] The features of the two men (including the fleshy earlobes) correspond fairly well if one allows for the different expression; the ensign's apparent height and age seem about the same, as does the date of the two paintings. Slive placed the present picture between 1630 and 1633; the man's costume, particularly the style of the collar, suggests a date toward the end of this period, or perhaps about 1634.

Even an erroneous attempt to identify the sitter with a figure in one of Hals's great group portraits of the Haarlem civic-guard companies would draw attention to the importance of these pictures to Hals's individual portraits dating from the 1620s and early 1630s. The difference, for example, between this painting and portraits by Van Dyck (such as that of Frans Snyders in the Frick Collection, New York) lies, insofar as expressiveness is concerned, in the more active, even jaunty stance of the figure here, the more momentary play of features and position of one of the hands, and the warmer, seemingly more accessible attitude of the model. These qualities distinguish Hals's interpretation of his clients from the more patrician presentation of Van Dyck (whose importance for Hals, nonetheless, has been insufficiently considered) and may have been inspired in part by Hals's repeated rendition of group portraits as congenial banqueting scenes.

The Taft painting dates from the same period (ca. 1634) in which Hals began another group portrait, *"The Meagre Company,"* which was finally completed three years later by Pieter Codde (Amsterdam, Rijksmuseum). This militia piece inspired Van Gogh's praise of Hals's palette: "all one family of gray. But wait! . . . the most beautiful blacks."[4] Here the values are much more restricted than in the figure Van Gogh described, but light, medium, and dark slashes streak the suit and cape in a manner that almost justifies Van Gogh's reference to "poles of electricity."

In 1825 the painting was listed in a Dutch sale together with a pendant, but the latter picture has never convincingly been identified.

1. Seymour Slive, *Frans Hals*, vol. III, London, 1974, p. 52, under no. 85.

2. William R. Valentiner, *Frans Hals: Paintings in America*, Westport, Conn., 1936, no. 44 (rejected in Slive, vol. III, p. 52).

3. Slive, vol. II, 1970, pls. 126–27.

4. Quoted more extensively in Slive, vol. I, 1970, pp. 137–38.

Provenance Sale (supplementary) in Utrecht, June 27, 1825, no. 153, sold for 200 florins with a pendant; Charles Pillet, Paris (in 1883); [Lawrie, London]; Arthur Sanderson, Edinburgh (in 1902); [Scott and Fowles, New York, in 1906]; Taft collection, 1906.

1931.450

Exhibitions London, Royal Academy (Burlington House), *Winter Exhibition of Old Masters,* 1902, no. 101; Detroit Institute of Arts, *An Exhibition of Fifty Paintings by Frans Hals,* Jan. 10–Feb. 28, 1935 (cat. by William R. Valentiner, no. 22, as about 1634 and proposing the subject to be Tieleman Roosterman); Cleveland Museum of Art, *Twentieth Anniversary Exhibition,* 1936 (*Catalogue of the Twentieth Anniversary Exhibition of the Cleveland Museum of Art: The Official Art Exhibit of the Great Lakes Exposition,* p. 89, no. 220, pl. LII, as *Michiel de Wael[?]*); San Francisco, Palace of Fine Arts, *Golden Gate International Exposition,* 1939, no. 79; New York, World's Fair, *Masterpieces of Art,* 1940 (*Catalogue of European and American Paintings, 1500–1900 [Masterpieces of Art],* by Walter Pach, p. 62, no. 81, as De Wael, about 1634); Cincinnati Art Museum, *Masterpieces of Art,* 1941, no. 32; Montreal, Museum of Fine Arts, *Masterpieces of Painting,* 1942; Columbus Gallery of Fine Arts, Ohio, *Masterpieces of Painting,* 1950; Minneapolis Institute of Fine Arts, *Great Portraits by Famous Painters,* 1952 (cat., no. 8); Newark Museum, N.J., *Old Masters from American Collections,* 1956; Columbus Gallery of Fine Arts, Ohio, *International Masterpieces,* 1956.

Literature Wilhelm von Bode, *Studien zur Geschichte der holländischen Malerei,* Brunswick, 1883, p. 85, no. 73, under Paris, collection of Charles Pillet, and as about 1630, known as *Der Bürgermeister;* Ernst Wilhelm Moes, *Iconographia Batavia,* Amsterdam, 1897–1905, vol. II, p. 566, no. 8794–3, as in the collection of Sanderson at Learmouth Terrace and as representing Michiel de Wael; Gerald S. Davies, *Frans Hals,* London, 1902, p. 65, note 1, as De Wael; *Daily Telegraph* [London], Jan. 14, 1902; *The Times* [London], Jan. 21, 1902; *Athenaeum* [London], Mar. 1, 1902; "Old Masters at the Royal Academy," *The Magazine of Art,* vol. XXVI (1902), p. 226; Ernst Wilhelm Moes, *Frans Hals: Sa Vie et son oeuvre,* Brussels, 1909, p. 104, no. 83; Arthur Hoeber, "Some Pictures from the Collection of Mr. and Mrs. Charles P. Taft," *The International Studio,* vol. XXXIX (1909–10), p. LXXIV; William Walton, "Exhibition in New York of Paintings from the Collection of Mr. and Mrs. Charles P. Taft," *Burlington Magazine,* vol. XVI (1909–10), p. 368; Cornelis Hofstede de Groot, *A Catalogue Raisonné of the Works of the Most Eminent Dutch Painters of the Seventeenth Century,* vol. III, London, 1910, p. 72, no. 242, stating that "there is apparently no evidence for the identification of the sitter as M. de Wael"; "Art Notes," *The Evening Post* [New York], Feb. 28, 1914, p. 7; Gustav Kobbe, "Noted Art Collectors Send Their Famous Old Masters for Loan Exhibition of Dutch Art in New York," *New York Herald*, Mar. 1, 1914; Wilhelm von Bode and Moritz Julius Binder, *Frans Hals: Sein Leben und seine Werke*, vol. II, Berlin, 1914, p. 56, no. 168, pl. 102 (same in English ed., 1914); Maurice W. Brockwell, *A Catalogue of Paintings in the Collection of Mr. and Mrs. Charles P. Taft*, New York, 1920, pp. 60–64, no. 17, quoting at length from reviews, articles, and books of 1897–1914; William R. Valentiner, *Frans Hals, des Meisters Gemälde (Klassiker der Kunst)*, Berlin and Leipzig, 1923, pp. 120 (ill.), 314, doubting the identification with De Wael; William R. Valentiner, *Frans Hals: Paintings in America*, Westport, Conn., 1936, no. 44, proposing the subject to be Tieleman Roosterman; "Cleveland Exhibits," *The Art Digest*, vol. x, no. 18 (July 1, 1936), p. 20; W. M. Milliken, "World Art at Cleveland," *The American Magazine of Art*, vol. XXIX (1936), pp. 436 (ill.), 438; Gerrit David Gratama, review of Valentiner, 1936, *Burlington Magazine*, vol. LXXI (1937), p. 49, wondering whether the De Wael identification might not be right; *Coronet*, vol. v, no. 4 (Feb. 1, 1939), p. 14 (ill.); *The Art Digest*, vol. XIII, no. 12, (Mar. 15, 1939), p. 47; Hans Tietze, *Masterpieces of European Painting in America*, New York, 1939, p. 165; *Catalogue of the Taft Museum*, 1939 and 1958, no. 242; Seymour Slive, *Frans Hals*, vol. II, London, 1970, pl. 131, and vol. III, 1974, pp. 51–52, no. 85, and p. 54 under no. 93, as about 1630–33, the subject unidentified; Claus Grimm, *Frans Hals: Entwicklung, Werkanalyse, Gesamtkatalog*, Berlin, 1972, p. 203, no. 80, fig. 111, as about 1636; Claus Grimm and E. C. Montagni, *L'Opera completa di Frans Hals*, Milan, 1974, pp. 98–99, no. 108, as about 1635; Norbert Middlekoop and Anne van Grevenstein, *Frans Hals: Leven, werk, restauratie*, Haarlem and Amsterdam, 1988, p. 77, fig. c; Claus Grimm, *Frans Hals: Das Gesamtwerk*, Stuttgart and Zurich, 1989, p. 200, fig. 113a (detail of face), and p. 273, no. 29 (ill.), as ca. 1626, on the basis of the erroneous De Wael identification.

1931.450

Frans Hals

Portrait of a Seated Man Holding a Hat
Portrait of a Seated Woman Holding a Fan

ca. 1650
Oil on canvas: 1931.451, 109.8 x 82.5 cm (43¼ x 32½ in.); 1931.455, 109.5 x 82.5 cm (43⅛ x 32½ in.)

In these pendant pictures a rather young married couple is depicted in three-quarter length and seated. Their side chairs are frontal, the figures turned toward each other; they look at the viewer with uneffusive smiles. The man's suit and the woman's dress are quietly fashionable costumes of about 1650. The man holds his hat in his lap, the woman a closed fan in her left hand. These two paintings are among Hals's most engaging companion pictures. They form an ideal complement to the earlier *Portrait of a Man*, since the artist's style evolved considerably during the intervening years.

This development may correspond to some extent with the differences that have been discerned between two generations in Holland. It has often been suggested that the men and women of the independent nation's nascent years (i.e., Hals's own contemporaries) were self-assertive types who gave their children a more stable society.[1] The idea might be illustrated by the three Hals portraits in the Taft Museum, although the sitters themselves are unknown. The hypothesis raises the question (familiar

from Van Dyck studies) of "self-projection" of Hals's own disposition at the ages of about fifty and sixty-five. Finally, it should be stressed that the more restrained and subtle qualities of the later works respond, at the measured pace of Hals's mature years, to broad stylistic changes in Dutch art dating from the 1630s and 1640s. The *Portrait of a Man* of about 1634, for example, is at ease in the company of Rembrandt's lively *Portrait of a Man Rising from His Chair*, dated 1633 (see 1931.409, p. 158), while the later pendant pictures may likewise be compared with Rembrandt portraits dating from the middle years of the century.

These broad remarks may be admissible here since they clarify the many discrete considerations involved in the seemingly straightforward task of designing portraits such as these. At the same time they may reveal how surprisingly subjective our responses to portraits can be. Thus, Seymour Slive, when about thirty years younger than he is now, saw the sitter in the *Portrait of a Seated Man* as "bolt up-right . . . ready to spring," while the woman, "with one arm hooked over the back of the chair," was presumed "more informal—perhaps more at ease—than many of her countrywomen."[2] To the present writer, by contrast, these portraits, and many others by Hals from the 1640s, appear more reserved than his earlier inventions, although the sitters, to be sure, still seem unaffected and accessible. Their complementary positions, seated diagonally on nearly frontal chairs, strengthen the sense of volume and align the figures with the frames (at the lower corners especially) in a way that suggests their weight or, more subjectively, their "substance." Hals understood intuitively from long experience that this literally sedate presentation of the sitters would set off their smiling expressions, foil the fluid strokes of color, and intensify the impressions of movement and light. Similarly, the sober palette is relieved by the brightly painted faces and hands and by such incidentals as the red chair seat below the man's hat, the green chair back supporting the woman, and of course the entire front of her dress, which might distract the viewer from her husband were it not for her fan pointing in his direction.

The more concrete questions of authorship (raised by Van Dantzig and Grimm; see Literature) and of the woman's possible identity (considered by Brockwell; see Literature) are laid to rest by Slive's catalogue entries of 1974 and 1989 (see Literature). In his 1971 monograph Grimm cites the Taft pendants as by Frans Hals the Younger, and in the concordance of his 1989 monograph as from Hals's workshop, group A, to be associated with the anonymous Meister der Fischerkinder. Whatever doubts one might have about Grimm's workshop hypothesis must be accompanied in this case by an account of the paintings' quality and especially by an understanding of their seriously worn condition.

Slive's dating to 1648–50 is supported by the style of the sitters' dress, which in the portrait of the woman would encourage a date of 1650 rather than slightly earlier. In her article refuting (along with Moes-Veth) Van Dantzig's doubts about this canvas and the woman's costume, Mevr. der Kinderen-Besier describes her dress as modern and highly chic in its time, which is about 1650.[3]

1931.451

1931.455

A small, late copy of the portrait of the woman (San Antonio, Tex., private collection, in 1980) is described by Slive in the 1989 Hals exhibition catalogue.[4] The copy may be British (and probably nineteenth century) in view of its apparent provenance and that of the Taft portraits.

1. This and similarly broad generalizations frequently are made in reference to Merry Company scenes painted by Hals, Buytewech, and other artists active in Haarlem during the second decade of the century. Thus Jan Kelch (in Peter C. Sutton et al., *Masters of Seventeenth-Century Dutch Genre Painting*, exh. cat., Philadelphia Museum of Art, 1984, p. 171), discussing Buytewech's *Merry Company in the Open Air* (ca. 1616–17, Berlin, on extended loan to the Gemäldegalerie), states that "this painting is Buytewech's observation of his own generation, the first to enjoy a carefree life in the Dutch Republic after the wars of independence against Spain." The Taft Museum's couple would belong to the generation following Buytewech's, when, according to Slive (in Seymour Slive, Jakob Rosenberg, and E. H. ter Kuile, *Dutch Art and Architecture: 1600–1800*, Baltimore, 1966, p. 43), "Dutch burghers were not as aggressive as their fathers had been. They preferred to be seen as dignified syndics, rather than boisterous soldiers." Obviously, this much-recycled reading of history through pictures, rather than vice versa, should be practiced parsimoniously.

2. From Seymour Slive, *Frans Hals*, exh. cat., Frans Halsmuseum, Haarlem, 1962, p. 69.

3. Johanna Henriëtte der Kinderen-Besier, "Het Kostuum der Vrouw op het aan Frans Hals Toegeschreven Portret te Cincinnati," *Maandblad voor Beeldende Kunsten*, vol. XVII (1940), p. 205. The author accordingly reproduced a drawing of this picture in her classic study, *Spelevaart der Mode*, Amsterdam, 1950, pp. 151, 153, fig. 128. Compare her fig. 132d, after a portrait by Bol dated 1650, which would tend to support this date for the Taft paintings.

4. See Seymour Slive, ed., *Frans Hals*, exh. cat., National Gallery of Art, Washington, D.C., 1989, p. 309.

Provenance James, fourth lord Talbot of Malahide (1805–1883), Castle Malahide, near Dublin (see Brockwell 1920, pp. 106–7, on the paintings in this collection); Richard Wogan Talbot, fifth lord Talbot of Malahide (before 1908); [Sulley, London, in 1908]; [Scott and Fowles, New York, in 1909]; Taft collection, 1909.

Exhibitions New York, Scott and Fowles, 1909 and 1914; Haarlem, Frans Halsmuseum, *Frans Hals*, 1937 (cat., *Frans Hals Tentoonstelling*, p. 49, nos. 95, 96, pls. 95, 96); New York, Schaeffer Galleries, *Frans Hals*, 1937 (cat., *Paintings by Frans Hals*, nos. 22, 23); New York, World's Fair, *Masterpieces of Art*, 1939 (*Catalogue of European Paintings and Sculpture from 1300 to 1800*, p. 90, no. 87 [*Man* only and incorrectly as lent by the Cincinnati Art Museum]); San Francisco, Palace of Fine Arts, *Golden Gate International Exposition*, 1940 (cat., p. 14, no. 190 [*Man*], ill. p. 41); City Art Museum of St. Louis, *Fortieth Anniversary Exhibition*, 1947 (*Woman*); Los Angeles County Museum, *Loan Exhibition of Paintings by Frans Hals, Rembrandt*, 1947 (cat., p. 22, nos. 16, 17, pls. 16, 17); New York, The Metropolitan Museum of Art, and Toledo Museum of Art, *Dutch Painting: The Golden Age*, 1954–55 (cat., nos. 32, 33 [ill.]); Haarlem, Frans Halsmuseum, *Frans Hals*, 1962 (cat. by Seymour Slive, pp. 68–69, nos. 59–60, pls. 63, 64); Cleveland Museum of Art, *Style, Truth, and the Portrait*, Oct. 1–Nov. 10, 1963; New York, The Metropolitan Museum of Art, and Cincinnati, Taft Museum, *Dutch Couples: Pair Portraits by Rembrandt and His Contemporaries*, 1973–74 (brochure by John Walsh [Metropolitan]; brochure by Jane Merkel [Taft]); Washington, D.C., National Gallery of Art [also London and Haarlem], *Frans Hals*, 1989–90 (cat. ed. by Seymour Slive, nos. 63, 64, pp. 309–11).

Literature Arthur Hoeber, "Some Pictures from the Collection of Mr. and Mrs. Charles P. Taft," *The International Studio*, vol. XXXIX (1909–10), p. LXXIV; William Walton, "Exhibition in New York of Paintings from the Collection of Mr. and Mrs. Charles P. Taft," *Burlington Magazine*, vol. XVI (1909–10), p. 368, pls. I, 1, and 2; Elisabeth Luther Cary, "Some Masters of Portraiture," *Putnam's Magazine*, vol. VII (Feb. 1910), pp. 525, 527 (ill.); *Connoisseur*, vol. XXXVI (1913), pp. 99, 120 (*Man* ill. and cited), 173, 188 (*Woman* ill. and cited); *The Evening Post* [New York], Feb. 28, 1914, p. 7 (*Woman* mentioned); *New York Herald*, Mar. 1, 1914 (*Man* described); *New York Tribune*, Mar. 1, 1914 (both portraits ill.); Wilhelm von Bode and Moritz Julius Binder, *Frans Hals: Sein Leben und seine Werke*, vol. II, Berlin, 1914, nos. 253–54, pls. 162–63; Maurice W. Brockwell, *A Catalogue of Paintings in the Collection of Mr. and Mrs. Charles P. Taft*, New York, 1920, pp. 104–10, nos. 27, 28, quoting at length from the preceding articles; William R. Valentiner, *Frans Hals, des Meisters Gemälde (Klassiker der Kunst)*, Berlin and Leipzig, 1923, pp. 238–39 (ill.), 321, as dating from the late 1640s; William R. Valentiner, *Frans Hals: Paintings in America*, Westport, Conn., 1936, nos. 89, 90; Horst Gerson, "The Frans Hals Exhibition at Haarlem," *Burlington Magazine*, vol. LXXI (1937), p. 139; *The Art Digest*, vol. XI, no. 17 (June 1, 1937), pp. 5 (*Woman* ill.), 6; Abraham Bredius, letter to *De Telegraaf*, Sept. 28, 1937, praising the two pictures; Edgar P. Richardson, "Hals, An Important Showing," *Parnassus*, vol. IX, no. 6 (Nov. 1937), pp. 5, 7 (*Woman* ill.); Alfred M. Frankfurter, "Celebrating the Return of Hals," *The Art News*, vol. XXXVI, no. 7 (Nov. 13, 1937), p. 12 (*Woman* ill.); *The Art Digest*, vol. XII, no. 4 (Nov. 15, 1937), p. 7; *Magazine of Art*, vol. XXX, no. 12 (Dec. 1937), p. 744; *Coronet* (June 1939), pp. 56, 57 (both ill. in color); *Catalogue of the Taft Museum*, Cincinnati, 1939 and 1958, nos. 477 (*Man*), 479 (*Woman*) (both ill.); Maurits Michel van Dantzig, "Twee Portretten van Frans Hals of . . . Moderne Vervalschingen?" *Maandblad voor Beeldende Kunsten*, vol. XVII (1940), pp. 149–52; A. J. Moes-Veth, "Nog Eens: Twee Portretten van Frans Hals," *Maandblad voor Beeldende Kunsten,* vol. XVII (1940), pp. 202–4; Johanna Henriëtte der Kinderen-Besier, "Het Kostuum der Vrouw op het aan Frans Hals Toegeschreven Portret te Cincinnati," *Maandblad voor Beeldende Kunsten*, vol. XVII (1940), pp. 205–6; *The Art Digest*, vol. XIV, no. 18 (July 1, 1940), p. 8; *The Art News*, vol. XL, no. 1 (Feb. 1, 1941), p. 17; Gerrit David Gratama, *Frans Hals*, The Hague, 1943, pls. 96, 97; Johanna Henriëtte der Kinderen-Besier, *Spelevaart der Mode*, Amsterdam, 1950, pp. 151, 153, fig. 128 (*Woman*); Seymour Slive, *Frans Hals*, vol. I, London, 1970, pp. 158–59, vol. II, 1970, pls. 268–70, and vol. III, 1974, p. 89, nos. 173, 174; Claus Grimm and E. C. Montagni, *L'Opera completa di Frans Hals*, Milan, 1974, pp. 113–14, nos. 270, 271, noting that Grimm excluded the works from his 1972 monograph, assigning them to Frans Hals the Younger; Claus Grimm, *Frans Hals: Das Gesamtwerk*, Stuttgart and Zurich, 1989, p. 285, as from Hals's workshop; E. Hendriks and K. Levy-van Halm (in collaboration with J. R. J. van Asperen de Boer), "Report Concerning a Preliminary Technical Investigation of Paintings Exhibited during the Frans Hals Exhibition, Held from May 11 to July 22, 1990, in the Frans Hals Museum, Haarlem," Haarlem, Feb. 1991, pp. 2, 16, 17, 33, on technical qualities found in these and other paintings by Hals.

1931.451, 1931.455

Style of Frans Hals

A Young Boy with a Flute and Another Child behind Him

Seventeenth century, probably 1620s
Oil on panel, 35 x 32.9 cm (13¾ x 13 in.)

A young boy, laughing or smiling broadly, is seen in bust length on this round panel. He holds a simple flute in his right hand. Behind him another boy, apparently younger still, looks on.

Many small paintings of this type and style are known. A few are authentic works by Hals; some are contemporary with his career; and a good number date from after his lifetime (often from the second half of the nineteenth century).[1] Three bust-length pictures of a young boy, each on a round panel about 29.2 centimeters (11½ in.) in diameter, are unquestionably autograph and set a standard by which similar paintings may be judged. The most familiar tondo of the three is the *Laughing Boy* in the Mauritshuis, the Hague,[2] while the example closest in composition to the Taft painting is the *Laughing Boy with a Soap Bubble* in a private collection in Hollywood, California.[3] These pictures and the third, *Laughing Boy Holding a Flute* in Sussex, are convincingly dated by Slive to the early 1620s.[4]

The Taft picture appears to be the best of six panels depicting the same subject in the narrowest sense.[5] Slive rejects them all but suggests that they may depend, ultimately, on a lost original. There is every reason to think that this is so, since the composition and subject are characteristic of Hals's small genre paintings dating from the 1620s. The Sussex picture and two groups of small panels painted in Hals's manner represent a laughing boy with a flute.[6] Older boys with a flute appear in two somewhat later paintings by Hals (ca. 1627): one of the two tondos in Schwerin[7] and the canvas of more conventional size in Berlin-Dahlem.[8]

The present picture, when compared with an original work like the *Laughing Boy* in the Mauritshuis, appears to be far less fluidly painted and at the same time less successful in suggesting three-dimensional form and space. The placement, color, and size of a brushstroke from Hals's own hand are determined primarily by the stroke's descriptive function, especially when the task is to articulate facial features. By contrast, the apparent looseness of a stroke — its broad, rough, and rhythmic quality — conveys the more fleeting impressions of action, light, and atmosphere. Achieving a balance between potentially antagonistic qualities required considerable care in the course of execution and exceptional technical skill. Few of Hals's numerous copyists and imitators understood this, to judge by their usually hasty attempts to approximate his style. Here, for example, the main figure's face is awkwardly brushed in ill-assorted colors; the child's cheeks resemble a flat surface with a few dents. Hair, skin, and cloth are all of one dull texture and all in one plane. The boy's expression, too, is superficial, since the smile bears little organic relation to the structure of the face. The eyes are similarly simplified.

In execution, then, the Taft picture could not be by Hals, nor is it consistent with the styles of his close associates such as Judith Leyster and Dirck Hals. However, the painting does appear to be an object from Hals's immediate circle of the 1620s. Whether it is from his workshop is unclear; the term suggests a secondary responsibility with which Hals, in this case, need not be charged.

A figure with a flute is often considered to have been an allegory of the sense of hearing and was certainly read as such in a set of images depicting the Five Senses.[9] The Taft painting and most similar pictures of young boys (the usual jacket and collar suggest that all these youthful figures are male) cannot be shown to have belonged to a set. It seems likely that many of these mod-

1931.401

est pictures were sold singly or in pairs and that the flute is a conventional and comparatively unimportant motif.

The subject of these paintings is essentially the charm, the innocence, and the happiness of the children, a theme dear to the Dutch, as it seems to have been to Hals, who had several children of his own. In this light, the much-repeated idea that these pictures were painted just for pleasure appears true enough.[10] They were, however, certainly salable, as were the small single-figure works by Hals's pupils Adriaen Brouwer and Adriaen van Ostade. In fact, the little wooden panels on which these images were painted (especially those that are actually cut round) would have to have been ordered from a panel maker, not picked up whenever the artist was in the mood. The many repetitions reveal that these works were popular in price and subject, rather than personal and "priceless," as is, for example, Rubens's small portrait of his daughter, Clara Serena, in the collection of the princes of Liechtenstein.[11]

1. Seymour Slive, *Frans Hals*, vol. III, London, 1974, pp. 18–19, nos. 27–29, and pp. 35–36, nos. 58, 59, for genuine works of this type; pp. 128–31, nos. D1–D8, figs. 101–21, for the doubtful and rejected pictures. See also Claus Grimm and E. C. Montagni, *L'Opera completa di Frans Hals*, Milan, 1974, pp. 115–18, nos. 281–317.

2. Slive, vol. II, 1970, pl. 49, and vol. III, pp. 18–19, no. 29. For color plates and commentaries, see also Hans R. Hoetink, ed., *The Royal Picture Gallery Mauritshuis*, Amsterdam and New York, 1985, pp. 192–93, no. 37; and Ben Broos, in *De Rembrandt à Vermeer: Les Peintres hollandais au Mauritshuis de la Haye*, exh. cat., Grand Palais, Paris, 1986, pp. 227–31, no. 28.

3. Slive, vol. II, pl. 51, and vol. III, p. 18, no. 28.

4. Slive, vol. II, pls. 49–51; a pair of circular panels in Schwerin, nos. 58, 59, and pls. 91–95, are dated by Slive to about 1626–28 and are also reproduced by Broos.

5. Slive, vol. III, pp. 130–31, group D6.

6. The two groups are listed under D4 and D5 in Slive, vol. III, pp. 129–30; no. 1 (fig. 108) under D5, *Boy with a Flute*, in the collection of Mrs. E. W. Edwards, Cincinnati, is now in the Cincinnati Art Museum and is reproduced in Grimm and Montagni as no. 308.

7. Slive, vol. II, no. 59, pl. 92 (see note 4).

8. Slive, vol. II, no. 25, pl. 45, as ca. 1623–25; Jan Kelch in Peter C. Sutton et al., *Masters of Seventeenth-Century Dutch Genre Painting*, exh. cat., Philadelphia Museum of Art, 1984, pp. 209–10, no. 47, pl. 17, as ca. 1627 (see Kelch's note 12 on the date).

9. For example, the series by Dirck Hals reproduced in Slive, vol. I, p. 79, fig. 57; on this subject, see Kelch's comments and notes in Sutton et al., pp. 209–10.

10. For such a comment, see Slive, vol. I, p. 75.

11. *Liechtenstein: The Princely Collections*, exh. cat., The Metropolitan Museum of Art, New York, 1985, pp. 324–26, no. 204.

Provenance Mathieu Neven (sale, Cologne, Mar. 17, 1879, p. 30, no. 85); Eduard, baron von Niesewand, Mühlhausen (by Cologne) (sale, London [Christie's?], June 9, 1886, no. 52); [Scott and Fowles, New York, by 1905]; Taft collection, 1905.

Exhibitions Düsseldorf (Kunstakademie?), 1886, no. 134; Detroit Institute of Arts, *An Exhibition of Fifty Paintings by Frans Hals*, Jan. 10–Feb. 28, 1935 (cat. by William R. Valentiner, no. 5 [ill.], as the autograph version, about 1625, probably representing one of Hals's children); Milwaukee Art Center, *The Artist Looks at Children*, Oct. 31, 1959–Feb. 14, 1960; Cincinnati, Taft Museum, *In the Manner of the Master: Issues of Attribution in the Taft Museum's Collections*, Oct. 10, 1990–Jan. 20, 1991.

Literature Wilhelm von Bode, *Studien zur Geschichte der holländischen Malerei*, Brunswick, 1883, p. 88, no. 115, as a replica of Slive, vol. III, 1974, no. D6.2; Cornelis Hofstede de Groot, *A Catalogue Raisonné of the Works of the Most Eminent Dutch Painters of the Seventeenth Century*, vol. III, London, 1910, p. 36, no. 132, as signed with a monogram and as a replica of Slive, vol. III, 1974, no. D6.2; Wilhelm von Bode and Moritz Julius Binder, *Frans Hals: Sein Leben und seine Werke*, vol. I, Berlin, 1914, no. 28, pl. 12c; Maurice W. Brockwell, *A Catalogue of Paintings in the Collection of Mr. and Mrs. Charles P. Taft*, New York, 1920, pp. 65–66, wrongly as on canvas; William R. Valentiner, *Frans Hals: Paintings in America*, Westport, Conn., 1936, no. 9 (ill.), as painted about 1623–25; *Catalogue of the Taft Museum*, Cincinnati, 1939 and 1958, no. 131 (ill., 1958 ed.); Seymour Slive, *Frans Hals*, vol. III, London, 1974, p. 130, no. D6.1, as not by Hals, nor is any known version; Claus Grimm and E. C. Montagni, *L'Opera completa di Frans Hals*, Milan, 1974, pp. 116–17, no. 306a (ill.).

1931.401

Imitator of Frans Hals

Singing Youth with a Boy at His Right

Probably nineteenth century
Oil on canvas, 60.3 x 50.8 cm (23¾ x 20 in.)

A young man in a tall, feathered hat is shown bust length with an open songbook before him. His left hand is raised in a gesture that in seventeenth-century pictures indicates the keeping of musical meter. Behind him another boy joins in. The corner of a room is suggested in the right background.

Before the winter of 1938–39 when this canvas was acquired by Dr. and Mrs. William Semple, it had a secure place in the literature of Frans Hals. William Valentiner, the preeminent exponent of Northern European painting in America during the

1962.6

1930s (and a key figure in collecting circles, both in New York and in the Midwest),[1] was especially supportive of this picture. He published it in the catalogue for the 1909 Hudson-Fulton exhibition at the Metropolitan Museum of Art and in standard monographs of 1921 and 1936. He also placed it in the Detroit exhibition of 1935 and the Haarlem-New York exhibition of 1937 (see Exhibitions and Literature). The next mention of the painting in print is in Slive's complete catalogue of 1974 (the work is not cited in Claus Grimm's monograph of 1972; see Literature), in which the author, repeating opinions he expressed to the Taft Museum in letters of 1963 and 1964, lists the picture among his rejected attributions and considers it "patent" that it was not painted by Hals.[2] Slive compares it with two paintings of singing boys, one of them very similar to the Taft picture, which Valentiner published in his 1935 article on new Hals discoveries and which Slive suggests are "modern imitations."[3]

The present picture appears to form a group with Valentiner's two additions to Hals's oeuvre, although it might be regarded as the best of the three dubious works. The subjects are essentially the same, and the styles of execution, including specific passages such as the white shirt and the upraised hand, are as consistent with each other as they are alien to autograph paintings by Hals. Similarly, seventeenth-century costume is approximated naïvely in each of the three images.[4]

Even when the Taft picture is considered independently, one feels confident that the term "modern imitation" is appropriate. Nothing about the painting or its support suggests a seventeenth- or eighteenth-century origin. Indeed, the most plausible date would seem to be not long before the picture's first appearance in a London sale of 1876. One recalls the enthusiasm of

Manet for Frans Hals's fluid style and genre subjects; his *Le Bon Bock* in the Philadelphia Museum of Art was painted in 1873 with Hals very much in mind and was described by Manet's Belgian friend Alfred Stevens as "pure Haarlem beer."[5] Surely other, lesser artists of Manet's period painted imitations of Hals, in many cases for the "old-master" markets in England and France.

1. Maurice H. Sterne, *The Passionate Eye: The Life of William R. Valentiner*, Detroit, 1980.

2. Seymour Slive, *Frans Hals*, vol. III, London, 1974, p. 139, no. D29: the author also mentions "two distinct systems of paint in some areas" that are revealed by radiographs.

3. William R. Valentiner, "New Additions to the Work of Frans Hals," *Art in America*, vol. XXIII, no. 3 (June 1935), figs. 9, 10, listed as nos. 1 and 2 in Slive, vol. III, p. 139, under no. D29.

4. The hat in the Taft painting is perhaps the least anachronistic of the three forms of headgear and may have been adopted from a contemporary costume print such as those made by Willem Buytewech. Compare also the hats in Hals's early portraits of men such as the one of 1619 in Dijon and the one in Kassel of about the same date (Slive, vol. II, 1970, pls. 24, 25).

5. Quoted by Petra ten Doesschate Chu, *French Realism and the Dutch Masters*, Utrecht, 1974, p. 46. See also Peter Hecht, "Manet et les hollandais, ou la tradition du 'contemporain,'" *Septentrion, Revue de culture néerlandaise*, vol. XIII (1984), pp. 44–51.

Provenance Albert Levy (sale, London, June 16, 1876); [M. Colnaghi, London (according to Scott and Fowles)]; Etienne Martin, baron de Beurnonville (d. 1876; sale, Paris, May 9, 1881, no. 299); [Edouard Warneck, Paris]; [Galerie Sedelmeyer, Paris, reportedly in 1890]; Charles Stewart Smith, New York (by 1898–d. 1909); heirs of Charles Stewart Smith (sale, American Art Association, Anderson Galleries, New York, Jan. 4, 1935, "Valuable Paintings Including the Celebrated *Two Singing Boys* by Frans Hals," no. 56, sold for $20,000); [Stevenson Scott, 1935–37]; [Scott and Fowles, New York, 1937–38]; Dr. and Mrs. William Semple, Cincinnati 1938; Louise Taft Semple bequest, 1962.

Exhibitions New York, The Metropolitan Museum of Art, *The Hudson-Fulton Celebration*, 1909 (*Catalogue of a Collection of Paintings by Dutch Masters of the Seventeenth Century* [vol. I], by William R. Valentiner, p. 24, no. 23, as *Singing Boys*, about 1625, lent by Charles Stewart Smith, New York); Detroit Institute of Arts, *An Exhibition of Fifty Paintings by Frans Hals*, Jan. 10–Feb. 28, 1935 (cat. by William R. Valentiner); Haarlem, Frans Halsmuseum, *Frans Hals*, July 1–Sept. 30, 1937 (cat., p. 34, no. 21, as ca. 1623–25, lent by Stevenson Scott, New York); New York, Schaeffer Galleries, *Paintings by Frans Hals*, Nov. 9–23, 1937 (cat., no. 4, lent by Scott and Fowles, New York); Cincinnati, Taft Museum, *In the Manner of the Master: Issues of Attribution in the Taft Museum's Collections*, Oct. 15, 1990–Jan. 20, 1991.

Literature Wilhelm von Bode, *Studien zur Geschichte der holländischen Malerei*, Brunswick, 1883, p. 84, no. 48, as *Der Psalmensänger*, ca. 1650, in the 1881 baron von Beurnonville sale; William Roberts, *Memorials of Christie's . . .*, vol. II, London, 1897, p. 252, as *The Singer; Illustrated Catalogue of Three Hundred Paintings by Old Masters . . . Which Have at Various Times Formed Part of the Sedelmeyer Gallery*, Paris, 1898, p. 60, no. 48 (ill.); Gerald S. Davies, *Frans Hals*, London, 1902, p. 152, as *The Singer*, sold in 1876 for £267.10, and p. 153, as *Le Chanteur*, sold from the baron von Beurnonville collection in May 1881, for FF 1200 (£48); Ernst Wilhelm Moes, *Frans Hals: Sa Vie et son oeuvre*, Brussels, 1909, p. 110, as nos. 225, 226; Cornelis Hofstede de Groot, *A Catalogue Raisonné of the Works of the Most Eminent Dutch Painters of the Seventeenth Century*, vol. III, London, 1910, pp. 37–38, no. 135, as *Singing Boys*; Wilhelm von Bode and Moritz Julius Binder, *Frans Hals: Sein Leben und seine Werke*, vol. I, Berlin, 1914, no. 62, pl. 27c, as *Der Psalmsänger*; William R. Valentiner, *Frans Hals, des Meisters Gemälde (Klassiker der Kunst)*, Stuttgart, 1921, pp. 78 (ill.), 311, and 2d ed., Berlin and Leipzig, 1923, pp. 81 (ill.), 312; Franz Dülberg, *Frans Hals: Sein Leben und sein Werk*, Stuttgart, 1930,

p. 110; William R. Valentiner, "New Additions to the Work of Frans Hals," *Art in America*, vol. XXIII, no. 3 (June 1935), p. 100, comparing the Taft painting to two newly discovered works supposedly by Hals; Julius S. Held, "Frans-Hals-Ausstellung in Detroit," *Pantheon*, vol. XV (Jan.–June 1935), pp. 164, 166 (detail ill.), as part of a group of paintings dating from the 1620s and mostly representing the artist's children; William R. Valentiner, *Frans Hals: Paintings in America*, Westport, Conn., 1936, no. 6 (ill.); "Frans Hals, 'Laureate of Laughter,' Honored by His Native Haarlem," *The Art Digest*, vol. XI, no. 17 (June 1, 1937), pp. 6 (ill.), 7; Seymour Slive, *Frans Hals*, vol. III, London, 1974, p. 139, no. D29, fig. 148, as certainly not by Hals; Claus Grimm and E. C. Montagni, *L'Opera completa di Frans Hals*, Milan, 1974, pp. 116–17, no. 304.

1962.6

Adriaen van Ostade

Haarlem 1610–1685 Haarlem

Adriaen van Ostade, the son of a weaver, was baptized in Haarlem on December 10, 1610. Houbraken describes Van Ostade and Adriaen Brouwer as contemporary pupils of Frans Hals;[1] Brouwer clearly influenced Van Ostade's early style and subjects.[2] Van Ostade's career as a prolific painter and etcher of peasant life was pursued entirely in Haarlem, where he married a local woman in 1638, served as *hoofdman* (headman) of the painters' guild in 1647 and 1661, and was dean of the guild in 1662.[3] The artist's first wife died in 1642; in 1657 he married a Catholic woman from a respected Amsterdam family. The couple lived in one of Haarlem's best neighborhoods and had one daughter, whom Van Ostade raised after his wife's death in 1666. He died on April 27, 1685, and on May 2 was buried in Saint Bavo's. In early July the contents of his studio were auctioned; the newspaper announcement of June 19 mentions "over two hundred works from his hand and a great number by various masters, all his engraved plates as well as a great number of etchings, drawings, etc., by him and other masters."[4]

Van Ostade had many imitators and three gifted pupils: his short-lived brother, Isaack van Ostade (1621–1649); Cornelis Bega (1631/32–1664); and, very late in the master's life, Cornelis Dusart (1660–1704). Several hundred paintings, about fifty etchings, and some four hundred drawings and watercolors are considered to be by Van Ostade, who occasionally collaborated with his brother and employed Dusart as an assistant.[5]

1. Arnold Houbraken, *De Groote Schouburgh der Nederlantsche Konstschilders en Schilderessen*, Amsterdam, 1718–21, vol. I, pp. 320, 347.

2. On Van Ostade's early work, see Rüdiger Klessmann, "Die Anfänge des Bauerninteriors bei den Brüdern Ostade," *Jahrbuch der Berliner Museen*, vol. II (1960), pp. 92–115; and Bernhard Schnackenburg, "Die Anfänge des Bauerninteriors bei Adriaen van Ostade," *Oud Holland*, vol. LXXXV (1970), pp. 158–69.

3. Bernhard Schnackenburg, *Adriaen van Ostade, Isack van Ostade: Zeichnungen und Aquarelle*, vol. I, Hamburg, 1981, pp. 13–16, for dates pertaining to Van Ostade's life and family.

4. Schnackenburg 1981, p. 16.

5. No modern publication supersedes the slim monograph by Adolf Rosenberg, *Adriaen und Isack van Ostade*, Bielefeld and Leipzig, 1900, although Schnackenburg's discussion and catalogue of all the drawings and watercolors (1981) provide a good framework for the study of

Adriaen van Ostade's entire oeuvre. See also the studies listed in Schnackenburg's bibliography and the literature in Peter C. Sutton et al., *Masters of Seventeenth-Century Dutch Genre Painting*, exh. cat., Philadelphia Museum of Art, 1984, p. 282.

Adriaen van Ostade

Interior of an Inn with Three Men and a Boy

1656
Oil on panel, 33.8 x 39.5 cm (13¼ x 15½ in.)
Signed and dated lower left: *Av ostade 1656* (*Av* in monogram)

Although not familiar from the literature on the artist, this work is a characteristic — and characterful — picture from Van Ostade's mature period. Wilhelm von Bode, the eminent director of the State Museums in Berlin and an influential historian of Dutch art, wrote about this work to the firm of Agnew's, London, in 1905 (the year in which the Tafts bought the painting), stating that it was "certainly one of the finest picture[s] by the master, I saw for sale for years. It is fine in composition, full of life, beautiful in color. . . . I prefer these smaller pictures to the rich compositions of the artist, generally too crowded."[1]

The interior has long been considered "a carpenter's shop,"[2] which, like Gerard ter Borch's so-called *Instruction Paternelle* (the inscription on Johann Georg Wille's engraving of 1765),[3] is an eighteenth-century misconception that has lingered for nearly two hundred years. An independent reading of the subject was recorded by John Smith, who sold the painting in 1825 and described the setting simply as "a peasant's cottage."[4] Cornelis Hofstede de Groot, whose catalogue raisonné is based on Smith's, nonetheless repeated the information found in the catalogue of the 1841 sale, thereby reviving the idea of a "Joiner's Shop."[5]

Thus, in the English edition of Hofstede de Groot's German text one finds lines once written in French, in Paris, and no doubt in haste, to the effect that "the joiner in his working coat and cap holds a board which he has just prepared." A fresh perusal of the picture suggests that, on the contrary, the board in question has served for some time as a countertop above a sink, while the man, in nondescript peasant attire, lifts the lid in order to exercise his "gentleman's prerogative" (as the practice is known in England).

The only objects that would not be expected in almost any Dutch peasant cottage of the period are the chalkboard and small wooden shoe (presumably used as a chalk holder) nailed onto the rear wall. Strokes next to roman numerals record the number of drinks ordered by individual customers. The interior, then, as so often is the case in Van Ostade's oeuvre, is the main room of a modest dwelling that, as part of a common cottage industry, also functions as a local pub.[6]

Among the several signs of domesticity are the swift (a yarn winder) hanging overhead, the loft above the foreground, the earthenware cooking pot (with wooden lid) in a hanging trivet

1931.400

set on the floor, and the sewing basket on the bench. Accompanying the basket are a hand winder and a distaff, objects that appear frequently in paintings and etchings by Van Ostade, sometimes as the sole attributes of single figures — women and, less frequently, men.[7]

The man in the corner, a clay pipe in what may under the circumstances be called his free hand, turns his amused attention to the child who shyly shrinks from the offer of a glass of beer. The man wearing an apron in the foreground stokes the meager fire. The full wooden washtub to the right of the sink, the broken bench, and the remains of a caned chair seat in front of the staircase (itself uninviting) complete the impression of dilapidation: this is not the sort of place foreign travelers had in mind when they wrote in their letters and diaries about the extraordinary order of Dutch homes. One wonders whether the mangy little dog, its back turned to the company, might be waiting for the woman who seems so conspicuously absent here.

A survey of the artist's paintings, watercolors, and drawings shows that he routinely rendered figures and motifs similar to those found in the Taft picture, although in this composition he did not repeat passages from any other work. Indeed, the painting seems, at least in hindsight, to stand on or near the threshold between Van Ostade's early, unflinchingly dissolute scenes set in dismal inns and the quieter, tidier, more temperate subjects of the 1650s and 1660s. Although this transition has seemed to some scholars to coincide approximately with the artist's second marriage in 1657 to a woman from a prominent family, it would be naive to imagine her straightening up his disheveled settings (the "Peasant Bruegel fallacy").[8] He was already well-off and respected, a man whose knowledge of the art market — and of changing tastes during the 1650s — was obviously as acute as his observation of daily life.

1. Taft Museum files. The letter is handwritten on Staatliche Museen stationery and is dated "Charlottenbg / 28.VII 05." Bode's brief note, which obviously served as a certificate, refers to his having been shown the painting "last month."

2. In the *Catalogue d'une riche collection de tableaux des écoles flamande et hollandaise, recueillie par M. Héris de Bruxelles . . .* , Paris, 1841, pp. 50–51, no. 48, the painting is described as "La maison du menuisier, . . . Décrit, connu et gravé sous ce titre." The only provenance given is "collection d'Orsay." Numerous paintings from the collection of the comte d'Orsay were sold in Paris on June 7, 1779; Apr. 14ff., 1790; and Mar. 20, 1810. I have been able to check only the 1790 catalogue, which does not include the picture.

3. S. J. Gudlaugsson, *Gerard ter Borch*, The Hague, 1959–60, vol. II, no. 110.

4. John Smith, *A Catalogue Raisonné of the Works of the Most Eminent Dutch, Flemish, and French Painters*, vol. I, London, 1829, no. 145, who read the date as 1655.

5. Cornelis Hofstede de Groot, *A Catalogue Raisonné of the Works of the Most Eminent Dutch Painters of the Seventeenth Century*, vol. III, London, 1910, no. 404f., with no reference to Smith. See note 2 above for the sale catalogue that Hofstede de Groot cites.

6. Compare the inn depicted in Van Ostade's etching *Paying the Hostess*, reproduced in C. G. Boerner, *Adriaen van Ostade: Die schönsten Radierungen*, Düsseldorf, 1985, no. 46; again a yarn winder hangs from the rafters. See also nos. 31, 52.

7. See the following Van Ostade entry in this catalogue, note 10; and Linda Stone-Ferrier, *Images of Textiles: The Weave of Seventeenth-Century Dutch Art and Society*, Ann Arbor, Mich., 1985, pp. 84–95, on Exemplary Female Spinners and Winders.

8. Bruegel was wrongly presumed to be a peasant himself — similar to the "El Greco fallacy," presuming poor eyesight. Compare Jakob Rosenberg, Seymour Slive, and E. H. ter Kuile, *Dutch Art and Architecture, 1600–1800*, Baltimore, 1966, pp. 112–13. Boerner, nos. 31, 52, dated 1652 and 1647 respectively, are two of many earlier examples depicting tranquil family life in the same sort of setting.

Provenance Comte d'Orsay (sale, Paris, Mar. 20, 1810? [see note 2 above]; Jean-Louis Laneuville (1748–1826, portraitist and pupil of David;

sale, Paris, Nov. 6ff., 1811, for FF 2500, cited by Smith); John Smith, "Sold by the Writer . . . 1825, 250 gns." (according to Smith in 1829); William Beckford (in 1829); colonel de Biré (sale, M. Héris of Brussels, Paris, Mar. 25–26, 1841, no. 48, for FF 841 according to marginal note in catalogue in the Frick Art Reference Library); [Thomas Agnew and Sons, London, in 1905]; Taft collection, purchased through Scott and Fowles, New York, Sept. 30, 1905.

Exhibition Hartford, Conn., Wadsworth Atheneum, *Life in Seventeenth-Century Holland,* Nov. 21, 1950–Jan. 14, 1951 (cat., p. 23, no. 60, as *Interior of a Carpenter's Shop* and observing that "young men were taught their father's craft at an early age").

Literature John Smith, *A Catalogue Raisonné of the Works of the Most Eminent Dutch, Flemish, and French Painters,* vol. I, London, 1829, pp. 147–48, no. 145; Cornelis Hofstede de Groot, *A Catalogue Raisonné of the Works of the Most Eminent Dutch Painters of the Seventeenth Century,* vol. III, London, 1910, p. 263, no. 404f.; H. Mireur, *Dictionnaire des ventes d'art en France et à l'étranger pendant les XVIIIe et XIXe siècles,* vol. V, Paris, 1911, p. 28, under 1811, Laneuville; Maurice W. Brockwell, *A Catalogue of Paintings in the Collection of Mr. and Mrs. Charles P. Taft,* New York, 1920, no. 18; *Catalogue of the Taft Museum,* Cincinnati, 1939 and 1958, no. 133.

1931.400

Adriaen van Ostade

An Old Toper

ca. 1660–65
Oil on panel, 21.8 x 18.6 cm (8⅝ x 7⅜ in.)

A portly man of many years sits at a small table, presumably in a pub. He responds to viewers without looking directly at them and gestures toward his small, upraised glass. On the table are a pewter tankard (*wijnkan*), a clay pipe, and straws and a bowl of hot coals for lighting the pipe.

The painting is typical of Van Ostade in composition and execution. The rather low placement of a seated figure in the picture field, all the more remarkable now that an added strip has been removed from the bottom of the panel, occurs similarly in several small pictures by Van Ostade dating from his mature years and suggests that the viewer stands very close to the subject.

From about the mid-1640s onward, the artist made small paintings, etchings, and many drawings of single figures, usually in half or three-quarter length (often full-length in drawings), some of which obviously represent live models.[1] The paintings and etchings are not studies in the same sense as, for example, Rubens's "study heads"[2] but are independent works of art addressing various iconographic themes. Nonetheless, the single-figure compositions may be seen as part of a development leading away from the stock peasant types found in Van Ostade's oeuvre throughout the 1630s and early 1640s and toward the more individualized figures that occupy his domestic interiors of the 1650s and later years. A much subtler rendering of expression accompanies the painter's study of physiognomy;[3] the boorish caricatures and unrestrained animation of figures in the early works are replaced by quieter situations in which the figures talk and listen to each other and even when alone or silent seem to have some words in mind.[4] Perhaps, as in the case of Van

1931.420

Ostade's increasingly refined use of light and shadow, the influence of Rembrandt might be supposed, although an evolution from type to individual and from stagelike to lifelike expression may be discerned in the works of other Dutch genre painters, such as Gerard ter Borch (see 1931.398, p. 170), during the same period.[5]

Evidently, the same model as the old man seen here appears in another small panel, which is signed and dated 1664.[6] The figure is again seated, facing forward, in similar clothing, but wearing a broad-brimmed hat. Van Ostade may have referred to the same drawing from life for both paintings, since the expression is similar. However, in the 1664 panel the action differs — the man's head tilts the other way, his hands are folded, and his parted lips and reflective eyes suggest that he may be speaking thoughtfully, as if reminiscing or telling a story. A close comparison is worthwhile for two reasons. First, it provides some evidence for dating the Taft panel, which in previous publications was said to be signed and dated 1651 (the false signature was recently removed, and there is no longer any trace of a date).[7] Second, the two paintings demonstrate how Van Ostade made use of an actual model in his mature works. The man is searchingly described, but neither picture should be considered an essay in portraiture per se. The suggestion that the two compositions depend on a single drawing is supported by other instances of a figure with distinctive features occurring in the same pose with a similar expression, but with a different positioning of the hands, in two additional genre paintings by Van Ostade.[8]

The man's seemingly significant gesture and glance in the Taft painting encourage the interpretation of its subject, simple though it may seem. It is now widely known that many Dutch genre paintings dating from the 1640s through at least the 1670s embody ethical values such as the virtues of hard work, marital fidelity, domestic diligence, or temperance in the pursuit of life's little pleasures. Paintings that illustrate the transgression of these standards (such as those with titles like *The Idle Servant)* are rightly called moralizing and often include well-established symbols underscoring the point, which function like nagging notes left around the house.[9] In quite a few less reproachful pictures, however, a figure's virtue is described in a refreshingly forthright way. Ter Borch's woman at a spinning wheel, Vermeer's young woman with a basin and pitcher, and Van Ostade's (and Dou's) old woman at a window with a yarn winder employ common and, in these examples, utilitarian household objects to underscore the theme.[10] The present picture is probably best understood in the context of an appreciation of the pleasure afforded by a pipe and a little wine. The importance of moderation seems to be stressed by the small size of the man's glass and perhaps by the pipe's having been set down. The theme of temperance is common in Dutch genre paintings of the 1650s and 1660s and often involves the consumption of wine.[11]

This specific reading of the picture's meaning should not obscure the obvious delight Van Ostade took in observing humble objects and an interesting character, nor does it speak, by contrast, against his debt to older iconographic conventions. Approximately the same subject in the artist's student days, indeed in the work of his fellow pupil Brouwer, would most likely stand for the sense of taste, either as an independent picture or as one of a series of five paintings representing the senses.[12] Van Ostade's single-figure compositions can also be considered a final step, or step beyond, in respect to the Dutch tradition of depicting peasant types, although his subject, as here, is often not a peasant.[13] In this progress from Pieter Bruegel the Elder's sympathetic but mockable members of the underclass to Van Ostade's sober citizens, an actual historical development is broadly sketched: the modest means and even moderation of Van Ostade's old toper are signs of a prosperity that Bruegel's peasants never knew.

1. See, for example, Bernhard Schnackenburg, *Adriaen van Ostade, Isack van Ostade: Zeichnungen und Aquarelle*, vol. II, Hamburg, 1981, pp. 33, 57, 76–78, 139–65; C. G. Boerner, *Adriaen van Ostade: Die schönsten Radierungen*, Düsseldorf, 1985, nos. 7–12; K. G. Boon and J. Verbeek (succeeding Hollstein), *Dutch and Flemish Etchings, Engravings, and Woodcuts*, vol. XV, Amsterdam, n.d., pp. 6–11, etc.

2. Julius S. Held, *The Oil Sketches of Peter Paul Rubens*, vol. I, Princeton, 1980, pp. 597ff.

3. On the tradition that Van Ostade follows in this area, see Konrad Renger, *Adriaen Brouwer und das niederländische Bauerngenre, 1600–1660*, Munich, 1986, pp. 41–44.

4. On this development see Bernhard Schnackenburg, "Das Bild des bäuerlichen Lebens bei Adriaen van Ostade," in Justus Müller Hofstede and Herman Vekeman, eds., *Wort und Bild in der niederländischen Kunst und Literatur des 16. und 17. Jahrhunderts*, Erftstadt, 1984, pp. 30–42.

5. See the comments on Van Ostade's style in Horst Gerson, "Rembrandt en de schilderkunst in Haarlem," *Miscellanea I. Q. van Regteren Altena*, Amsterdam, 1969, pp. 140–42.

6. Cornelis Hofstede de Groot, *A Catalogue Raisonné of the Works of the Most Eminent Dutch Painters of the Seventeenth Century*, vol. III, London, 1910, no. 212k; sold at the Dorotheum, Vienna, Nov. 28–Dec. 1, 1967, and

shown at the Galerie Sanct Lucas, Vienna, in 1976. To judge from photographs, Hofstede de Groot's reading of the date as 1664 seems reliable. A man in the same pose with a similar hat but less individualized features occurs in a drawing exhibited at the Brod Gallery, London, July–Aug. 1962, no. 42.

7. No date or signature is mentioned by John Smith, *A Catalogue Raisonné of the Works of the Most Eminent Dutch, Flemish, and French Painters*, vol. IX, *Supplement*, London, 1852, p. 81, no. 6. In a letter of Sept. 24, 1986, Bernhard Schnackenburg agrees that the Taft painting may date from the first half of the 1660s.

8. For example, the man about to feed a baby in Van Ostade's peasant interior of 1651 in Buckingham Palace (Christopher White, *The Dutch Pictures in the Collection of Her Majesty the Queen*, Cambridge, 1982, no. 128, pl. 109) is repeated as a smoker in a small panel formerly in Amsterdam and recently acquired by a private collector in New York. The model appears to be the man seen in bust length in a drawing in the Albertina, Vienna; see Schnackenburg 1981, no. 291, pl. 138.

9. See the examples discussed in *Tot Lering en Vermaak*, exh. cat., Rijksmuseum, Amsterdam, 1976, and in *Die Sprache der Bilder*, exh. cat., Herzog Anton Ulrich-Museum, Brunswick, 1978.

10. The references here are to Ter Borch's painting in the Boymans-van Beuningen Museum (Stichting Willem van der Vorm), Rotterdam; Vermeer's canvas in the Metropolitan Museum of Art, New York; Dou's panel, *A Fisherman's Wife*, 1653, in the Rijksmuseum, Amsterdam; and a picture by Van Ostade, said to be signed and dated 1640, sold at Sotheby's, London, Dec. 8, 1976, no. 76.

11. See Schnackenburg 1984, pp. 33, 37, on the peasant drinking and smoking in moderation, often after working hard. Schnackenburg cites contemporary verses, such as an anonymous author's reference to drinking a "little pint" on Sunday afternoon (p. 37). See also Peter C. Sutton (citing Kurt Bauch) on "the theme of contentment with little" in connection with Pieter Codde's *Young Man with a Pipe* (Lille), in Peter C. Sutton et al., *Masters of Seventeenth-Century Dutch Genre Painting*, exh. cat., Philadelphia Museum of Art, 1984, p. 175. Samuel Pepys's diary entries for the years 1660–62 frequently mention tempering his consumption of wine for the sake of health and work. I am not convinced by Ivan Gaskell, *The Thyssen-Bornemisza Collection: Seventeenth-Century Dutch and Flemish Painting*, London, 1990, p. 250, where the man in the Taft painting is said to be drinking brandy, which might be seen as a sign of "decline in old age." Gaskell records this work as reportedly dated 1651 and as "whereabouts unknown."

12. Renger, pp. 39–41, on the Five Senses; see also Walter Liedtke, in *Liechtenstein: The Princely Collections*, exh. cat., The Metropolitan Museum of Art, New York, 1985, p. 190, on a series of small pictures by Brouwer representing the Seven Deadly Sins, particularly no. 3, *Luxury*, depicting a cavalier with a glass of wine. It remains possible that the Taft painting was once understood to represent the sense of taste, but it is doubtful that the picture would be understood primarily in this way unless it formed part of a series. There is no evidence for the latter, and there are other single pictures in which a solitary figure enjoys a pipe or a glass.

13. See Renger, p. 30, on Brouwer's types; on the precedent in Bruegel, see Konrad Oberhuber, "Pieter Bruegel und die Radierungsserie der Bauernköpfe," in Otto von Simson and Matthias Winner, eds., *Pieter Bruegel und seiner Welt*, Berlin, 1975, pp. 143–47, pls. 52–57. More immediate antecedents to Van Ostade's solitary drinkers include some figures drawn from life by Jacob de Gheyn II and Frans Hals's *Merry Drinker* (Amsterdam, Rijksmuseum) and similar pictures; on both artists, see Seymour Slive, *Frans Hals*, vol. I, London, 1970, pp. 107–11, and vol. II, 1970, pls. 105–7.

Provenance Jonkheer Johan Goll van Franckenstein, Amsterdam (sale, July 1, 1833, no. 59); baron de Varange (sale, Paris, May 26–27, 1852, no. 31, apparently bt. in); baron de [Varange] (sale, Paris, Apr. 25, 1857, no. 10); Emile Pereire (sale, Paris, Mar. 6, 1872, no. 144); Anatolii Nikolaevich Demidov [Demidoff], principe di San Donato, Florence (sale, Mar. 15ff., 1880, no. 1045); Charles T. Yerkes, Chicago (sale, New York, Apr. 8, 1910, no. 158, no. 68 in the *édition de luxe* of the sale cat.; see Literature); Taft collection, 1910.

Literature John Smith, *A Catalogue Raisonné of the Works of the Most Eminent Dutch, Flemish, and French Painters*, vol. IX, *Supplement*, London, 1852, p. 81, no. 6; W. Bürger [Théophile Thoré], "Galerie de Mm. Pereire," *Gazette des beaux-arts*, vol. XVI (1864), p. 308, as "un *Buveur*, le même bonhomme que van Ostade a peint plusiers fois"; F. G. Stevens, "Mr. Yerkes Collection at Chicago: The Old Masters, I," *The Magazine of Art*, vol. XVIII (1895), p. 101, as *The Old Toper*, signed and dated 1651; *Catalogue De Luxe of Ancient and Modern Paintings Belonging to the Estate of the Late Charles T. Yerkes*, American Art Association, New York, 1910, no. 68 (ill.); Cornelis Hofstede de Groot, *A Catalogue Raisonné of the Works of the Most Eminent Dutch Painters of the Seventeenth Century*, vol. III, London, 1910, p. 184, no. 144; Maurice W. Brockwell, *A Catalogue of Paintings in the Collection of Mr. and Mrs. Charles P. Taft*, New York, 1920, no. 53; *Catalogue of the Taft Museum*, Cincinnati, 1939 and 1958, no. 233; Ivan Gaskell, *The Thyssen-Bornemisza Collection: Seventeenth-Century Dutch and Flemish Painting*, London, 1990, pp. 250–51, fig. 1, as "whereabouts unknown."

1931.420

Rembrandt van Rijn
Leiden 1606–1669 Amsterdam

Rembrandt Harmensz. van Rijn was born in Leiden on July 15, 1606, the son of a miller, Harmen van Rijn, and Neeltgen van Zuytbroeck.[1] He learned to read and write in a city school, attended the Latin school in Leiden around 1615–19, and in 1620 enrolled at the University of Leiden with no intention, evidently, of being a regular student there. From about 1619 to 1622 Rembrandt was apprenticed to the Leiden painter Jacob van Swanenburgh and then (1623?) to the distinguished Amsterdam artist Pieter Lastman. Although he returned to Leiden after only half a year, his association with Lastman and his circle of history painters determined Rembrandt's style and choice of subject matter during the 1620s, opened his eyes to artists active in other cities (especially Amsterdam and Utrecht), and presumably gave him grand ideas about artistic achievement and patronage.

Rembrandt's work of the next several years in Leiden is remarkable for its accelerated development: the approximately fifty known paintings and many etchings of about 1626–31 begin with ambitious multifigure history pieces in a Lastman-like dramatic style and move on, as early as 1627, to paintings of one, two, or a few usually biblical figures whose realistic appearance and profound expressions are clearly based on close study of living models. Rembrandt's many representations of interiors, of still-life details, and of his own features (some of the self-portraits are studies of expression) reveal how important empirical study (which was both a personal inclination and a Leiden tradition) was and would remain in Rembrandt's art; but he also learned lessons in gesture, lighting, and staging from Caravaggesque compositions and from Hendrick Goudt's engravings after Adam Elsheimer. In the Leiden period Rembrandt seems to have shared a studio with Jan Lievens, and he was Gerrit Dou's teacher beginning in February 1628.

At some time near the end of 1631 Rembrandt took up residence in Amsterdam, where he was drawn, according to contemporary sources, by demand for his work. *The Anatomy Lesson of Dr. Tulp* (The Hague, Mauritshuis), painted by Rembrandt in 1632, is the greatest group portrait of the dozens by Dutch artists up to that date, while single and pendant portraits, such as the Taft Museum's *Portrait of a Man Rising from His Chair* (1633), made Rembrandt the most successful painter in Amsterdam during the 1630s. Six pictures of Christ's Passion, painted for the Stadholder Prince Frederick Hendrick, date from 1633 to 1639. Numerous other history paintings, such as *The Blinding of Samson* (Frankfurt, Städelsches Kunstinstitut), are also from these years.

In June 1634 Rembrandt married Saskia van Uylenburgh (1612–1642), the daughter of a prominent politician from Friesland and cousin of Hendrick van Uylenburgh, the Amsterdam art dealer with whom Rembrandt probably had dealings before leaving Leiden. The comfortable circumstances resulting from Saskia's dowry and Rembrandt's success may account for his reduced rate of production around 1636–38[2] and, more certainly, for his activity as an art collector during this period. A magnificent house in the Breestraat became Rembrandt's home and studio in 1639. *The Night Watch* (Amsterdam, Rijksmuseum), the famous group portrait of a company of civic guardsmen, was finished in 1642, and a number of Rembrandt's finest portraits (e.g., *The Preacher Anslo and His Wife* [Berlin, Gemäldegalerie, Staatliche Museen]) and biblical pictures date from the early 1640s. He was apparently less in demand during the following decades but exercised great influence on younger artists, such as his students Samuel van Hoogstraten and Carel Fabritius and his former pupils Govaert Flinck (see 1931.416, p. 160) and Ferdinand Bol.

The religious and other history paintings that date from the 1640s and 1650s (e.g., *Aristotle with a Bust of Homer*, 1653 [New York, The Metropolitan Museum of Art]) are more introspective than those of the 1630s; Rembrandt's use of light and shadow becomes a subtler dramatic device, suggesting the conflict of emotions and often of moral choice. A widower after 1642, Rembrandt raised his son Titus (1641–1668) with the help of his housekeeper, Geertge Dircx. Her intimate relationship with Rembrandt ended ignominiously for both parties in 1650. From about this time until her death in 1663, Hendrickje Stoffels was Rembrandt's devoted companion and model; in 1660 she and Titus formed a company to shield Rembrandt from his debts. His house and art collection were auctioned after his insolvency in 1656, and the last decade of his personal life was markedly difficult. However, it was during the 1650s and 1660s that Rembrandt painted many of his most profound religious pictures and imposing portraits, including *The Denial of Peter, The Jewish Bride*, and *The Syndics of the Cloth Drapers' Guild* (all three, Amsterdam, Rijksmuseum). The late self-portraits trace the artist's aging, careworn, but apparently peaceful features. Paintings date from the last year of his life; he died on October 4, 1669, and was buried two days later in the Westerkerk.

No biography — and to this date no book on the hundreds of paintings, drawings, and etchings Rembrandt left behind — conveys the measure of his achievement, which has affected artists and art lovers throughout Europe and America.[3] The nineteenth-century notion of Rembrandt as an isolated genius still survives in the form of popular misconceptions, such as the idea that he transcends his time and place. He does, but did not, as is apparent from a comparison with contemporary artists such as Velázquez and from a consideration of the many pupils, followers, and patrons for whom Rembrandt's work served as inspiration.

1. See Gary Schwartz, *Rembrandt: His Life, His Paintings*, New York, 1985, chap. 3, on the artist's family.

2. Compare the speculations of Schwartz, p. 194.

3. For general impressions of the artist and his work, Horst Gerson, *Rembrandt Paintings*, Amsterdam, 1968, and Bob Haak, *Rembrandt: His Life, His Work, His Time*, New York, 1969, remain the most satisfactory of recent efforts. Still a good read and an insight into the taste of an earlier time (that of the Tafts) is Emile Michel, *Rembrandt: Sa Vie, son oeuvre et son temps*, Paris, 1893. On the artist's self-image, see H. Perry Chapman, *Rembrandt's Self-Portraits*, Princeton, N.J., 1990.

Rembrandt van Rijn

Portrait of a Man Rising from His Chair

1633
Oil on canvas, 124 x 98.5 cm (48⅞ x 38¾ in.)
Signed and dated lower right: *Rembrandt.f / 1633*

This splendid picture and its companion, *Portrait of a Woman in an Armchair* (New York, The Metropolitan Museum of Art, fig. 1), are among the most remarkable examples of Rembrandt's prolific work as a fashionable portraitist in Amsterdam during the early 1630s.[1] The unusually active pose of the subject, who seems to be rising suddenly from his chair in response to a visitor, finds a rhythmic counterpart in the animated but much more reserved movement of the man's wife. In pose and expression she offers a calm, even reassuring resolution of the exuberance depicted in the Taft picture. Furthermore, when seen side by side, the portraits suggest two distinct yet complementary personalities, an impression that is lost or overwhelmed by the dynamic design of the *Portrait of a Man* when it is considered separately. Unfortunately, the two paintings have only rarely been brought together, which allows one to appreciate how consistent they are in coloring, lighting, their effects of fine materials, and atmospheric space.[2] The canvases are recorded in different English collections from the early nineteenth century.[3]

Pair portraits of this quality were usually installed in the most formal room of an upper-middle-class house. Although the evidence is slight, it seems that examples on this comparatively large scale were often separated by some distance (the male figures almost always placed deferentially to the woman's right); the space between them might have been filled by a fireplace or a freestanding cabinet. The size, the separation, and the tendency to hang pictures rather high (by later standards) as well as the contemporary custom of viewing paintings from a considerable distance with an eye to their subjects rather than style or technique encouraged the more imaginative portraitists

of the period to experiment with bold compositional ideas, such as active poses, strong silhouettes, low points of view, eye-catching accessories, illusionary effects of space, texture, and modeling, and dramatic use of light. Formal devices similar to those developed by Rembrandt during his first decade in Amsterdam are found in earlier portraits by Rubens, Van Dyck, and their predecessors Titian and Lotto.[4]

However, as in the case of Hals (see 1931.450, p. 141, and 1931.451, 455, p. 143) and, in a quieter way, Thomas de Keyser,[5] it appears that Rembrandt's work in the particularly Dutch genre of group portraiture inspired him to introduce innovative devices in his single and companion portraits: for example, the Taft figure's spontaneous pose and gesture, the parted lips, and the gaze that does not answer so much as it solicits the viewer's immediate attention.[6] *Woman in an Armchair* has, in fact, been compared with the uppermost figure in Rembrandt's *Anatomy Lesson of Dr. Tulp*, which dates from the previous year.[7] The similarity, while not obvious, is underscored by the way in which the Taft figure's reaction to the viewer recalls the next highest figure in the same important group portrait and also by the fact that the most conspicuous gesture in Rembrandt's portraiture to predate the present example is that of Dr. Tulp's left hand.

Another instance of a parallel in group portraiture, in this case dating from the same year, is found in the *Portrait of the Shipbuilder Jan Rijcksent and His Wife* (1633, London, Buckingham

Fig. 1 Rembrandt van Rijn, *Portrait of a Woman in an Armchair*, 1633. Oil on canvas, 126.2 x 100.5 cm (49¾ x 39½ in.). New York, The Metropolitan Museum of Art, gift of Mrs. Helen Swift Neilson, Chicago, 1943 (43.125).

1931.409

sources to mention; and no copies or graphic reproductions are known.

Finally, two aspects of the Taft painting should be mentioned here and will impress any visitor to the collection. First, the animation of the figure is complemented by strong, sensitive modeling and a compelling sense of space. These effects are somewhat diminished by the usual deepening with age of dark passages, so that folds in the costume and the distinction between the figure and background are no longer as clear as they once were. However, the fine transitions of light and shade still evident in the lace collar and cuffs, in the hands and face, and to some extent in the torso reveal both the extraordinary quality one expects in Rembrandt's major portraits of this period and also the illusionistic element that is often evident in paintings dating from around 1632–34.

Second, the costume itself is remarkable, although it and the attire of the *Woman in an Armchair* are not unusual for the years 1633 and 1634. Similar rosettes with gold aglets on the doublet are found in Rembrandt's *Portrait of Maerten Soolmans* and in Hals's *Portrait of Tieleman Roosterman,* both of which are dated 1634;[12] a very similar decoration, usually one bow with no aglets, occurs in female costumes of the same time, as in the Metropolitan Museum picture. It has frequently been observed that middle-class men and women of this generation in the Netherlands favored dark, conservative clothing that in its sobriety evokes the Calvinistic spirit but in its elegance, fineness, and exquisite detail concedes pride in their new prosperity. The emphasis here, in the costume and in the commission given to Rembrandt, is on the material side.

Palace), in which the standing woman, leaning, almost lunging forward with a message for the man, may be compared with the Taft figure, while the seated shipbuilder, one hand on the table, the other raised and holding dividers, has a quieter pose and reflective expression somewhat similar to those of the *Woman in an Armchair.* Here, Rembrandt reverses the distinction usually found in his pair and double portraits between the outgoing male and the more retiring female,[8] although to say this is to underestimate the subtlety of the double portrait (the shipbuilder's wife remains his subordinate) and the complexity of double portraits (especially those with a narrative element) as opposed to pendant single portraits. One recent writer makes this point but considers the Taft picture and its pendant to be a further development beyond the *Portrait of a Couple in an Interior* (1633, Boston, Isabella Stewart Gardner Museum) and then describes the *Shipbuilder and His Wife* as "the next logical step in this chain of development."[9] One could just as well see the *Shipbuilder and His Wife* as a new application of the approach worked out in *The Anatomy Lesson of Dr. Tulp* and conclude that the design of the Taft painting and its companion benefits from both of these impressive experiments in group portraiture, adopting their innovations to the much more restricted and usually more conservative format of pair portraits.[10]

All the more technical matters concerning the present picture have been presented at length in the new *Corpus of Rembrandt Paintings,* in which it is described as "a fairly well preserved, authentic work, reliably signed and dated 1633."[11] The radiographs are not revealing; there are no contemporary documents or

1. On portraits painted during the artist's first few years in Amsterdam, see Stichting Foundation Rembrandt Research Project, *A Corpus of Rembrandt Paintings,* vol. ii, Dordrecht, 1986; and David Smith, "Rembrandt's Early Double Portraits and the Dutch Conversation Piece," *Art Bulletin,* vol. lxiv (1982), pp. 259–88.

2. This impressed the writer forcefully when he saw the paintings side by side in 1985 in the conservation studio of the Metropolitan Museum of Art. The pictures were exhibited together in 1973–74 at the Metropolitan Museum and at the Taft Museum; their first reunion in well over a century was at the Detroit Institute of Arts in 1930 (see Exhibitions and William R. Valentiner, *Rembrandt Paintings in America,* New York, 1931, nos. 34, 35, pls. 34, 35). The pendants were first presented to the Dutch public at the Mauritshuis, the Hague, in 1990–91, and were then shown together in San Francisco (see Exhibitions).

3. The writer found no obvious connection between the well-known collector George O'Brien Wyndham, third earl of Egremont, who had the Metropolitan Museum painting at Petworth (by 1822), and the earl of Ashburnham. In 1850, when the Taft painting was sold in London, the title of earl was held by the Reverend Sir John Ashburnham, seventh baronet, who succeeded his elder brother Sir William Ashburnham on the latter's death in 1843. Ben Broos, *Great Dutch Paintings from America,* exh. cat., Mauritshuis, the Hague, 1990, nos. 51, 52, gives a lively account of the previous owners, in particular the earl of Ashburnham and the count of Pourtalès.

4. See the entry on Van Dyck's *Portrait of a Man, Probably Lucas van Uffel* in Walter A. Liedtke, *Flemish Paintings in the Metropolitan Museum of Art,* New York, 1984, pp. 58–59.

5. Compare Rudolf Oldenbourg, *Thomas de Keysers Tätigkeit als Maler,* Leipzig, 1911, pls. i, vii, viii, and especially xi (discussed pp. 38–39).

6. The importance of group portraiture for the composition of Rembrandt's single portraits is discussed in *Corpus,* vol. ii, p. 127.

7. The authors of the *Corpus* go so far as to state that the pose of the figure in *The Anatomy Lesson* "is here repeated faithfully" (vol. II, p. 382).

8. Compare the following, cited here with their numbers in the *Corpus*, vol. II: *A Couple in an Interior*, Boston, Isabella Stewart Gardner Museum (c 67, under the rejected attributions); the pendant portraits of Johannes Elison and Maria Bockenolle (A 98, A 99); the pendant portraits of Marten Soolmans and Oopjen Coppit (A 100, A 101); the so-called Van Beresteyn pair of portraits, New York, The Metropolitan Museum of Art (c 68, c 69, wrongly under rejected attributions); and the pair of pictures representing Jean Pellicorne and his son, and his wife and daughter, London, Wallace Collection (c 65, c 66, considered to be products of Rembrandt's workshop).

9. Smith, pp. 262, 268, 269 (the quote from p. 269).

10. Smith, p. 268, suggests that these two pictures "probably represent his first attempt at this kind of composition, and perhaps for that very reason they show more movement than later examples." This may very well be, but one must also take into account the character of the sitters, the artist's obvious interest in them as subjects, and the tendency, noticeable in Hals also, toward somewhat more reserved portraits from the mid-1630s onward (see 1931.451, p. 143).

11. *Corpus*, vol. II, p. 380.

12. *Corpus*, vol. II, no. A 100; Seymour Slive, *Frans Hals*, vol. II, London, 1970, pl. 154. The comparison with Rembrandt's *Portrait of Maerten Soolmans* was made independently by Broos, p. 379, fig. 3.

Provenance Earl of Ashburnham (sale, London, July 20, 1850, for £724 10s, to the London dealer Farrer, according to Hofstede de Groot); [Farrer, London]; comte de Pourtalès-Gorgier, Paris (sale, Mar. 27, 1865, no. 181, bought in, FF 34,500); comte Edmond de Pourtalès, Paris (lender to 1898 Amsterdam exhibition); [M. Knoedler, New York, by 1909]; [Scott and Fowles, New York]; Taft collection, Oct. 22, 1909.

Exhibitions Amsterdam, Stedelijk Museum, *Rembrandt Schilderijen*, 1898 (*De Rembrandt Tentoonstelling te Amsterdam*, by Cornelis Hofstede de Groot, no. 24 [ill.]); New York, Scott and Fowles, 1909 and 1914; New York, Knoedler & Co., *A Loan Exhibition of Twelve Masterpieces of Painting*, 1928, no. 8; Detroit Institute of Arts, *Paintings by Rembrandt*, 1930 (cat. by William R. Valentiner, no. 16 [ill.], exhibited with no. 17, the pendant now in the Metropolitan Museum); The Museum of Fine Arts, Houston, *The Human Image*, 1958 (cat., no. 42 [ill.]); Raleigh, North Carolina Museum of Art, *Masterpieces of Art: In Memory of William R. Valentiner, 1880–1958*, 1959 (cat., no. 71, fig. 129); Seattle, World's Fair, *Masterpieces of Art*, 1962 (cat., pp. 66–67, no. 26 [ill.]); New York, The Metropolitan Museum of Art, and Cincinnati, Taft Museum, *Dutch Couples: Pair Portraits by Rembrandt and His Contemporaries*, 1973–74 (brochure by John Walsh [Metropolitan]; brochure by Jane Merkel [Taft]); The Hague, Mauritshuis, and The Fine Arts Museum of San Francisco, *Great Dutch Paintings from America*, 1990–91 (cat. by Ben Broos et al., pp. 376–81, no. 51, and pp. 383–85, under no. 52).

Literature John Smith, *Catalogue Raisonné of the Works of the Most Eminent Dutch, Flemish, and French Painters*, vol. VII, London, 1836, p. 120, no. 332; Charles Blanc, *L'Oeuvre complet de Rembrandt*, Paris, 1859–61, vol. II, p. 451, as in the Galerie de Feu M. de Pourtalès-Gorgier; Paul Mantz, "La Galerie Pourtalès," *Gazette des beaux-arts*, vol. XVIII (1865), p. 105; Carel Vosmaer, *Rembrandt Harmens. van Rijn: Sa Vie et ses oeuvres*, The Hague, 1868, p. 433; Carel Vosmaer, *Rembrandt: Sa Vie et ses oeuvres*, The Hague, 1877, pp. 121, 500, with provenance and prices; Wilhelm von Bode, *Studien zur Geschichte der holländischen Malerei*, Brunswick, 1883, p. 597, no. 299; Eugène Dutuit, *L'Oeuvre complet de Rembrandt, Supplément: Tableaux et dessins*, Paris, 1885, p. 52, no. 224; Alfred von Wurzbach, *Rembrandt Galerie*, Stuttgart, 1884–86, no. 311; Emile Michel, *Rembrandt: Sa Vie, son oeuvre et son temps*, vol. I, Paris, 1893, p. 143 (English ed., London, 1903, pp. 109–10, 435); Wilhelm von Bode and Cornelis Hofstede de Groot, *The Complete Work of Rembrandt*, vol. II, Paris, 1897, pp. 9, 81–82, no. 100; O. von Schleinitz, "Die Rembrandt-Ausstellung in der Royal-Academy in London," *Kunstchronik*, n.s., vol. X (1898–99), col. 196; Malcolm Bell, *Rembrandt van Rijn and His Work*, London, 1899, p. 161, as in the collection of Countess Edmond de Pourtalès, Paris; H. F. Cook, "Correspondance d'Angleterre: L'Exposition

Rembrandt à Londres," *Gazette des beaux-arts*, vol. XXI (1899), p. 256; Adolf Rosenberg, *Rembrandt, des Meisters Gemälde (Klassiker der Kunst)*, Stuttgart and Leipzig, 1906, p. 77 (ill.); Jan Veth, *Rembrandts leven en kunst*, Amsterdam, 1906, p. 48; J. Six, "De teckniekvan Vermeer in 'Een Meyd die melk uytgiet,'" *Bulletin . . . Nederlandschen Oudheidkundigen Bond*, 2d ser., vol. I (1908), p. 3, note 1; William R. Valentiner, *Rembrandt, des Meisters Gemälde (Klassiker der Kunst)*, Stuttgart and Berlin, 1909, p. 96 (ill.); Elisabeth Luther Cary, "Some Masters of Portraiture," *Putnam's Magazine*, vol. VII (Feb. 1910), pp. 525–26 (ill.); Alfred von Wurzbach, *Niederländisches Künstler-Lexikon*, vol. II, Vienna and Leipzig, 1910, p. 408; Arthur Hoeber, "Some Pictures from the Collection of Mr. and Mrs. Charles P. Taft," *The International Studio*, vol. XXXIX (1910), pp. lxxi–lxxiv, pl. 73; William Walton, "Exhibition in New York of Paintings from the Collection of Mr. and Mrs. Charles P. Taft," *Burlington Magazine*, vol. XVI (1910), p. 368; *Connoisseur*, vol. XXXVI (May–Aug. 1913), p. 256, pl. p. 261; "Art Notes," *The Evening Post* [New York], Feb. 28, 1914, p. 7; Gustav Kobbe, "Noted Art Collectors Send Their Famous Old Masters for Loan Exhibition of Dutch Art in New York," *New York Herald*, Mar. 1, 1914; Cornelis Hofstede de Groot, *A Catalogue Raisonné of the Works of the Most Eminent Dutch Painters of the Seventeenth Century*, vol. VI, London, 1916, p. 346, no. 736, and p. 403, under no. 881; Maurice W. Brockwell, *A Catalogue of Paintings in the Collection of Mr. and Mrs. Charles P. Taft*, New York, 1920, p. xvi, no. 13; C. H. Collins Baker, *Catalogue of the Petworth Collection of Pictures in the Possession of Lord Leconfield*, London, 1920, p. 101; D. S. Meldrum, *Rembrandt Paintings with an Essay on His Life and Work*, London, 1923, pp. 51, 72, 189, pl. LXXXVIII; *The Art News*, vol. XXVIII, no. 28 (Apr. 12, 1930), p. 3, on the sale of the pendant to the Taft picture with a reference to the latter; W. Heil, "Die Rembrandt-Ausstellung in Detroit," *Pantheon*, vol. VI (1930), p. 380; F. Schmidt-Degener, in *Unknown Masterpieces*, ed. William R. Valentiner, London, 1930, under no. 51 (the pendant), as "probably a companion-piece"; William R. Valentiner, *Rembrandt Paintings in America*, New York, 1931, no. 34, pl. 34; Walter H. Siple, "The Taft Museum," *Bulletin of the Cincinnati Art Museum*, vol. IV (1933), p. 13; O. Benesch, *Rembrandt: Werk und Forschung*, Vienna, 1935, p. 14; Abraham Bredius, *Rembrandt Gemälde*, Vienna, 1935, pp. 172 (ill.), 341; *Loan Exhibition of Paintings, Drawings, and Etchings by Rembrandt and His Circle*, exh. cat., The Art Institute of Chicago, 1935, p. 17; *Coronet*, vol. V, no. 4 (Feb. 1, 1939), p. 12 (ill.); *Catalogue of the Taft Museum*, Cincinnati, 1939 and 1958, no. 275 (ill.); J. Q. van Regteren Altena, in Jan Veth, *Rembrandts leven en kunst*, Amsterdam, 1941, p. 73, identifying the subject as Constantijn Huygens; Harry B. Wehle, "A Fashionable Portrait by Rembrandt," *The Metropolitan Museum of Art Bulletin*, n.s., vol. II, no. 6 (Feb. 1944), pp. 178–80 (ill.), considering whether the New York and Taft paintings are a pair; *Loan Exhibition of Paintings by Frans Hals, Rembrandt*, exh. cat., Los Angeles County Museum of Art, 1947, p. 65; H. E. van Gelder, *Ikonographie van Constantijn Huygens*, The Hague, 1957, p. 36, rejecting Altena's identification of the sitter as Huygens; W. G. Constable, *Art Collecting in the United States of America: An Outline of a History*, London, 1964, p. 132; Kurt Bauch, *Rembrandt Gemälde*, Berlin, 1966, no. 366; Horst Gerson, *Rembrandt Paintings*, Amsterdam, 1968, pp. 276–77, 494, fig. 140; *The Age of Rembrandt: Dutch Paintings and Drawings of the Seventeenth Century*, exh. cat., National Museum of Western Art, Tokyo, 1968, no. 45; Giovanni Arpino and Paolo Lecaldano, *L'Opera pittorica completa di Rembrandt*, Milan, 1969, pp. 100–101, no. 125; Abraham Bredius, *Rembrandt: The Complete Edition of Paintings*, ed., Horst Gerson, London, 1969, pp. 147 (ill.), 562, no. 172, and p. 576, under no. 341; Jaap Bolton and H. Bolton-Rempt, *The Hidden Rembrandt*, Milan, 1976, and Chicago, 1977, p. 181, fig. 172; Karel Braun and Paolo Lecaldano, *Alle tot nu toe bekende schilderijen van Rembrandt*, Rotterdam, 1976, pp. 96–97, nos. 125–26 (ill.); David Smith, *The Dutch Double and Pair Portrait: Studies in the Imagery of Marriage in the Seventeenth Century*, Ann Arbor, Mich., 1978, pp. 271–72, fig. 102; W. Strauss and M. van der Meulen, *The Rembrandt Documents*, New York, 1979, p. 95; Howard Hibbard, *The Metropolitan Museum of Art*, New York, 1980, p. 336; David Smith, *Masks of Wedlock: Seventeenth-Century Dutch Marriage Portraits*, Ann Arbor, Mich., 1982, pp. 125–27, 129; *Masterpieces of the Dutch Golden Age*, exh. cat., High Museum of Art, Atlanta, 1985, p. 105; David Smith, "Rembrandt's Early Double Portraits and the Dutch Conversation Piece," *Art Bulletin*, vol. LXIV (1982), pp. 268–70, 273, fig. 17; S. Dickey, in *Dutch Painting in* the Age of Rembrandt from the Metropolitan Museum of Art, Picker Art Gallery, Colgate University, Hamilton, N.Y., 1983, p. 24; Walter A. Liedtke, *Flemish Paintings in the Metropolitan Museum of Art,* vol. I, New York, 1984, p. 60, note 9, comparing the rising figure in Rembrandt's *Syndics* in the Rijksmuseum, Amsterdam; Gary Schwartz, *Rembrandt: His Life, His Paintings,* Harmondsworth, 1985, p. 165, fig. 166; Stichting Foundation Rembrandt Research Project, *A Corpus of Rembrandt Paintings,* vol. II, Dordrecht, 1986, pp. 69, 127, 373, 378–83 (no. A 78), 391; J. and M. Guillard, *Rembrandt: The Human Form and Spirit,* Paris and New York, 1986, pp. 304–5, fig. 359; Peter C. Sutton, *A Guide to Dutch Art in America,* Grand Rapids, Mich., 1986, p. 60, fig. 85; Christian Tümpel, *Rembrandt: Mythos and Methode,* Antwerp, 1986, pp. 86 (ill.), 412, no. 200; Ernst van de Wetering, *Studies in the Workshop Practice of the Early Rembrandt,* vol. III, Amsterdam, 1986, p. 69; Ruth K. Meyer, "The Tafts of Pike Street," *Apollo,* n.s., vol. CXXVIII, no. 322 (Dec. 1988), pp. 388, 392–93 (ill.); Walter Liedtke, "Reconstructing Rembrandt: Portraits from the Early Years in Amsterdam (1631–34)," *Apollo,* n.s., vol. CXXIX, no. 327 (May 1989), pp. 326, 329, fig. 5; Walter Liedtke, "Dutch Paintings in America: The Collectors and Their Ideals," in Ben Broos et al., *Dutch Paintings from America,* exh. cat., Mauritshuis, The Hague, 1990, pp. 46–47, fig. 33; David Torbet Johnson, "Taft Museum," *Ventura,* vol. IV, no. 16 (June–Aug. 1991), p. 136 (ill.).

1931.409

1931.402

Follower of Rembrandt

An Elderly Woman

Probably mid-seventeenth century
Oil on wood, 64.8 x 52.1 cm (25½ x 20½ in.)
Signed and dated (falsely) lower left: *Rembrandt / f 1642*

There can be little doubt that this falsely signed and dated painting is the work of a seventeenth-century follower, probably a pupil, of Rembrandt, who himself painted pictures that are very similar in subject and superficially similar in style. The master's mature manner, as imitated here, features the "impasto-ridden use of paint,"[1] which, during the eighteenth century, drew remarks such as "picking up Rembrandt by the nose"[2] but which, during the seventeenth century and again during the nineteenth (one might compare the present sitter's face to Courbet's craggy cliffs), inspired honest students and copyists as well as less innocent admirers.

It should not be surprising that this somewhat unfamiliar work must be stricken from Rembrandt's oeuvre, although in 1965 Bauch considered it not only genuine but as belonging to a series of studies after the same model.[3] During the past twenty years our knowledge, or at least our idea, of Rembrandt's role as a teacher and of his many pupils and followers has changed significantly.[4] Paintings that virtually defined what was typical of the master, such as the famous *Man in the Golden Helmet* (Berlin, Gemäldegalerie, Staatliche Museen), have recently been assigned to students (usually anonymous) with little opposition from the academic community.[5] The process of "deattribution" is a commentary on, not a contribution to, the history of taste, which has had many moments of excess in regard to Rembrandt. Brockwell, for example, considered the present picture "techni-

cally, even finer" than Rembrandt's *Portrait of a Man Rising from His Chair,* which helps explain how the Tafts could have purchased *An Elderly Woman* in 1908 for the exorbitant price of $60,000.[6]

The Taft picture is executed on a scale somewhat larger than that of most study heads by Rembrandt and his immediate followers. The cheerful expression seems alien to the master, the modeling even more so. There is some sense of solid form in the main features but not in the contours of the face, ear, and brow. The brushwork in the face is not as thick as it appears in reproduction; however, it is arbitrary — a manner rather than a method — to a degree not found in autograph works. Even more unexpected in a painting supposedly by Rembrandt or by one of his close followers is the flat brushwork in the headdress, which flows around the face with careless disregard for the laws of perspective and gravity.

These shortcomings, and probably the most broadly brushed areas especially, led Gerson to consider the Taft painting to be an imitation "of a later century."[7] However, the support, the paint surface, and in some passages (including the signature) the execution appear consistent with seventeenth-century methods and materials. Unfortunately, the panel is backed and cradled, preventing examination of the wood. However, a smaller painting in the National Gallery of Art, Washington, D.C. (fig. 1), which is so similar in execution that it may well be by the same hand, is on a panel that has been dendrochronologically dated to the mid-seventeenth century.[8] Furthermore, the style of the Washington picture, while exhibiting some of the same troubling qualities as the present painting, is more clearly charac-

Fig. 1 Follower of Rembrandt van Rijn, *Head of an Aged Woman*, ca. 1645. Oil on panel, 21 x 17 cm (8¼ x 6¾ in.). Washington, D.C., National Gallery of Art, Widener Collection, 1942.9.64.

teristic of Rembrandt's circle. The old woman's wrinkled face is treated as an opportunity to display an impasto technique, but at the same time the features and the white head cover (especially at the edge) are articulated convincingly. In summary, the Washington and Cincinnati pictures exaggerate a few qualities that the painter considered Rembrandtesque but do not go beyond what one finds elsewhere in Rembrandt's circle; no passage, considered in the context of the composition as a whole, reveals an artistic conception distinctive of a later period.

It may appear that the small panel in the National Gallery is by a better artist, but it would be more appropriate to suggest that the style of execution evident in both paintings is less successful when employed on a larger scale. The pattern of strokes and touches in the face of the two figures is very much the same, as are such discrete elements as the strong black line running around the front of the hood, the pink touches around the eyes, and the form of the signature, which in both pictures is to the left near the woman's shoulder, with *Rembrandt* above a lowercase *f* (for *fecit*) and the date. The most similar paintings by Rembrandt, *Old Woman in a Hood* in Moscow (Bredius 383) and *Old Woman in an Armchair* in Leningrad (Bredius 381), are both dated 1654; the Washington panel is dated — perhaps spuriously — 1657. The Taft picture is dated 1642, not 1652 as Bredius and Bauch believed, although in correcting them Gerson conceded that "the later date would indeed fit better with the type of model"[9] and, one would add, with the manner of execution. It is not inconceivable that the signature and date here are contemporary with the picture and that the work was deliberately back-dated to gain some distance from Rembrandt's contemporary canvases. In any case, the Taft painting probably dates from the 1650s.

The name of a known Rembrandt follower, Abraham van Dijck, has been tangentially connected with the Washington picture. Van Dijck did paint a similar model in *The Old Procuress* of about 1655–60 in the Hermitage, Saint Petersburg, and in other works.[10] The style of the Taft picture does not recall that of Van Dijck's securely attributed paintings, but the similarity of subject adds some support to the idea that the painter may have been, as Van Dijck probably was, Rembrandt's pupil during the 1650s.

1. Stichting Foundation Rembrandt Research Project, *A Corpus of Rembrandt Paintings*, vol. II, Dordrecht, 1986, p. 652.

2. Anthony Bailey, *Rembrandt's House*, Boston, 1978, p. 201. Compare Chardin's panel after a similar Rembrandt subject, published by Pierre Rosenberg, "Chardin Studies," *Burlington Magazine*, vol. CXXIX (1987), p. 116, fig. 47.

3. Kurt Bauch, *Rembrandt Gemälde*, Berlin, 1966, nos. 271 (Taft), 273 (Washington; fig. 1, here), 274 (St. Petersburg, *Old Woman*, dated 1654), 275 (Moscow, *Old Woman*, dated 1654), 276 (Copenhagen); see also no. 277.

4. See especially Werner Sumowski, *Gemälde der Rembrandt-Schüler*, Landau (Pfalz), 1983–; and Albert Blankert et al., *Rembrandt: The Impact of a Genius*, Amsterdam, 1983.

5. The Berlin picture was closely studied and reattributed at the Gemäldegalerie itself and is discussed by Jan Kelch, *Der Mann mit dem Goldhelm* (Bilder im Blickpunkt), Berlin, 1986.

6. Maurice W. Brockwell, *A Catalogue of Paintings in the Collection of Mr. and Mrs. Charles P. Taft*, New York, 1920, p. xvi; the price is given on Scott and Fowles's invoice of Jan. 22, 1908, in which the Tafts also receive a credit of $18,000 for a painting by Constable. The figure of $60,000 is ten times the record-setting price paid by John G. Johnson at about the same time for Rogier van der Weyden's monumental *Crucifixion Diptych* in Philadelphia.

7. Horst Gerson, in Abraham Bredius, *Rembrandt: The Complete Edition of the Paintings*, London, 1969, p. 580, under no. 382.

8. Per Arthur Wheelock (see note 10); the tree was cut no earlier than 1633.

9. Gerson, p. 580.

10. Arthur Wheelock, curator of Dutch and Flemish paintings at the National Gallery of Art, Washington, D.C., kindly examined the painting with the writer in July 1987 and provided a draft of his entry for the forthcoming catalogue of Dutch paintings in which Van Dijck is tentatively brought into consideration. The paintings by Van Dijck cited by Wheelock are in Sumowski, vol. I, nos. 367 (St. Petersburg), 370, 372, 375, and 377.

Provenance William Ponsonby, ninth earl of Drogheda (1846–1908), Moore Abbey, Monasterevan, County Kildare, Ireland; Sir Hugh P. Lane, London (by 1903); [Dowdeswell and Dowdeswell, London]; [Scott and Fowles, New York, in 1908]; Taft collection, Jan. 22, 1908.

Exhibitions London, Guildhall, Corporation Art Gallery, *A Selection of Works by Early and Modern Painters of the Dutch School*, 1903, no. 135; New York, Scott and Fowles, 1914, no. 6; Raleigh, North Carolina Museum of Art, *Rembrandt and His Pupils*, 1956 (cat. by William R. Valentiner, no. 23); Milwaukee Art Institute, *Six Great Painters*, 1957.

Literature Sir [William] Martin Conway, *Great Masters, 1400–1800*, London, 1903, sec. XXIII, large photogravure reproduction and broad commentary; Wilhelm von Bode and Cornelis Hofstede de Groot, *The Complete Work of Rembrandt*, vol. VIII, Paris, 1906, pp. 39, 130, pl. 584, as "somewhat caricatural in expression"; William R. Valentiner, *Rembrandt,* *des Meisters Gemälde (Klassiker der Kunst)*, Stuttgart and Berlin, 1909, pp. 349 (ill.), 560; "Art Notes," *The Evening Post* [New York], Feb. 28, 1914, p. 7; Gustav Kobbe, "Noted Art Collectors Send Their Famous Old Masters for Loan Exhibition of Dutch Art in New York," *New York Herald*, Mar. 1, 1914; William R. Valentiner, *The Art of the Low Countries*, Garden City, N.Y., 1914, p. 247, no. 60; Cornelis Hofstede de Groot, *A Catalogue Raisonné of the Works of the Most Eminent Dutch Painters of the Seventeenth Century*, vol. VI, London, 1916, p. 251, no. 496; Maurice W. Brockwell, *A Catalogue of Paintings in the Collection of Mr. and Mrs. Charles P. Taft*, New York, 1920, p. xvi, no. 15; William R. Valentiner, *Rembrandt Paintings in America*, New York, 1931, no. 112, pl. 112; Abraham Bredius, *Rembrandt Gemälde*, Vienna, 1935, p. 16, no. 382, pl. 382; *Catalogue of the Taft Museum*, Cincinnati, 1939 and 1958, no. 238 (ill.); Paul L. Grigaut, "Rembrandt and His Pupils in North Carolina," *The Art Quarterly*, vol. XIX (1956), p. 410, note 2, on the reading of the date; Kurt Bauch, *Rembrandt Gemälde*, Berlin, 1966, no. 271; Abraham Bredius, *Rembrandt: The Complete Edition of the Paintings*, ed. Horst Gerson, London, 1969, pp. 298 (ill.), 580, no. 382.

1931.402

1962.1

⁊

Imitator of Rembrandt

Rembrandt Leaning on a Windowsill

Probably early eighteenth century
Oil on canvas, 82.5 x 68.3 cm (32½ x 26⅞ in.)
Signed and dated (falsely) lower right: *Rembrandt. f 1650*

A man resembling Rembrandt is portrayed half length leaning on a stone windowsill. He rests his head on his right hand and smiles at the viewer. The large hat of soft material, the jacket, and the cape recall costumes worn by Rembrandt in self-portraits of about 1640–50.

This intriguing picture is not well known, having been in private collections until 1962 and first published, as a *Self-Portrait* by Rembrandt, in 1922.[1] Valentiner catalogued the painting in 1923 and 1931; he considered "the delicacy of execution and the rather fluid color" to be characteristic of Rembrandt's work around 1650.[2] When the canvas was exhibited in New York in 1933, the journalist Elisabeth Luther Cary, in comparing this work to Rembrandt's *Self-Portrait*, also dated 1650, in the Widener Collection, concluded that "it calls for credulity to accept these two Rembrandts as one and the same personality."[3] Glück (1928) and Bredius (1935) also doubted the identification of the sitter with Rembrandt. Bauch (1966) adopted this view but wondered whether the subject might be another artist, considering the unconventional costume ("with slashed sleeves and a beret") and informal pose.[4] Rembrandt was rejected as the sitter and, for the first time, as the author of the painting by Gerson in 1968. He knew the picture only from a photograph but was "not convinced that the attribution is correct."[5] More recent monographs on Rembrandt do not mention the work,[6] which members of the Rembrandt Research Project consider a later imitation.[7]

The question of how closely the sitter resembles Rembrandt is rendered less urgent by the current consensus that the painting is not by him. The slightly uncertain likeness in a picture of considerable quality might lead one to conclude that the artist had only limited evidence of Rembrandt's appearance, rather than to suppose, with Glück and Bredius, that this is Rembrandt's portrait of a man who happened to look like him. The execution, as discussed below, is much less reminiscent of Rembrandt than is the subject's smiling face. However, the portrait does not appear to have been based on a single self-portrait by Rembrandt, on a portrait of the master by one of his pupils or contemporary followers, or on a print after such a work. The picture might be described as an imitation or (more kindly) an imaginary self-portrait, that is, a historical portrait of Rembrandt that employs a Rembrandtesque composition and brushwork inspired, if not well informed, by an idea of the artist's style during the appropriate period (about 1645–55).

The most similar self-portraits by Rembrandt in regard to facial features include the familiar *Self-Portrait at the Age of Thirty-four* (1640) in the National Gallery, London, and the half-length *Self-Portrait* (1652) in the Kunsthistorisches Museum, Vienna. The sitter here seems closer in age to the artist as he appears in the Vienna painting; indeed, the date of 1650 on the Taft picture is plausible. All that can be said of the costume is that it bears a broad resemblance to the style of dress that Rembrandt wears in self-portraits of the 1640s; the floppy beret, slashed sleeves, and cloak are found in various forms in several pictures, in which, however, they are usually described with closer attention to their distinctive details. The *Self-Portrait* in Windsor Castle, signed and dated 1642 (Bredius 37), should be mentioned here not only in regard to the costume and the artist's appearance but because the painting has only recently been considered as "a later imitation, possibly from the second half of the eighteenth century."[8]

In bright light the Taft picture appears very thinly painted in broad strokes over the brown background. This is especially evident in the costume (including the oversized beret), but even the hands — one gloved and formless, the other bare but revealing no interest in anatomy — lack the kind of attention to modeling that even a minor pupil of Rembrandt would have given them. The face is more carefully developed and borrows a scheme of lighting found in Rembrandt's self-portraits,[9] but the feathery brushwork fills in areas and sketchily suggests forms, the eyebrows for example, in a manner foreign to Dutch painting during the seventeenth century. If one forgets for a moment the charm of the image as a whole and isolates such details as the eyes and considers their physical relationship to each other and to the structure of the head, then one can only wonder at the state of Rembrandt connoisseurship during the first half of this century. The palette alone, with red smoldering through a simple scheme of charcoal and brown, takes one (so to speak) to the other side of De Gelder (d. 1727) from Rembrandt, while the fluid technique, like this very type of fancy portrait, seems directly of the eighteenth century and anticipatory of Fragonard's *portraits de fantaisie.*[10]

Not only Rembrandt's reputation but also imitations of his style flourished during the eighteenth century, first in France with such figures as Alexis Grimou and Jean Raoux (and very differently, Chardin), then in Germany and England.[11] In these countries and even in Italy, Rembrandt's single figures, his "characters," were found to be far more impressive than his historical subjects; his greatest achievement was the self-portrait, an assessment made without any idea of how extensively the artist had worked on this theme. In England painters such as Thomas Hudson, Nathaniel Hone, John Opie, Thomas Barker, and Sir Joshua Reynolds (the last as early as 1751) paid an egocentric tribute to the master by depicting themselves (as well as others) in Rembrandtesque portraits, usually in half length.[12]

Although one would not closely associate the Taft picture with any one of the artists named above, it is easy to imagine it as having been painted in France or England during the first half of the eighteenth century. The Rembrandt Research Project (RRP), in a first draft of their forthcoming catalogue entry on this work, suggests a French imitator active at the end of the seventeenth century or in the period 1700–1720.[13] A later dating is discouraged by the presence of azurite, which was largely replaced by Prussian blue in European paintings dating from after about 1720. At the same time, Karen Groen of the RRP describes the ground ("one layer of lead white with umber and charcoal black") as unfamiliar from paintings of the Rembrandt school.

The RRP's attribution of the picture to a French rather than an English or other imitator is plausible in terms of taste and technique; Paul-Ponce Robert's casual *Study of a Woman* of 1722 (Lille, Musée des Beaux-Arts) is, for example, one of several early-seventeenth-century French paintings that offers interesting analogies in subject and style.[14] Ernst van de Wetering's argument is based mainly on his view that the artist benefited from a close study of Rembrandt's *Girl Leaning on a Windowsill*

of 1645 (London, Dulwich Picture Gallery), which in the 1690s was taken from Amsterdam to Paris by Roger de Piles and remained in France until the early 1770s.[15] Van de Wetering feels that not only the arrangement and painterly treatment of the architecture are generally the same but also that discrete passages of execution are remarkably similar. This relationship between a then-famous work by Rembrandt and the Taft picture and the RRP's conclusion that the signature appears to have been inscribed by the painter of the latter work suggest that it was conceived as something less than an honest homage to the master.

1. Cornelis Hofstede de Groot, *Die holländische Kritik der jetzigen Rembrandt-Forschung und neuest wiedergefundene Rembrandtbilder,* Stuttgart and Berlin, 1922, pp. 43–48, no. 11. The term "first published," when used by authors such as Valentiner, usually refers to a reproduction but until now has led cataloguers to assume that this picture had not been mentioned previously in print.

2. William R. Valentiner, *Rembrandt Paintings in America,* New York, 1931, no. 104.

3. Elisabeth Luther Cary, review of Knoedler exhibition, *New York Times,* Apr. 16, 1933; the review is quoted on the invoice given by Knoedler and Co. to Mr. Semple on Dec. 25, 1934.

4. See Literature under Glück, Bredius, and Bauch; the latter's view follows Wilhelm Pinder, *Rembrandts Selbstbildnisse,* Königstein im Taunus, 1956, p. 82.

5. Horst Gerson, *Rembrandt Paintings,* Amsterdam, 1968, p. 500, under no. 301; and Abraham Bredius, *Rembrandt: The Complete Edition of the Paintings,* ed. Horst Gerson, London, 1969, p. 550, under no. 41. The comment quoted here appears in both books.

6. Except Jaap Bolton and H. Bolton-Rempt, *The Hidden Rembrandt,* Milan, 1976, and Chicago, 1977, p. 193, no. 379.

7. Letter to the writer from J. Bruyn, dated Sept. 10, 1986. Bruyn and Simon Levie studied the painting in June 1972 and "felt sure that this was one of the cases where one could with some confidence think of a later imitation. Neither the brushwork nor the colour-scheme convinced us of a 17th-century origin."

8. Christopher White, *The Dutch Pictures in the Collection of Her Majesty the Queen,* Cambridge, 1982, p. 112, citing the supporting opinions of the Rembrandt Research Project (letter of 1972) and of the conservator Herbert Lank.

9. For example, Bredius, nos. 42, 43, 44, and paintings of other models, such as *A Bearded Man in a Cap* in the National Gallery, London (Bredius 283).

10. See Mary D. Sheriff, "Invention, Resemblance, and Fragonard's *Portraits de fantaisie,*" *Art Bulletin,* vol. LXIX (1987), pp. 77–87. It should be added that the inscription, too, suggests a later date, since the *1* and *5* in the date do not follow seventeenth-century forms.

11. Horst Gerson, *Ausbreitung und Nachwirkung der holländischen Malerei des 17. Jahrhunderts,* Haarlem, 1942, pp. 87–96 (on the eighteenth-century French response to Rembrandt), 301–2, 316–20, 333–34, 343–44 (the same in Germany and Austria), 445–50 (in England). See also S. Heiland and H. Lüdecke, *Rembrandt und die Nachwelt,* Leipzig, 1960; Franklin W. Robinson, "Rembrandt's Influence in Eighteenth-Century Venice," *Nederlands Kunsthistorisch Jaarboek* (identified as *NKJ* below), vol. XVIII (1967), pp. 167–96; Horst Gerson, "Imitaties naar Rembrandt door Thomas Worlidge, 1700–1766," *NKJ,* vol. XXI (1970), pp. 301–7; Jan Bialostocki, "Rembrandt and Posterity," and Jean Cailleux, "Esquisse d'une étude sur le goût pour Rembrandt en France au XVIIIe siècle," *NKJ,* vol. XXIII (1972), pp. 131–57, 159–66; Ina Marie Keller, *Studien zu den deutschen Rembrandtnachahmungen des 18. Jahrhunderts,* Berlin, 1981; and especially, *Rembrandt in Eighteenth-Century England,* Yale Center for British Art, New Haven, 1983. The following remarks principally depend on Christopher White's two essays

in the New Haven catalogue, "Rembrandt: Reputation and Collecting" and "Rembrandt's Influence on English Painting."

12. *Rembrandt in Eighteenth-Century England*, pls. 12–14, 20, 22, 29, 30; pls. 49, 50 (etchings by Pond and Worlidge); see also p. 92 in the biography on Benjamin Wilson; and pp. 106–17, for White's list of paintings and drawings by or thought to be by Rembrandt in England during the eighteenth century.

13. Draft of a forthcoming *Corpus* entry kindly sent to the writer by Ernst van de Wetering, Dec. 1992. Karen Goren provided a copy of her technical analysis in Sept. 1991.

14. See *Masterworks from the Musée des Beaux-Arts, Lille*, exh. cat., The Metropolitan Museum of Art, New York, 1992, no. 22. The arrangement of a figure leaning on a windowsill goes back to Dutch sources such as prints and paintings by Adriaen van Ostade and fancy portraits of the Rembrandt school (see especially Ferdinand Bol's *Portrait of a Young Man*, 1647, sold at Christie's, London, Dec. 13, 1991, no. 32; A. Blankert, *Ferdinand Bol*, Doornspijk, 1982, no. 100, pl. 109).

15. RRP entry (see note 13). This relationship was first noted by Bruyn in his letter of 1986 (see note 7). For the Rembrandt, see Peter Murray, *Dulwich Picture Gallery: A Catalogue*, London, 1980, p. 101, no. 163. Joshua Reynolds's copy of the Dulwich canvas (ca. 1780) makes for an interesting comparison and is reproduced in Bob Haak, *Rembrandt: His Life, His Work, His Time*, New York, 1969, fig. 310.

Provenance Marivaux, Paris (in 1806; sale, Paris, Jan. 27, 1806); Count F. W. Rostopchin, Moscow (sale, London, 1844, to P. Norton, according to Hofstede de Groot, 1916 and 1922); sold by Norton to Th. Gurle (T. Garle?) (after 1854; sale, London, May 24, 1862, to J. Smith); [John Smith, in 1862]; Sir John Poynder Dickson-Poynder, Lord Islington (b. 1866), Rushbrook Hall, near Bury St. Edmunds, and 20 Portman Square (Home House), London, according to Knoedler's; [Lewis and Simmons, London, according to Hofstede de Groot, 1922]; Nils B. Hersloff, West Orange, N.J. (before 1922–34); [M. Knoedler, New York, in 1934]; Mr. and Mrs. William Semple, Cincinnati (in 1934); Louise Taft Semple bequest, 1962.

Exhibitions Detroit Institute of Arts, *Paintings by Rembrandt*, 1930 (cat. by William R. Valentiner, no. 66); New York, M. Knoedler, *Rembrandt Exhibition*, Apr. 1933; The Art Institute of Chicago, *A Century of Progress: Exhibition of Paintings and Sculpture*, 1934 (cat., p. 19, no. 106, pl. XX, as *Self-Portrait*, signed and dated 1650, lent by Hersloff); Cleveland Museum of Art, *Twentieth-Anniversary Exhibition*, 1936 (*Catalogue of the Twentieth-Anniversary Exhibition of the Cleveland Museum of Art, The Official Art Exhibit of the Great Lakes Exposition*, p. 92, no. 230, as *Self-Portrait*, dated 1650).

Literature John Smith, *A Catalogue Raisonné of the Works of the Most Eminent Dutch, Flemish, and French Painters*, vol. VII, London, 1836, p. 85, no. 206, as representing Rembrandt and as in the Marivaux collection, Paris, 1806; Ernst Wilhelm Moes, *Iconographia Batavia*, vol. II, Amsterdam, 1905, p. 316, no. 100, under subject no. 6693 (Rembrandt), as sold from the collection of T. Garle, London, 1862; Cornelis Hofstede de Groot, *A Catalogue Raisonné of the Works of the Most Eminent Dutch Painters of the Seventeenth Century*, vol. VI, London, 1916, p. 290, no. 593b, with important details of provenance for the period 1806–62; Cornelis Hofstede de Groot, *Die holländische Kritik der jetzigen Rembrandt-Forschung und neuest wiedergefundene Rembrandtbilder*, Stuttgart and Berlin, 1922, pp. 43–48, no. 11, fig. 11, as signed and dated 1660, but wondering whether the date might really be 1650 (judging only from a photograph), with further details of provenance; William R. Valentiner, *Rembrandt, wiedergefundene Gemälde (1910–1922)*, Berlin and Leipzig, 1923, p. 96 (ill.); Gustav Glück, "Rembrandts Selbstbildnis aus dem Jahre 1652," *Jahrbuch der kunsthistorischen Sammlungen in Wien*, n.s., vol. II (1928), pp. 317–28, reprinted in Gustav Glück, *Aus drei Jahrhunderten europäischer Malerei, Gesammelte Aufsätze*, vol. II, Vienna, 1933, p. 296, as a wonderful portrait of a man of about forty, dated 1660, impossible that it represents Rembrandt (Valentiner, editorial comment on p. 347, corrects the date to 1650 and suggests that Glück, had he known this, would not have doubted the identification of the sitter as Rembrandt); William R. Valentiner, *Rembrandt Paintings in America*, New York, 1931,

no. 104, pl. 104, correcting the date to 1650; Elisabeth Luther Cary, review of Knoedler exhibition, *New York Times*, Apr. 16, 1933; Royal Cortissoz, review of Knoedler exhibition, *New York Herald Tribune*, Apr. [16?], 1933; R. Flint, "Knoedler Holds Rembrandt Show to Aid Charity," *Art News*, vol. XXXI, no. 30 (Apr. 22, 1933), p. 4, as *Portrait of the Artist*, loaned by Lord Islington; Ella Simons Siple, "A Rembrandt Exhibition in New York," *Burlington Magazine*, vol. LXII (Apr. 1933), p. 190, pl. B, as a *Self-Portrait* dated 1660, once owned by Lord Islington, now in the Hersloff collection; Forbes Watson, "Gallery Explorations," *Parnassus*, vol. V, no. 111 (Apr. 1933), p. 2, as *Self-Portrait*, dated 1650, "a firm and mellow masterpiece"; "Rembrandt Loan Exhibition," *Connoisseur*, vol. XCI (Apr. 1933), p. 276; Alfred M. Frankfurter, ed., "New York's First Rembrandt Exhibition," *The Fine Arts*, vol. XX, no. 1 (May 1933), p. 9 (ill.), as *Portrait of the Artist*, 1660, and p. 50; "Knoedler Sells Fine Rembrandt," *Art News*, vol. XXXIII, no. 17 (Jan. 26, 1935), p. 8 (ill.); Abraham Bredius, *Rembrandt Gemälde*, Vienna, 1935, pl. 41, and p. 4, as dated 1650, not a self-portrait, recently sold from the Hersloff collection to another American owner; Wilhelm Pinder, *Rembrandts Selbstbildnisse*, Königstein im Taunus, 1956, p. 82, as "probably an artist, but surely not Rembrandt himself"; Kurt Bauch, *Rembrandt Gemälde*, Berlin, 1966, no. 399, as perhaps an artist, not Rembrandt; Horst Gerson, *Rembrandt Paintings*, Amsterdam, 1968, pp. 356, 381 (ill.), 500, no. 301, as *Man Leaning in a Windowsill*, and for the first time doubting the attribution to Rembrandt; Abraham Bredius, *Rembrandt: The Complete Edition of the Paintings*, ed. Horst Gerson, London, 1969, pp. 37 (ill.), 550, no. 41, repeating opinions of Gerson 1968; Jaap Bolton and H. Bolton-Rempt, *The Hidden Rembrandt*, Milan, 1976, and Chicago, 1977, p. 193, no. 379 (ill.), as *Self-Portrait?*.

1962.1

Govaert Flinck
Cleves 1615–1660 Amsterdam

A merchant's son from Cleves, which at that time belonged to Prussia, Flinck was born on January 25, 1615. Houbraken elaborates a long account of Flinck's childhood commitment to art, which was supported by Lambert Jacobsz., a visiting Mennonite preacher and painter from Leeuwarden, to which Flinck soon moved. A biblical picture by Jacobsz., signed and dated 1629, in the Rijksmuseum, Amsterdam, is interesting for the light it sheds on Flinck's early style.

It was probably during the early 1630s that Flinck, like Jacobsz.'s pupil Jacob Backer, moved from Leeuwarden to Amsterdam. Flinck must have come into contact with Rembrandt through Hendrick van Uylenburgh, a Mennonite art dealer who had business with Jacobsz. as well as with Rembrandt.[1] Like the latter, Flinck rarely left the city and never went abroad; Rembrandt's compositions, manner of execution, figure types (even their homeliness), and great success as a portraitist sufficed to fire the younger artist's imagination.

By 1645, when Flinck married at the age of thirty, he had been working independently as a portraitist and history painter for about ten years and was already financially secure. A number of important commissions date from the 1640s, such as the large group portraits of the governors of the Amsterdam musketeers (1642), the company of Captain Bas (1645), and the Amsterdam civic guard celebrating the Peace of Münster (1648), all in the Rijksmuseum, Amsterdam. Houbraken relates that Flinck had a valuable collection of ancient sculpture, paintings and drawings, and armor and orientalia; moved in high social circles; and was a friend of the distinguished burgomasters Cornelis and Andries de Graeff.[2]

Through the 1640s, Flinck, along with such contemporary portraitists as Bartholomeus van der Helst and Ferdinand Bol, turned to a lighter, looser style based on Flemish models. He painted portraits of eminent figures, including the prince-elector of Prussia (1652) and Count Johan Maurits van Nassau (1653 and ca. 1658?).[3] In 1651 Flinck's first wife died, and in 1656 he married a wealthy woman. In the same year he painted his enormous history of Marcus Curius Dentatus, one of several lucrative commissions he fulfilled for the new Town Hall of Amsterdam.[4] In November 1659, Flinck was assigned another dozen compositions for the same building at one thousand guilders each, but he died on February 2, 1660, having completed only some preliminary work.

Flinck enjoyed the kind of career that his famous master might have envied, but his success had more to do with charm, fashion, good connections, and the readability of his history pictures than with his superficial command of Rembrandt's manner.[5] The Flemification of his style served him less well in murals than in easel pictures, especially portraits; a few female figures are unforgettable.[6]

1. See J. W. von Moltke, *Govaert Flinck, 1615–1660,* Amsterdam, 1965, p. 10, note 1; and, more informatively, Bob Haak, *Rembrandt: His Life, His Work, His Time,* New York, 1969, pp. 79, 131. Haak states flatly that Flinck arrived in Amsterdam between 1631 and 1633 and "became Rembrandt's pupil in Hendrick Uylenburgh's home." See also Gary Schwartz, *Rembrandt: His Life, His Paintings,* Harmondsworth, 1985, chap. 20.

2. Arnold Houbraken, *De Groote Schouburgh der Nederlantsche Konstschilders en Schilderessen,* Amsterdam, 1718–21, vol. II, p. 22.

3. Moltke, p. 11 and nos. 198, 214.

4. Moltke, p. 90, no. 113, pls. 22, 23. Neil Maclaren, *The Dutch School,* National Gallery Catalogues, London, 1960, p. 131, seems to confuse the date of this picture with that of *The Wisdom of Solomon* (1658; Moltke, no. 30).

5. See, for example, Flinck's *Diana and Endymion,* exhibited in *Liechtenstein: The Princely Collections,* exh. cat., The Metropolitan Museum of Art, New York, 1985, pp. 264–65, no. 167, from which a few of my lines are repeated here.

6. See Moltke, no. 390 and compare no. 80.

Govaert Flinck

A Young Man in a Feathered Beret

ca. 1636
Oil on panel, 58.7 x 47.9 cm (23⅛ x 18⅞ in.)

A young man in fanciful attire is depicted in bust-length, three-quarter view. Strong light from the left falls mostly on his face and on the wall behind him. His feathered beret and tunic are decorated with gold chains, which, with the costume as a whole, derive from early portraits by Rembrandt.

In 1923 one of the founding fathers of the history of Dutch art, Abraham Bredius, took aim at two others, Cornelis Hofstede

1931.416

de Groot and Wilhelm von Bode, using this picture as ammunition.[1] Bredius had already published the panel as a self-portrait by Bol.[2] The Dutchman described the work as "a charming picture, strongly influenced by Rembrandt . . . in the splendid Taft Collection in Cincinnati." He continued: "I was told there that Dr. Bode at the first moment he saw it thought it to be an early Rembrandt. No wonder, since Dr. Bode, in his big work on Rembrandt, reproduced as by that master an old, weak, free copy after this painting in the Brunswick Gallery [fig. 1]."[3]

The debate about Bol, which went on with other authors,[4] was laid to rest by Albert Blankert, who rightly rejected the painting as by the artist and as a portrait of him.[5] Bol's early work (for example, *Portrait of a Lady,* signed and dated 1642, New York, The Metropolitan Museum of Art) is in a style different from and clearly later than that found here,[6] which is, whatever the quality, characteristic of Rembrandt's circle around 1635.[7] Blankert also rejected the Brunswick version as a Bol, concurred with Moltke that the latter picture is not by Flinck either,[8] suggested that both paintings are "weak derivations from a signed Flinck in the State Collection Wawel at Cracow" (Moltke, no. 246, pl. 33), and described the Taft panel more specifically as a "German (or maybe French) work of the 17th or 18th century."[9] However, Blankert recently admitted to the writer that he has never been to the Taft Museum and that his conclusion, which follows Moltke's view of the Brunswick picture (perhaps eighteenth century, based on the Cracow painting), was based solely on the perusal of photographs about twenty years ago.[10]

My own estimate of the painting's quality accords with that of the older scholars who saw it as the work of Rembrandt or Bol.[11] However, the picture's style, as suggested by the references to the Cracow panel, is consistent with that of signed works by

Flinck dating from the mid-1630s. The figure in the Cracow panel is very similar to this one in the generalized form of the head; the pattern of shadow cast to the right of the nose, brow, cheek, and chin; the drawing of the eyes, especially the lids; the treatment of the full coiffure; and the articulation of chains and other costume details. Other paintings by Flinck that bear close comparison to the Taft picture in both subject and style include the so-called *Rembrandt in a Feathered Beret and Gorget* of 1636 formerly in Lausanne; *Young Man in a Feathered Beret and Jeweled Chains* of 1637 in the Hermitage, Saint Petersburg; *Self-Portrait* of 1639 in the National Gallery, London; *Portrait of a Young Man* in the National Gallery of Ireland; and the presumed *Self-Portrait* of 1643, sold at Sotheby's, London, December 11, 1985.[12] The Taft painting may be placed with the earlier pictures in this group, which are smoother and simpler in execution than those of about 1640. A likely date would thus be about 1636.

The Brunswick version, even allowing for its poor condition, is distinctly inferior in quality and is very likely an old copy of the present picture, modified at the neckline of the costume and by the implausible addition of the figure's right hand and a sword hilt. That the latter motif was adopted from the Cracow painting suggests that the Brunswick panel was produced in Flinck's studio.[13]

1. Abraham Bredius, "Self-Portraits by Ferdinand Bol," *Burlington Magazine*, vol. XLII (Jan.–June 1923), pp. 81–82, which on the whole responds to a pamphlet published by Hofstede de Groot.

Fig. 1 Copyist of Ferdinand Bol, *Self-Portrait in a Feathered Beret,* perhaps eighteenth century. Oil on panel, 81 x 59.5 cm (32 x 23½ in.). Brunswick, Herzog Anton Ulrich-Museum.

2. Abraham Bredius, "Drei frühe Werke von Ferdinand Bol," *Kunstchronik*, n.s., vol. XXV (1913–14), col. 611. The painting has hung as a work by Bol until the present research on this catalogue, although doubts have been expressed previously.

3. Bredius 1923, pp. 81–82. Bode's "big work" is Wilhelm Bode, assisted by Cornelis Hofstede de Groot, *The Complete Work of Rembrandt*, vol. III, Paris, 1899, p. 68, no. 162, on the painting in Brunswick, with no mention of the Taft picture.

4. Cornelis Hofstede de Groot, "Self-Portraits by Ferdinand Bol," *Burlington Magazine*, vol. XLIII (July–Dec. 1923), pp. 27–28; John C. Van Dyke, *Rembrandt and His School*, New York, 1923, p. 53; J. H. J. Mellaart, "Self-Portraits by Ferdinand Bol," *Burlington Magazine*, vol. XLIII (Oct. 1923), p. 153, accepting all the Bol self-portraits advanced by Bredius 1923 (the Taft painting is not mentioned explicitly). Mellaart refers to Hofstede de Groot's article as "a counterblast on the subject."

5. Albert Blankert, *Ferdinand Bol, 1616–1680: Rembrandt's Pupil*, Doornspijk, 1982, p. 170, no. R 75; the Brunswick picture is no. R 76.

6. Blankert, no. 122, pl. 131.

7. Examples can be found in Werner Sumowski's six-volume corpus, *Gemälde der Rembrandt-Schüler*, Landau (Pfalz), 1983–, under Dou, Flinck, Van Gherwen, De Joudreville, etc. Blankert, pp. 57–58, briefly discusses the painting of *tronies* (literally, "faces"), which he describes as "representations of a single figure, usually half-length, wearing fancy costume instead of contemporary dress." This type of picture, which is very common in Rembrandt's oeuvre and his circle but hardly is restricted to them, is a difficult subject in search of a rather subtle scholar.

8. J. W. von Moltke, *Govaert Flinck, 1615–1660*, Amsterdam, 1965, pp. 244–45, no. 95.

9. Blankert, p. 170, under no. R 75.

10. In conversation with the writer, Nov. 1986.

11. The authors cited in notes 1–4 and Lionel Cust, "The So-Called 'Young Sampson,'" *Burlington Magazine*, vol. XXVI (1914), p. 256, as "a portrait of Bol by himself."

12. For these pictures and the Cracow painting, see Sumowski, vol. II, nos. 658, 663, 664, 666, 680, and 689; Moltke, pls. 32, 33 (Cracow), 35, 36, 48; H. Potterton, *Dutch Seventeenth- and Eighteenth-Century Paintings in the National Gallery of Ireland*, Dublin, 1986, no. 319, fig. 58.

13. Rüdiger Klessmann's very tentative attribution of the Brunswick painting (*Die holländische Gemälde*, Herzog Anton Ulrich-Museum, Brunswick, 1983, p. 113, no. 239) to Philips Koninck, whose name was proposed by Gerson, does not take into account the Taft picture (which is not even mentioned) and may be dismissed on the basis of comparisons with the superficially similar works by that artist or by his cousin Salomon Koninck. Dr. Klessmann and the writer examined the Brunswick picture together in July 1988.

Provenance P. Mersch (sale, Galerie Georges Petit, Paris, May 28, 1909, no. 4 [ill.], as by Bol); [Scott and Fowles, New York, in 1912]; Taft collection, 1912.

Exhibitions New York, Schaeffer Gallery, *Self-Portraits by Artists of Many Countries*, 1940; Indianapolis, John Herron Art Museum [also San Diego], *The Young Rembrandt and His Times*, 1958 (cat. by David Carter, no. 17, as by Bol).

Literature Abraham Bredius, "Drei frühe Werke von Ferdinand Bol," *Kunstchronik*, n.s., vol. XXV (1913–14), col. 611 (ill.), as by Bol; Lionel Cust, "The So-Called 'Young Sampson,'" *Burlington Magazine*, vol. XXVI (1914), p. 256, pl. B, as by Bol; Maurice W. Brockwell, *A Catalogue of Paintings in the Collection of Mr. and Mrs. Charles P. Taft*, New York, 1920, no. 9, as by Bol; Abraham Bredius, "Self-Portraits by Ferdinand Bol," *Burlington Magazine*, vol. XLII (Jan.–June 1923), pp. 81–82, pl. V, fig. K, as by Bol; Cornelis Hofstede de Groot, "Self-Portraits by Ferdinand Bol," *Burlington Magazine*, vol. XLIII (July–Dec. 1923), pp. 27, 28, doubting Bredius; John C. Van Dyke, *Rembrandt and His School*, New York, 1923, p. 53, as by Bol, along with the Brunswick picture; *Catalogue of the Taft Museum*, Cincinnati, 1939 and 1958, no. 234, as by Bol; Robert Goldwater, "Artists Painted by Themselves: Self-Portraits from Baroque to Impressionism," *Art News*, vol. XXXVIII, no. 26 (Mar. 30, 1940), p. 9; A.

Dobrzycka, "Autoportrety Ferdinanda Bola," *Biuletyn Historii Sztuki i Kultury*, vol. xviii (1956–57), pp. 419–27, fig. 2; J. W. von Moltke, *Govaert Flinck, 1615–1660*, Amsterdam, 1965, p. 244, under no. 95 (the Brunswick picture); Albert Blankert, *Ferdinand Bol, 1616–1680: Rembrandt's Pupil*, Doornspijk, 1982, p. 170, no. R 75, as not by Bol.

1931.416

Jeronimus van Diest

The Hague 1631–after 1675 The Hague?

Jeronimus (Jeronymus, Hieronymus) van Diest, son of the marine painter Willem van Diest (The Hague? before 1610–after 1663 The Hague?), was probably born at the Hague in 1631 and evidently died there after 1675.[1] He married at the Hague in 1655; his son Adriaen was born on December 12 of that year. In 1663 Van Diest was cited as a member of the painters' confraternity at the Hague, to which he presented a picture of "calm waters with various ships." In 1671–72 he served as "headman." His paintings, when signed, bear the initials i.v.d.

Van Diest's style of depicting ships on rivers or at sea derives directly from that of his father, whose most obvious debts are to Jan Porcellis and Simon de Vlieger. Jeronimus and to a lesser extent Willem were also familiar (through Jan van Goyen at the Hague?) with new developments in Haarlem and Amsterdam during the middle decades of the century. Their paintings of about 1650 onward are often remarkably similar to the calm atmospheric scenes of De Vlieger's pupil Jan van de Cappelle and of Hendrick Dubbels, and to Salomon van Ruysdael's river views of the 1640s and 1650s in the case of pictures like the one discussed below.[2]

1. F. Willis in Thieme-Becker, vol. ix, p. 251, who is more reliable than other lexicographers such as Nagler and Swillens.

2. On the Van Diests' style, see Laurens J. Bol, *Die holländische Marinemalerei des 17. Jahrhunderts*, Brunswick, 1973, pp. 162–69, and Hans-Ulrich Beck, *Künstler um Jan van Goyen*, Doornspijk, 1991, pp. 144–49 on Jeronimus van Diest, pp. 150–58 on Willem van Diest.

1962.3

Stechow, the acknowledged authority on Salomon van Ruysdael, saw the Taft painting for the first time in 1963, he doubted the attribution and suggested the name of Jeronimus van Diest as "more reasonable."[3] In 1964, Seymour Slive agreed that the picture appeared to be by one of Van Ruysdael's followers.[4]

Firsthand study of paintings of this type by Salomon van Ruysdael, Willem van Diest, and Jeronimus van Diest leaves no doubt in the writer's mind that Stechow was right. The panel of this size in the Rijksmuseum, Amsterdam (fig. 1), signed i.v.d., is entirely consistent with the Taft picture both in execution and in palette, which includes the same shades of rose and blue in the sky.[5] Works of this period by Willem van Diest seem less skillfully composed and more prosaically painted than those by his son, whose differences from Van Ruysdael are not easily de-

Jeronimus van Diest

Sailboats on a River with Fishermen Setting out a Net

ca. 1655–60
Oil on panel, 33.7 x 34.9 cm (13¼ x 13¾ in.)

This small panel is very closely related to the river views that Salomon van Ruysdael painted between about 1650 and 1660.[1] Not only is the composition comparable, but the drawing of the sailboats, the figure style, and the brushwork employed to describe the water's surface, the distant strip of land, and the cloudy sky are so reminiscent of the Haarlem painter's work that the picture was considered by Hofstede de Groot to be "a genuine and characteristic work," as indeed it would be by many modern scholars of Dutch art.[2] However, when Wolfgang

Fig. 1 Jeronimus van Diest, *River View*, ca. 1655–60. Oil on panel, 31.5 x 37 cm (12½ x 14½ in.). Amsterdam, Rijksmuseum-Stichting.

scribed.[6] Nonetheless, there is a taut, calligraphic quality in Van Ruysdael's drawing (especially evident in the quick curves of his sails and rigging) and a sureness of touch throughout, which are not found in the Van Diests' less spontaneous manner.

1. Comparable compositions by Salomon van Ruysdael are in the Gemäldegalerie, Staatliche Museen, Berlin (inv. no. 901A), and in the Boymans-van Beuningen Museum, Rotterdam. See also Wolfgang Stechow, *Dutch Landscape Painting of the Seventeenth Century*, London, 1966, figs. 220−21, 224−26, 228−29, for similar pictures by Jan Porcellis, Jan van Goyen, and Van Ruysdael.

2. Undated certificate of Cornelis Hofstede de Groot in the files of the Taft Museum.

3. Stechow's opinion was reported in a letter of Sept. 3, 1963, from Richard Buck, conservator at the Intermuseum Laboratory, Oberlin, Ohio, where the panel had been sent for examination (and subsequent treatment). Stechow did not include the Taft painting in the second edition of his monograph, *Salomon van Ruysdael*, 1st ed., 1938, Berlin, 1975. See also Stechow's last essay on the artist, "A River View by Salomon van Ruysdael," *Bulletin of the Cleveland Museum of Art*, vol. LX (1973), pp. 222−31.

4. Letter from Seymour Slive to Katherine Hanna, Mar. 24, 1964. Taft Museum files.

5. P. J. J. van Thiel et al, *All the Paintings of the Rijksmuseum in Amsterdam*, Amsterdam and Maarssen, 1976, p. 194, no. A2503, seen by the writer in the museum's study collection in Nov. 1986.

6. The firm of P. de Boer, Amsterdam, has a large photograph archive of paintings by Willem and Jeronimus van Diest and had three marine views by Willem van Diest when the writer visited the gallery in 1986.

Provenance Said to have been purchased in England by F. Steinmeyer, Lucerne (in 1936); [Lucerne Fine Art Company (according to Knoedler files)]; [Knoedler, New York, 1938−40]; Oliver B. James (in 1940); [Knoedler, New York, 1941−46]; Jane Taft Ingalls, Cleveland (in 1946); Jane Taft Ingalls bequest, 1962.

Exhibitions The Hague, Kleykamp Galleries, *Oude Hollandsche en Vlaamsche Meesters*, 1928, no. 37; Amsterdam, Goudstikker Galleries, *Salomon van Ruysdael*, Jan.−Feb. 1936 (cat., p. 22, no. 44, as from the collection of F. Steinmeyer, Lucerne, and with a starred catalogue number indicating that the picture was for sale); New York, M. Knoedler, *Masters of the Seventeenth Century*, Feb. 5−24, 1945.

1962.3

Jacob Isaacksz. van Ruisdael

Haarlem 1628/29−1682 Amsterdam

The son of Isaack Jacobsz. van Ruisdael, an art dealer, frame maker, and occasional landscapist (no works by him are known), Jacob Isaacksz. probably studied with his father and with his well-known uncle, Salomon van Ruysdael.[1] Ruisdael's earliest paintings include thirteen landscapes dated 1646 and sixteen dated 1647.[2] These remarkably accomplished views of trees, farmland, and the dunes near Haarlem owe less to Salomon van Ruysdael than to the sensitive woodland and river landscapes of Cornelis Vroom.[3] An important complement to his Haarlem experience was Ruisdael's trip through the eastern Dutch provinces and western Germany (Westphalia) during the early 1650s, very probably with his friend and sometime collaborator Nicolaes Berchem. Not only the castle of Bentheim but the border region's rugged, rolling hills, rich in rocks, trees, and fast-flowing streams, captured the Haarlemer's imagination, which

was always responsive first to nature, however much his style was informed by both earlier and contemporary art.

Around 1656 or 1657 Ruisdael moved from Haarlem to Amsterdam where his views of terrain very different from the lowlands of northern Holland found an appreciative clientele. His attraction to northern, but not Dutch, motifs was probably encouraged by the paintings and prints of Allart van Everdingen, who had traveled in Norway and Sweden and had popularized Scandinavian views. However, Ruisdael continued to paint dune and river landscapes and during the 1660s broadened his horizons to include distinctly Dutch views of extensive plains. These may have been inspired by the panoramic landscapes of Philips Koninck but remained entirely personal explorations of Ruisdael's immediate environment. Such distinctive images as his severe winter scenes, distant views of Haarlem, stormy seascapes, a few town views, and the famous *Mill at Wijk bij Duurstede* (after 1668; Amsterdam, Rijksmuseum) are testaments to Ruisdael's inventiveness, expressive powers (which were celebrated by Goethe in his essay "Ruisdael als Dichter"), and stature as the leading landscape painter of the period (the so-called classical phase of about 1650−75).

The question whether Ruisdael became a surgeon is almost too marginal to mention here;[4] however, it does appear that he was less active as a painter during the 1670s. He probably died in Amsterdam but was buried in Haarlem on March 14, 1682. He left behind his pupil Meyndert Hobbema (see 1931.407, p. 166), a good number of followers and imitators, perhaps a thousand paintings (about seven hundred are known today), dozens of drawings,[5] and some excellent early etchings.[6]

1. For a good introduction to the formerly confusing figure of Jacob Salomonsz. van Ruysdael (Salomon's son, 1629/30−1681), see Neil Maclaren, *The Dutch School*, National Gallery Catalogues, London, 1960, pp. 375−76.

2. According to Seymour Slive, *Jacob van Ruisdael*, exh. cat., Mauritshuis, the Hague, and Fogg Art Museum, Cambridge, Mass., New York, 1981, p. 20. This catalogue will be the best survey of the artist's work until Slive's monograph is completed.

3. George Keyes, *Cornelis Vroom, Marine and Landscape Artist*, printed Ph.D. diss., Utrecht, 1975.

4. See Maclaren, p. 354, and Slive, pp. 19−20.

5. Jeroen Giltay, "De Tekeningen van Jacob van Ruisdael," *Oud Holland*, vol. XCIV (1980), pp. 141−208.

6. Slive, pp. 231−60.

Jacob van Ruisdael

Farmhouses on a High Road

ca. 1658−60
Oil on canvas, 57.5 x 67.9 cm (22⅜ x 26¾ in.)
Signed lower left: *JvRuisdael* (*JvR* in monogram)

The topography, the castle in the background, and the distinctive type of domestic architecture depicted here reflect the artist's wanderings in western Germany.[1] The turreted tower is derived from one at Bentheim Castle, the somewhat unimposing struc-

1931.391

ture that Ruisdael used with romantic exaggeration in a few paintings of 1651–53.[2] In the most memorable of them, the Beit collection picture dated 1653, half-timbered houses very similar to those in the Taft painting are tucked among the trees on the precipitous slope, which is Ruisdael's revision of the actual site. A windmill appears in the distance, as does the top of one here. The arrangement of the composition also recalls paintings of about 1653, for example, *Landscape with Cottages and a Blasted Tree,* dated 1653 (New York, Helena Trust).[3]

Ruisdael painted views of Bentheim and the surrounding area in later years as well, and the Taft picture appears most closely associated with a few examples from the late 1650s. Two canvases that probably date from this period (formerly in Berlin and in Vienna) represent roads ascending steeper slopes past half-timbered houses, above which the tower of Bentheim Castle is visible.[4] In composition, the present painting stands between these views (which recall the dramatic topography of the early 1650s) and another canvas of the late 1650s in which the same kind of houses and similar figures are placed over ground no more uneven than that in the foreground here.[5] Thus, the Taft picture, to judge from its composition and manner of execution, probably dates from the later 1650s and is certainly later than the earliest Bentheim views of about 1651–53.[6]

Smith, in 1835, thought the painting excellent, but turned "a little too dark." Kurt Simon, in a letter dated 1932, cites Smith but suggests that the canvas is "perhaps an old copy, though I do not know the original."[7] There are a few indifferent passages in the picture, such as the rounded trees in the distance, and the touch throughout is less lively than in Ruisdael's well-preserved works of this period. However, the writer finds sufficient accounting for any deficiencies in the condition report

of 1974, which advises removal of the "moderately thick" discolored varnish, "thorough cleaning," and replacement of the "brittle and desiccated" lining already adhered to the canvas. The strongest parts of the picture, which include the brushstrokes in the sky that let the rusty ground layer show through, are entirely characteristic of Ruisdael and would not likely be realized so well even in an excellent copy of the period.

As usual, the view presented here by the artist is carefully constructed and for the most part invented, although it is probably based on faithful drawings made around Bentheim. A rough road descends from the castle, branches toward the viewer, and evidently continues back to the left where a man and, farther on, two other figures make their way. In the foreground a woman and a small boy are reflected in a large puddle, and a puppy runs down to them from the house. A man leans on the lower half of the Dutch door. The cut stones to the right are similar to those used to build the steps; together with the logs and the woman's market basket, they suggest the self-sufficiency of rural life, as does the design of the central cottage, which has a large doorway between its two small wings. This type of structure, which combines a modest farmhouse with cow or horse stalls under one roof, was especially common in the eastern Netherlands and Westphalia and is still seen today in those parts of Europe where heat is carefully conserved.[8]

The lord Ashburton who, according to Smith, owned this picture was one of England's most distinguished collectors during the early nineteenth century.[9]

1. See Josef Schepers, *Haus und Hof westfälischer Bauern,* Münster, 1976, who is cited by Seymour Slive in his entries on three of Ruisdael's Bentheim views in *Jacob van Ruisdael,* exh. cat., Mauritshuis, the Hague, and Fogg Art Museum, Cambridge, Mass., New York, 1981, pp. 50–55, nos. 12–14. Under no. 12, Slive mentions a drawing of Bentheim, dated

1650, by Nicolaes Berchem, with whom Ruisdael probably traveled in Westphalia.

2. Compare the photograph of Bentheim reproduced in Sliye, p. 54.

3. Walter Liedtke, *The Golden Ambiance: Dutch Landscape Painting in the Seventeenth Century,* exh. cat., Minskoff Cultural Center, New York, 1985, no. 11; and Cornelis Hofstede de Groot, *A Catalogue Raisonné of the Works of the Most Eminent Dutch Painters of the Seventeenth Century,* vol. IV, London, 1912, no. 793.

4. Jakob Rosenberg, *Jacob van Ruisdael,* Berlin, 1928, nos. 10, 11, pls. 90, 91, paintings from private collections in Berlin and in Vienna.

5. Rosenberg, no. 510 (*Dorfstrasse*), pl. 82, as with Agnew's, London.

6. This conclusion was reached with the patient help of Seymour Slive (meeting in Mar. 1988).

7. Letter from Kurt E. Simon dated Nov. 7, 1932, in the files of the Cincinnati Art Museum.

8. In Ter Borch's *Horse Stall,* 1654, now in Malibu, J. Paul Getty Musuem (S. J. Gudlaugsson, *Gerard ter Borch,* the Hague, 1959–60, no. 109), the same kind of structure is seen from the inside (the woman enters the stall from the house).

9. As noted by Dr. Waagen in Frank Herrmann, *The English as Collectors,* New York, 1972, pp. 150–51.

Provenance R. de Verdier, Général Laneuville (sale, Paris, Mar. 13ff., 1813, no. 69, to "Monmaison"); Alexander Baring, first baron Ashburton (by 1835); by descent to Francis Denzil Edward Baring, fifth baron Ashburton, The Grange, Alresford, Hants.; [Agnew's, London (in 1907)]; [Scott and Fowles, New York (by Jan. 1908)]; Taft collection, Jan. 10, 1910.

Exhibition New York, Scott and Fowles, 1914.

Literature John Smith, *A Catalogue Raisonné of the Works of the Most Eminent Dutch, Flemish, and French Painters,* vol. VI, London, 1835, p. 48, no. 154, as sold from the Verdier collection in 1816, "now in the collection of the Right Hon. Alexander Baring," as an "excellently painted picture" that "has become a little too dark"; Cornelis Hofstede de Groot, *A Catalogue Raisonné of the Works of the Most Eminent Dutch Painters of the Seventeenth Century,* vol. IV, London, 1912, p. 254, no. 811, as with Agnew's, London, in Jan. 1908, which acquired the collection of Lord Ashburton, The Grange, "as a whole" in Aug. 1907 (perhaps also identical to Hofstede de Groot, no. 35, *The Castle of Bentheim,* "dark in tone"); "Art Notes," *The Evening Post* [New York], Feb. 28, 1914, p. 7; Gustav Kobbe, "Noted Art Collectors Send Their Famous Old Masters for Loan Exhibition of Dutch Art in New York," *New York Herald,* Mar. 1, 1914; Maurice W. Brockwell, *A Catalogue of Paintings in the Collection of Mr. and Mrs. Charles P. Taft,* New York, 1920, no. 78; Jakob Rosenberg, *Jacob van Ruisdael,* Berlin, 1928, p. 104, no. 509, as with Agnew's in 1908, and as possibly also identical with Rosenberg, no. 16 (Hofstede de Groot, no. 35); *Catalogue of the Taft Museum,* Cincinnati, 1939 and 1958, no. 158.

1931.391

Meyndert Hobbema
Amsterdam 1638–1709 Amsterdam

Meyndert Lubbertsz. Hobbema, son of Lubbert Meyndertsz. (Meyndert's son), was baptized in Amsterdam on October 30, 1638, and rarely left the city (except, presumably, for a few hours of sketching) until his death on December 7, 1709. Jacob van Ruisdael, who was only a few years older than Hobbema, was his teacher during the second half of the 1650s.[1] Early works by Hobbema show the influence of Ruisdael's uncle, Salomon van Ruysdael, and perhaps of Cornelis Vroom. However, Jacob van Ruisdael was Hobbema's main source of inspiration, and in some paintings of the early 1660s he adopted his master's com-

positional ideas. During 1663 and 1664 Hobbema's style became calmer and more luminous; the space is generally more open and the touch more fluid than in Ruisdael's comparable works (i.e., mostly woodland views). Picturesque motifs such as water mills and cottages convey a sense of well-being in the country-side, which was a view of rural life entertained in Amsterdam sitting rooms.

Hobbema married a burgomaster's kitchen maid in 1668 and received a well-paid civic post as a wine gauger. From then on he appears to have painted only occasionally and for pleasure, or so it seems in the famous *Avenue at Middelharnis* of 1689 (London, National Gallery).

Although highly gifted as a painter and exceedingly productive during his fairly short career, Hobbema may be considered (like Jan van der Cappelle and even Jan van der Heyden) something of a dilettante. Most of his work was based on art, not nature, although it nonetheless reveals a distinctive disposition, especially when compared to his teacher's typical images. The subjects of Hobbema's landscapes are those one encounters on walks out of town, a choice of locale that aligns him with a tradition in Amsterdam and Haarlem dating from the first decades of the century (prints by Claes Jansz. Visscher and Jan van de Velde, for example).[2] There are always houses and other signs of life and, in an oeuvre full of countless clouds and trees, never an ominous shadow.

1. Compare Neil Maclaren, *The Dutch School,* National Gallery Catalogues, London, 1960, pp. 163–64; Van Ruisdael was a resident of Amsterdam by June 1657 but probably was there earlier. He testified in July 1660 that Hobbema had "served and learned with me for a few years."

2. See Irene de Groot, *Landscape Etchings by the Dutch Masters of the Seventeenth Century,* Maarssen, 1979; and especially David Freedberg, *Dutch Landscape Prints of the Seventeenth Century,* British Museum Prints and Drawings Series, London, 1980.

Meyndert Hobbema

Farmland with a Pond and Trees

ca. 1663–64
Oil on canvas, 96.5 x 128.3 cm (38 x 50½ in.)
Signed lower right: *m. hobbema*

Georges Broulhiet, the author of the standard monograph on Hobbema, referred to this large canvas as "de la série des grands chefs-d'oeuvre de l'apogée," while Smith, with British succinctness, called it "A Capital Picture."[1] Indeed, the painting is exceptional even in comparison with many of Hobbema's major works, for the formulaic quality that is often sensed in his compositions is here dispelled by the naturalistic breadth and continuity of the view and by the number of attractive motifs and passages of painterly interest. Thus, one is hardly aware when before the picture itself of its division into two principal recessions, a scheme that ultimately descends from forest views painted some sixty years earlier.

1931.407

The view to the left, over water and under trees, is open in every direction through silhouetted tree trunks, with sunlight flooding the deeper spaces and catching the bouquetlike bunches of leaves. Such visual incidents serve to slow the pace of the eye as it takes in the plants in the foreground, the cows at the edge of the pool, a dog to the left, two goats farther back, and the bright picturesque area in the left background. Similarly, to the right, Hobbema's familiar farmhouse and mill are set deep within a space (with a pond, fields, and other buildings) that could be a separate landscape, but light blends all the more distant areas together as well as into the clouds and sky. One might, for a moment, incautiously characterize the composition as a Ruisdael-like woodland view leading to pastures such as Adriaen van de Velde painted; and further, this fortunate juxtaposition— or rather, synthesis— has the kind of continuity between foreground and background that Philips Koninck established in his panoramic landscapes of about the same time.

This image is not entirely subjective, since the Taft picture must date from about 1663–64, when Hobbema, having closely followed a number of Ruisdael's compositions, began to free himself from his teacher's sense of structure in favor of more extensive and open views.[2] Broulhiet suggests that a very similar canvas by Hobbema (formerly in the Porgès collection) is loosely patterned after a design by Ruisdael, quite as another composition by Hobbema (Broulhiet, no. 201), dated 1664, is based on one of Ruisdael's schemes.[3] The Taft painting repeats many of the motifs found in the Porgès version, but it is not merely a replica. In fact, one feels fairly confident in placing the present picture slightly later, as the variant and not the model, since it represents a further development away from Ruisdael and toward Hobbema's more independent compositions of

around 1665. In the present painting, for example, the eye is carried through the foreground and into the left background with greater ease, and the trees extend slightly farther to the right, a construction that, with the central cow, tends to lead the viewer's eye smoothly from the shadowy pool to the open road and fields.

Smith assigned the figures to Adriaen van de Velde, who often added figures and animals to paintings by Jacob van Ruisdael, Philips Koninck, and other artists active in Amsterdam. The finely modeled figures in the right foreground — two boys, leading a bull (the rear guard ringing a bell), and a woman apparently removing some uninvited item from a young man's hair — are clearly Van de Velde's work.[4]

In previous publications the painting was erroneously said to have been in the collection of the countess of Holderness. It is now known that the duke of Bridgewater bought the picture in Amsterdam, probably a year or two before it was sold at Christie's in 1802.[5]

1. Georges Broulhiet, *Meindert Hobbema*, Paris, 1938, p. 409, under no. 239, where John Smith (*A Catalogue Raisonné of the Works of the Most Eminent Dutch, Flemish, and French Painters,* vol. vi, London, 1835, p. 117, no. 10) is quoted.

2. See Wolfgang Stechow, *Dutch Landscape Painting of the Seventeenth Century,* London, 1966, pp. 77–78.

3. See Broulhiet, pp. 41–42, 408–9, nos. 236 (Ruisdael in the M. Kann sale, 1911), 238 (Hobbema in the Porgès collection), and 239 (Taft Museum), which are reproduced on pp. 220–21; p. 403, no. 201 (Hobbema, 1664), citing a painting by Ruisdael (Broulhiet, no. 136) as a prototype. On these comparisons and for other "works of this group" by Hobbema, see Peter C. Sutton et al., *Masters of Seventeenth-Century Dutch Landscape Painting,* exh. cat., Museum of Fine Arts, Boston, 1987, p. 349.

4. Sutton, p. 349, agrees. His photographs, no. 45 and pl. 108, show the

painting before its restoration in 1987 when a large vertical strip of paint loss was revealed. The only original part of the two cows and the cowherd in the middle of the picture is the front half of the cow to the right. Cleaning also revealed two figures walking in the sunlit area farther back to the left; evidently, they were painted, and painted out, by Hobbema.

5. This information was kindly provided by Burton Fredericksen, director of the Provenance Index, The Getty Art History Information Program, in a letter to the Taft Museum dated Apr. 20, 1990. An annotation in a copy of the Holderness sale catalogue in the library of the Rijksmuseum, Amsterdam, reads, "put in by Christie; formerly purchased by the Duke of Bridgewater for 700 Gns — exchanged for a picture by Wm Vander Velde with Mr. Foster, who sold it to Mr. Slade" (for whom Christie may have been acting). The duke of Bridgewater's great collection of paintings included at least five works by Willem van de Velde; their dates of acquisition are not recorded.

Provenance Amsterdam sale (around 1800); Francis Egerton, third duke of Bridgewater (before 1802); Mr. Foster; Mr. Slade; (countess of Holderness sale, Christie's, London, Mar. 6, 1802, no. 76 [put in by Christie; sold to Tracy for £294]); Charles Hanbury Tracy (1802; in 1835 [according to Smith]); Anatolii Nikolaevich Demidov [Demidoff], principe di San Donato, Florence (sale, Mar. 15ff., 1880, no. 1103 [ill.]); E. Secrétan, London (sale, Christie's, July 13, 1889, no. 6, for £5,460); Samuel Cunliffe-Lister, first baron Masham, Swinton Park, Masham, Yorkshire (d. 1906); [Scott and Fowles, New York, in 1907]; Taft collection, 1907.

Exhibitions London, British Institution, 1821, no. 129, and 1832, no. 56; New York, Scott and Fowles, 1909 and 1914; Boston, Museum of Fine Arts [also Amsterdam and Philadelphia], *Masters of Seventeenth-Century Dutch Landscape Painting*, 1987–88 (cat. by Peter C. Sutton et al., pp. 348–49, no. 45, pl. 108).

Literature William Buchanan, *Memoirs of Painting, with a Chronological History of the Importation of Pictures by the Great Masters into England since the French Revolution*, vol. 1, London, 1824, p. 318, no. 76; John Smith, *A Catalogue Raisonné of the Works of the Most Eminent Dutch, Flemish, and French Painters*, vol. vi, London, 1835, p. 117, no. 10; Frank Cundall, *The Landscape and Pastoral Painters of Holland*, London, 1891, p. 158, referring to the painting's high price in the 1880 sale; Arthur Hoeber, "Some Pictures from the Collection of Mr. and Mrs. Charles P. Taft," *The International Studio*, vol. xxxix (1909–10), p. lxxiv; Cornelis Hofstede de Groot, *A Catalogue Raisonné of the Works of the Most Eminent Dutch Painters of the Seventeenth Century*, vol. iv, London, 1912, p. 389, no. 106; "Art Notes," *The Evening Post* [New York], Feb. 28, 1914, p. 7; Gustav Kobbe, "Noted Art Collectors Send Their Famous Old Masters for Loan Exhibition of Dutch Art in New York," *New York Herald*, Mar. 1, 1914; Maurice W. Brockwell, *A Catalogue of Paintings in the Collection of Mr. and Mrs. Charles P. Taft*, New York, 1920, pp. 70–72, no. 20; Georges Broulhiet, *Meindert Hobbema*, Paris, 1938, pp. 41–42, 221 (ill.), 409, no. 239; *Catalogue of the Taft Museum*, Cincinnati, 1939 and 1958, no. 470; Peter C. Sutton, *Dutch Art in America*, Grand Rapids and Kampen, 1986, p. 61, fig. 87; E. John Walford, *Jacob van Ruisdael and the Perception of Landscape*, New Haven and London, 1991, p. 134.

1931.407

Aert van der Neer

Gorinchem ca. 1603/4–1677 Amsterdam

Aernout (Aert) van der Neer was born in Gorinchem (Gorkum) around 1603–4; in May 1642 he was said to be about thirty-eight years old.[1] The town of Gorinchem lies near the union of the Meuse (Maas) and Waal rivers, equidistant from Rotterdam to the west and Utrecht to the north. The biographer Arnold Houbraken reports that Van der Neer began painting as an amateur while working as a steward for a wealthy family.[2] Around 1632 he moved to Amsterdam[3] where his son, the more successful painter Eglon van der Neer, may have been born in 1634.[4] Another son, Johannes, was probably born in Amsterdam around 1637–38; he became his father's imitator.[5]

Two artists from Gorinchem, the Camphuysen brothers (Raphael and Joachim Govertsz.), were instrumental in Van der Neer's early development as a landscape painter (his earliest known dated picture is from 1635).[6] It has been noted in this connection that the woman Van der Neer married in Gorinchem bore the not very common name of Lysbeth Goverts (Govert's daughter); thus, Van der Neer was probably the brother-in-law of Raphael and Joachim Govertsz.[7] This would help to explain his close relationship with these rather minor artists, an association that continued beyond his early years. In 1642 Raphael Camphuysen was a witness at the baptism in Amsterdam of a daughter born to the Van der Neers.[8]

As one might expect of any artist active in Amsterdam, particularly one who never studied under an important master, Van der Neer gleaned ideas from a considerable variety of sources. His compositions, which he often recycled, are invariably related to those of earlier artists. Stechow stresses the importance of the Flemish immigrant Alexander Keirincx for Van der Neer's landscapes of about 1635; both Stechow and Bachmann mention Gillis d'Hondecoeter; and Bachmann maintains that the origins of Van der Neer's style also may be traced by way of the Camphuysens to Roelant Savery in Utrecht.[9] Comparisons between Van der Neer's paintings of about 1635–50 and typical pictures by Savery and by Gillis van Coninxloo illuminate the eclectic quality of Van der Neer's trees (often shaped like broccoli *en branche*) and the derivation of his tunnel-like recessions from the imaginary woodland views of Flemish artists. This tradition trained the Dutchman's eye for the picturesque.

Van der Neer's more empirical effects, by contrast, depend both on the pioneer works of Dutch painters and printmakers and on his independent observations. The most important antecedents to Van der Neer's well-known nocturnal views are found among Hendrick Goudt's engravings after Elsheimer, Jan van de Velde's etchings after Willem Buytewech, and paintings of villages at night by Esaias van de Velde and his cousin Jan.[10] Not only the night views but also the winter landscapes (an important subgenre of Van der Neer's oeuvre) and, in general, the compositional schemes of Esaias van de Velde and the slightly later Haarlem artists Jan van Goyen, Salomon van Ruysdael, and Pieter de Molijn determined Van der Neer's development.

This heritage does not, however, explain Van der Neer's remarkable achievement. Whatever their sources, the winter scenes and nocturnes, with their curved horizons and naturalistic qualities of light, color, and atmosphere, are now appreciated as individual and exceptional examples of Dutch landscape painting during its most mature period. Like other distinctive talents of the 1650s and 1660s — for example, Pieter de Hooch and Emanuel de Witte, both of whom also studied optical effects — Van der Neer nonetheless found little fame and no fortune: the pub he ran may have been as modest as the one depicted by Van Ostade (see 1931.400, p. 148). The great number of pictures he painted, the declining quality of his late work, and his specialization in subjects that presumably sold (however cheaply) were probably all aspects of his unsuccessful campaign against personal poverty.

1. Abraham Bredius, "Aernout (Aert) van der Neer," *Oud Holland,* vol. XVIII (1900), p. 71.

2. Arnold Houbraken, *De Groote Schouburgh der nederlantsche konst-schilders en schilderessen,* Amsterdam, 1718–21, vol. III, p. 172.

3. According to Fredo Bachmann, *Aert van der Neer,* Bremen, 1982, p. 10.

4. For his biography, see Neil Maclaren, *The Dutch School,* National Gallery Catalogues, London, 1960, pp. 265–66; and Walter Liedtke in *Liechtenstein: The Princely Collections,* exh. cat., The Metropolitan Museum of Art, New York, 1985, p. 272.

5. Bachmann, pp. 126–27.

6. According to Maclaren, p. 260, who follows the entry in Thieme-Becker, vol. XXV, p. 374, on this point. On Van der Neer's development, see Bachmann and three articles by the same author: "Zur Datierung der Frühwerke und der Mondscheinlandschaften des Aert van der Neer," *Weltkunst,* vol. XXXVIII (Aug. 1968), pp. 705–7; "Die Brüder Rafel und Jochem Camphuysen und ihr Verhältnis zu Aert van der Neer," *Oud Holland,* vol. LXXXV (1970), pp. 243–50; and "Die Herkunft der Frühwerke des Aert van der Neer," *Oud Holland,* vol. LXXXIX (1975), pp. 213–22. Joachim Camphuysen had moved to Amsterdam in 1621; Raphael, in 1626.

7. Liedtke, p. 255.

8. Maclaren, p. 260 and note 9, citing Bredius, p. 75; but Bredius gives this information with no further comment on p. 70, note 1. The proper reference is Abraham Bredius and Ernst Wilhelm Moes, "De Schilders Camphuysen," *Oud Holland,* vol. XXI (1903), pp. 193–219, as cited by Bachmann, 1970, p. 243.

9. Keirincx and D'Hondecoeter had also worked in Utrecht before moving to Amsterdam. In this paragraph and below I am compressing my discussion on Van der Neer's style and sources from Liedtke, pp. 255–56.

10. Specific examples and references to appropriate literature are cited in Liedtke, pp. 255–56.

Aert van der Neer

An Extensive Valley with a Distant City

ca. 1662–65
Oil on canvas, 76.5 x 103.8 cm (30⅛ x 40⅞ in.)
Signed lower right: AV DN (in two monograms)

This is an exceptionally large, splendid, and brightly lit landscape by Aert van der Neer, who generally produced small cabinet paintings in which moonlight or streaking sunlight is employed for picturesque and often jewel-like effect. The intimacy of the artist's familiar village and rural scenes is here abandoned in a sweeping valley view, although the two hunters in the foreground, the three men talking in the middle distance, and the almost Claudean (or rather, Cuyp-like) glow of the setting sun establish Van der Neer's usual mood of peace and comfort, of rest and reflection at the end of a lovely day.

One of the few published comments on this picture, that it "suggests no specific time of day," is precisely the wrong thing to say about this or almost any other work by Van der Neer.[1]

The color of the sky, the alignment of the church, the behavior of the figures, and perhaps even the location of the cows would imply that the sun is setting, not rising, and that the hunter in the foreground, his bag full, is heading home.

Valentiner's verbal opinion that this work is early, very good, and unusual in Van der Neer's oeuvre can be contested only insofar as the picture is clearly a mature work.[2] Indeed, were no other painting by Van der Neer known, this canvas, when compared to the works of other landscapists active in Amsterdam, would have to be placed close to Philips Koninck's panoramic views of eastern Dutch farmland, to Ruisdael's similarly extensive scenes, and to the high points of Hobbema's career: that is, in the 1660s. Fredo Bachmann, in his chapter on Van der Neer's style during this decade, considers the Taft painting a "late work of high quality" in which the artist's freedom from older formulas is obvious.[3]

The qualities of light and especially of space in this picture cannot be conveyed adequately in reproduction. The wide-angle view of the foreground, with directions of view leading from the lower frame to the right and left (the latter prospect entering an Elsheimer-like corner of shadowy foliage and tree trunks soon to be forsaken by the sun), is so all-encompassing of the distant city, valley, and rolling hills that the composition seems to require its considerable size. One has a similar sensation before a panel in Leipzig, in which the broad embrace of the foreground, although framing a different subject, is employed in quite the same way.[4] Even such compositional elements as the fence parallel to the picture plane and the tree to the right (again, with a man sitting near it) present close points of comparison with the Taft painting, although the latter's structure seems subtler, at once more complex and relaxed (described by Bachmann as an *Auflösung*). These observations support a date a little later than the Leipzig picture (ca. 1660), or about 1662–65, which is the period implied, if not stated, in Bachmann's monograph. His mention of motifs reminiscent of Jan Wijnants, incidentally, is no more relevant than the above references to other contemporary landscapists and is less illuminating than Stechow's conception of the painting as a *Rubenstyp*.[5]

1. *Catalogue of the Taft Museum,* Cincinnati, 1939 and 1958, no. 129.

2. William R. Valentiner, undated note in Taft Museum files.

3. Fredo Bachmann, *Aert van der Neer, 1603/4–1677,* Bremen, 1982, p. 137.

4. Bachmann, p. 121 and fig. 95, evidently as about 1660. The Leipzig panel is much smaller, 40 x 53 cm (15¾ x 20⅞ in.). See also the large ex-Thyssen picture, a winter landscape of the early 1660s (Bachmann, pp. 133–34, fig. 104, and color pl. p. 111), in which the wide-angle effect is enhanced by very near *repoussoirs* (a fence and blasted trees) and the rapid recession of the foreground.

5. Wolfgang Stechow in a letter to Bachmann, who quotes it p. 137.

Provenance [Scott and Fowles, New York, in 1911]; Taft collection, 1911.

Exhibition Art Association of Montreal, *Benefit Exhibition for Children of Great Britain, Netherlands, and Other Occupied Countries,* Mar. 9–Apr. 9, 1944.

Literature Cornelis Hofstede de Groot, *A Catalogue Raisonné of the Works of the Most Eminent Dutch Painters of the Seventeenth Century,* vol. VII, London, 1923, p. 471, no. 618, as "A Large Landscape. In the col-

1931.468

lection of C. P. Taft, Cincinnati" with no further information; Maurice W. Brockwell, *A Catalogue of Paintings in the Collection of Mr. and Mrs. Charles P. Taft*, New York, 1920, pp. 143–44, no. 40; *Catalogue of the Taft Museum*, Cincinnati, 1939 and 1958, no. 129; Fredo Bachmann, *Aert van der Neer, 1603/4–1677*, Bremen, 1982, p. 137, fig. 111.

1931.468

Gerard ter Borch

Zwolle 1617–1681 Deventer

Ter Borch's training began in the small eastern Dutch town of Zwolle, where he was taught by his father, Gerard ter Borch the Elder, a little-known artist.[1] In 1634 the young Ter Borch went to the thriving art center of Haarlem and studied with the landscape painter Pieter de Molijn. A period of *Wanderjahre* followed; according to Houbraken, Ter Borch traveled to England (where he was cited in July 1635), France, Germany, Spain, and Italy.[2] He probably returned to the Netherlands before 1640.

Ter Borch's genre paintings and portraits of the 1640s depend on the works of Amsterdam and Haarlem artists, and during the mid-1640s prominent Amsterdam patrons sat for small portraits by Ter Borch. The artist was in Münster during the peace negotiations of 1646–48 and painted individual portraits of Dutch and Spanish dignitaries as well as the historic group portrait *The Swearing of the Oath of Ratification of the Treaty of Münster, May 15, 1648* (London, National Gallery). Ter Borch was recorded in Amsterdam in November 1648, and in April 1653 he witnessed a deposition in Delft along with the twenty-year-old Jan Vermeer.[3] In February 1654 Ter Borch married in Deventer where he became a citizen in 1655 and appears to have spent the rest of his life.

Like Ter Borch's native Zwolle, Deventer is in the province of Overijssel, rather far from the main centers of Dutch art. None-theless, he was not destined to become a provincial painter. His father had lived in Italy and encouraged Ter Borch and his sister, Gesina (his model in a number of genre scenes), to study art and literature at an early age. Ter Borch's travels, too, were probably initiated by his father. At the same time, the artist's early training in Overijssel, well removed from the provinces of Holland and Utrecht, may partly explain his later independence from obvious conventions of composition. The small full-length portraits that he painted from around 1640 onward, for example, are more similar to his early sketchbook studies from life than to most contemporary Dutch portraits, although examples by the older Amsterdam artist Thomas de Keyser may have impressed Ter Borch. Similarly, his genre paintings dating from after 1650, while sophisticated in iconography and style, are remarkable for their naturalistic treatment of interior space, the portraitlike individuality of figures, and the sensitivity with which the artist interprets human situations. Ter Borch seems to stand apart even from those painters who influenced him, such as Pieter Codde and Willem Duyster; from those with similar interests, such as Gabriel Metsu; and from those he inspired, such as Caspar Netscher, whom Houbraken mentions as being Ter Borch's pupil in Deventer.

1. On Ter Borch's early life and family, see S. J. Gudlaugsson's exemplary monograph, *Gerard ter Borch*, the Hague, 1959–60, vol. I, chaps. II–IV.

2. Arnold Houbraken, *De Groote Schouburgh der Nederlantsche Konstschilders en Schilderessen*, the Hague, 1718–21, vol. III, p. 34.

3. J. M. Montias, "New Documents on Vermeer and His Family," *Oud Holland*, vol. XCI (1977), pp. 280–81, no. 46a. It was around this time or slightly later that Ter Borch painted a portrait of his cousin Hartogh van Moerkerken with his wife and son; the family lived near Delft in a village outside the Hague (see *The Jack and Belle Linsky Collection in the Metropolitan Museum of Art*, New York, 1984, pp. 86–88). Ter Borch is also mentioned in connection with Delft in Walter A. Liedtke, *Architectural Painting in Delft*, Doornspijk, 1982, p. 63.

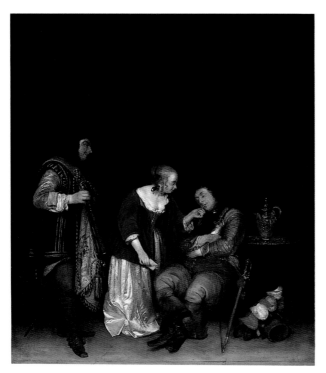

1931.398

Gerard ter Borch

The Sleeping Soldier

ca. 1656–57
Oil on canvas, 65.3 x 55 cm (25¾ x 21⅝ in.)
Signed on hat: GTB (in monogram)

A young Dutch officer is asleep in a chair; his raffishly feathered hat has fallen to the floor. The woman he was visiting has shown in another cavalier (both men wear spurs) who serves as regimental trumpeter, messenger, and, in this case, Amor *à rebours*: the letter the woman holds must be the sleeping officer's order to report for duty. The casual way in which the young woman wears her elegant attire — her housecoat open to reveal an enticingly low neckline — intimates that she is not shy around men, even when one of them is a stranger. She tickles the sleeping soldier's lips with a straw. That her life-style is comfortable is suggested not only by her dress but by the handsomely draped bed, the doorway surmounted by a round pediment, the large clothing trunk behind the trumpeter, and especially the lavish basin and pitcher on the table.

Gudlaugsson's date of about 1656–57 for this painting is strongly supported by his close study of Ter Borch's development and by comparisons with works by contemporary genre painters such as Gabriel Metsu and Frans van Mieris.[1] The Taft picture thus dates from two or three years later than Ter Borch's first mature genre scenes, such as versions of *Parental Admonition*

in Amsterdam and Berlin;[2] nonetheless, it remains one of the first paintings in which he arrives at his characteristic combination of realism and embellishment, of substance and surface, of plainness and luxury. Whereas, for instance, the figures in the pictures of the mid-1650s are set back in space, clearly separated, and supported by a strict structure of simple doorways and furniture, here and in similar paintings of about 1657–58 they are moved forward and grouped closely together, like objects in a still life by Kalf, whose work is also brought to mind by Ter Borch's increased attention to rich materials, fine details, and shimmering plays of light.

Some of the same objects and articles of clothing occur in two other paintings of about the same date: *Carousing Soldiers* in the baroness de Rothschild collection, Paris, and *The Refused Letter* in the Alte Pinakothek, Munich, in which another *stadstrompet* (a similar silver trumpet, dated 1659, is displayed in the Centraal Museum, Utrecht), a comparable basin and pitcher, a plumed chapeau, a white satin skirt, and the trumpeter's striped uniform create exquisite and admirably understated pictorial effects.[3]

Unfortunately, the condition of the Taft painting does not allow one to appreciate fully the achievement that it was, since the dark colors have darkened considerably, obscuring the background and diminishing the impression of depth and atmosphere. The jewel-like dots of light, by contrast, are mostly later additions of a sort sympathetic to Ter Borch's technique, but lacking his sophistication. Some suggestion of his subtlety survives in the tonal harmony of the whole; the primary colors — blue, red, and yellow — are darkened and discreetly distributed within the overall arrangement of subdued shades.

In 1692 the present picture was sold at the Hague with a pendant, which may have gone to a different buyer at that time and which is identified by Gudlaugsson as a poorly preserved painting by Ter Borch in a private collection in Paris.[4] The Paris painting was recently sold at Sotheby's, Monaco, and the dimensions and the complementary subjects and compositions of the two pictures support their interpretation as a pair.[5] The pendant represents a well-dressed woman seated in a comfortable although sparely appointed room where she is served a beverage — not wine, as Gudlaugsson assumes — by a page. His tray is steadied by a gentleman, evidently the woman's husband, whose hat and cape suggest that he has just come in from outside.[6] Thus, two different ways of life are contrasted, one of them stable and serious (if pleasant, in the measured manner of joys that endure), the other fugitive and frivolous. Each woman is the center of her world — one as a wife, one as a demimondaine. It should be added that the Taft painting, as a conversation piece, stands very well on its own and was probably painted before the Paris picture. The latter's import, by contrast, is largely lost when the painting is considered independently.

The composition of the Taft painting appears to have impressed Ter Borch's pupil Caspar Netscher, to whom Gudlaugsson attributes three or four variants.[7]

1. S. J. Gudlaugsson, *Gerard ter Borch*, the Hague, 1959–60, vol. I, captions to pls. 121 and 122 (the supposed pendant, discussed below), and vol. II, pp. 133–34, no. 121.

2. Gudlaugsson, nos. 110–I, 110–II.

3. The Paris and Munich pictures are Gudlaugsson, nos. 123 and 124 of "about 1656–57" and "about 1657," respectively.

4. Gudlaugsson, vol. II, pp. 135–36, no. 122, a canvas, 64 x 54 cm.

5. Sotheby's, Monaco, *Importants Tableaux anciens*, Dec. 2, 1989, no. 324. It is identified as *Couple buvant du vin servi par un page*, oil on canvas, 64 x 54 cm: "Le Taft Museum de Cincinnati conserve un *Soldat endormi* . . . conçu en pendant de notre tableau et réalisé avec lui vers le milieu des années 1650" (p. 44).

6. Except for this tentative observation, I am following Nanette Salomon's discussion of these pictures in "Dreamers, Idlers, and Other Dozers: Aspects of Sleep in Dutch Art," Ph.D. diss., Institute of Fine Arts, New York University, 1984, pp. 102–6, figs. 90, 91. Salomon, p. 105, sees the man as about to leave, as will the sleeping soldier in the Taft picture, but the behavior of the three figures and even that of the dog suggests that the time is late in the day, a reading that would strengthen, not weaken, Salomon's comparison. See Peter C. Sutton et al., *Masters of Seventeenth-Century Dutch Genre Painting*, exh. cat., Philadelphia Museum of Art, 1984, no. 36, for Jacob Duck's earlier example of a woman tickling a sleeping soldier.

7. Gudlaugsson, vol. II, pp. 134–35, nos. 121a–d, pl. XII, fig. 2 (no. 121a). See also Salomon, pp. 105–7.

Provenance Johan van Tongeren (sale, the Hague, Mar. 24, 1692, with a pendant); A. van Hoek (sale, Amsterdam, Apr. 7, 1706, no. 34?); George Alan, fifth viscount Midleton (d. 1848), Peper-Harow, near Godalming, Surrey (sale, Christie's, London, July 31, 1851, no. 77, for £299 5s.); Henry Harvey, London (in 1868); William Harvey, London (in 1895); [Scott and Fowles, New York, in 1916]; Taft collection, 1916.

Exhibitions Leeds, Corporation Art Gallery, 1868, no. 652; London, Guildhall Art Gallery, 1895, no. 111; Denver Art Museum, *Baroque Art*, 1971.

Literature Gerard Hoet, *Catalogus of Naamlyst van Schilderyen . . . ,* vol. I, the Hague, 1752, p. 13, no. 57, recording the 1692 sale; John Smith, *A Catalogue Raisonné of the Works of the Most Eminent Dutch, Flemish, and French Painters*, vol. IV, London, 1833, p. 117, no. 3, and p. 131, no. 43 (in each case, it is not certain that the Taft painting is meant); Cornelis Hofstede de Groot, *A Catalogue Raisonné of the Works of the Most Eminent Dutch Painters of the Seventeenth Century*, vol. V, London, 1913, pp. 31–32, no. 77, with some errors of provenance; Maurice W. Brockwell, *A Catalogue of Paintings in the Collection of Mr. and Mrs. Charles P. Taft*, New York, 1920, pp. 40–41, no. 11; *Catalogue of the Taft Museum*, Cincinnati, 1939 and 1958, no. 128; E. Plietzsch, *Gerard ter Borch*, Vienna, 1944, pp. 13, 49; S. J. Gudlaugsson, *Gerard ter Borch*, the Hague, 1959–60, vol. I, pp. 111–12, 280, pl. 121, and vol. II, pp. 133–34, no. 121, and p. 135, under no. 122; Otto Naumann, *Frans van Mieris*, vol. I, Doornspijk, 1981, pp. 74–75, fig. 111; Peter C. Sutton et al., *Masters of Seventeenth-Century Dutch Genre Painting*, exh. cat., Philadelphia Museum of Art, 1984, p. 190, note 9; Sotheby's, Monaco, *Importants Tableaux anciens*, Dec. 2–3, 1989, under no. 324 (*Couple buvant du vin servi par un page*), p. 44.

1931.398

Jan Steen

Leiden 1625/26–1679 Leiden

Steen was described as twenty years old when he enrolled at the University of Leiden in November 1646. In March 1648 he became a founding member of the artists' guild in his native town. Houbraken says that Steen was a pupil of Jan van Goyen, but the landscapist sold his house in Leiden in November 1631 and became a citizen of the Hague in March 1634.[1] Steen married Van Goyen's daughter Margaretha (Grietje) at the Hague in December 1649 and was recorded there in July 1654. Steen may have studied with his father-in-law during the early 1650s (most

of Steen's landscape paintings appear to date from around 1648–52), although at this stage of his career he would not have been a pupil in the usual sense.[2] Steen's father leased a brewery for him in Delft between 1654 and 1657.[3] From 1656 to 1660 the painter lived in Warmond near Leiden, and in 1661 he entered the artists' guild in Haarlem. He is cited there, although infrequently, until 1670 when he inherited his father's house in Leiden. A widower from May 1669, Steen lived his last decade in Leiden where he remarried in 1673 and served as an officer of the guild (as dean in 1674). He was buried in the Pieterskerk on February 3, 1679.[4]

Steen painted a fair number of history pictures as well as landscapes and portraits, but by far the greatest part of his large oeuvre consists of genre scenes.[5] Most of them are satirical, which sets Steen apart from other Dutch painters of everyday life, particularly those of his own rather than the preceding generation.[6] His humor, while distinctive, is drawn from sources in popular literature and comic theater and may represent a light side of Leiden academic life.[7] He also drew from pictorial examples, which probably included prints after Pieter Bruegel the Elder and paintings by Adriaen Brouwer.

The finely rendered details in some of Steen's work seem typical of the Leiden school, but his fluid technique, with which he achieved broad and occasionally brilliant effects (especially in passages of drapery and daylight),[8] testifies to Steen's study of art from outside his native town and lends support to Weyerman's statement that the artist was influenced by Knüpfer, Van Ostade, and Van Goyen.[9] Steen's figures are similar to those of the leading Flemish painter of the day, Jacob Jordaens, in that stock types mingle successfully in the genre scenes with figures modeled on real people.[10]

1. Arnold Houbraken, *De Groote Schouburgh der Nederlantsche Konstschilders en Schilderessen*, Amsterdam, 1718–21, vol. III, p. 13.

2. Karel Braun, *Alle tot nu toe bekende schilderijen van Jan Steen*, Rotterdam, 1980, pp. 86–89, and color pls. on pp. 17–19.

3. The portrait of a man and his daughter known as the *Burgomaster of Delft* is dated 1655 and is set on a quay in Delft; see *Treasure Houses of Britain*, exh. cat., National Gallery of Art, Washington, D.C., 1985, p. 365, no. 294. However, Steen seems to have spent little time in Delft.

4. For further information about Steen's wife, children, and personal life, see Braun, pp. 11–14.

5. On the history pictures, see Baruch D. Kirschenbaum, *The Religious and Historical Paintings of Jan Steen*, New York, 1977.

6. Hence the title of Lyckle de Vries's exemplary dissertation, "Jan Steen 'de kluchtschilder,' " Rijksuniversiteit Groningen, 1977.

7. S. J. Gudlaugsson, *The Comedians in the Work of Jan Steen and His Contemporaries*, Soest, the Netherlands, 1975, Dutch ed., the Hague, 1945.

8. As, for example, in the Linsky *Dissolute Household* (see *The Jack and Belle Linsky Collection at the Metropolitan Museum of Art*, New York, 1984, no. 31) and in *Merry Company on a Terrace*, also in the Metropolitan Museum (inv. no. 58.89).

9. Jacob Campo Weyerman, *De Levensbeschryvingen der Nederlandsche Kunstschilders*, vol. II, the Hague, 1729, p. 348.

10. In addition to the literature cited above, the reader might consult Peter C. Sutton, "Jan Steen, Comedy and Admonition," *Bulletin* [Philadelphia Museum of Art], vol. LXXVIII, nos. 337–38 (Winter 1982–Spring 1983), and a few of the bibliographical items listed on pp. 62–63.

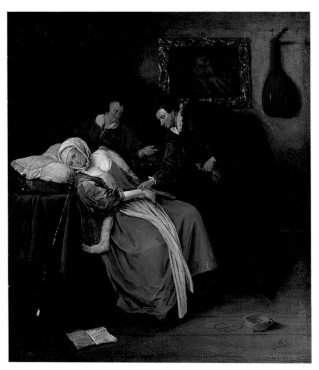

1931.396

℀

Jan Steen

The Doctor's Visit

ca. 1663
Oil on panel, 44.5 x 37.1 cm (17½ x 14⅝ in.)
Signed lower right: *JStEEn* (JS in monogram)

A pretty, buxom, and seemingly silly young woman in modish attire assumes a languorous pose while a doctor of questionable credentials feels her pulse. The lady's maid smiles and gestures toward the physician who, to judge from his expression, has, like the servant, seen young women in this condition before. Steen's own prescription is written in the booklet (similar in format to a book of amorous poems, which the artist in his own way makes of it) that is lying on the floor: *hier baet / geen medicÿn / want het is / minepÿn* (a rhyming verse that translates, "no medicine is of use, for it is lovesickness").[1]

A contemporary viewer could have supplied the verse, having been given so many visual clues. The lute hanging on the wall, for example, recalls Dutch scenes of courtship and, more specifically, the word *luit,* which is indelicate slang pertaining to female anatomy.[2] The painting between the lute and the more obviously suggestive bed depicts Venus and Adonis — appropriately, a beauty grazed by Cupid's arrow and the handsome man she loses and laments.[3] In this context the outsized and provocatively pointing bedwarmer certainly serves as a male counterpart to the lute, quite as do pipes and pots, spoons and bowls in other entertaining works by Steen.

The pot of coals in the foreground has been pulled out of the footwarmer beneath the lady's left foot to facilitate the ribbon test, a quack technique for detecting pregnancy. Another test for the same condition, performed by dubious doctors who were thereby known as *piskijkers* (from *kijken,* meaning "to look"), was the visual analysis of a urine sample, a practice denounced in Dutch medical books of the period. A small bottle of urine stands on the table to the left next to a large tome probably meant to represent just such an imposing if rarely read treatise on diseases and cures.[4]

The doctor's outdated doublet and ruff along with his tall hat accent the angularity of his ungainly figure, which complements a face that would be hard to place in a contemporary series of university portraits.[5] His boomeranglike posture may be accentuated by an unseen sword hilt under the back of his mantle but in any case is meant to look ridiculous, the kind of exaggeration that Steen must have seen in the costumes of the comic stage.[6] Thus it is not unexpected that the simple, frontal arrangement of the setting here and in other similar scenes by Steen resembles a stage set with a backdrop and a few props, whereas in his other domestic interiors of the 1650s and 1660s a less schematic description of space is often impressively suggestive of an actual architectural environment.

The first of Steen's pictures of doctors and lovesick women is probably the panel in Prague, which dates from about 1659–60.[7] By this time the artist had developed his distinctive style and was adept at compositional variation, a talent that is particularly evident in his many stagings of this kind of scene.[8] About eighteen examples are listed in Braun's catalogue raisonné and are dated from around 1660 to 1670–72; a review of Braun's small reproductions shows that ten of the compositions dating from the early to mid-1660s include the usual three characters — doctor, maid, and maiden — but in constantly changing configurations and domestic interiors.[9] The closest correspondence between any of the compositions is that between the Taft picture and the panel in the Hermitage, in which the young woman's pose and dress are almost the same, and the table, bed, and bowl of hot coals are similarly positioned.[10] However, the maid and the doctor strike entirely different poses, and the back wall has a window (no painting or lute) through which a young man peeks into the room. Braun dates the Saint Petersburg and Cincinnati paintings to about 1665, while De Vries places the present picture around 1661.[11] Comparisons with other paintings of the same subject and with Steen's pictures of different subjects but similar compositions and style suggest to this writer that Braun's and De Vries's datings define extremes and that the Taft picture was painted around 1663.

With the exception of the simple and surprisingly original canvas in the Rijksmuseum, Amsterdam — which subtly rearranges the elements present in the Taft picture minus the maid, the bedwarmer, and the painting on the wall — all the later interpretations are more elaborate, beginning with the approximately contemporary panel in the Museum Boymans-van Beuningen, Rotterdam.[12] Here the same message lies on the floor, but the young woman is in bed, the doctor writes a prescription at the table, and a laughing maid, old man, and young boy armed with an erect enema complete the composition. Another painting of lovers in a landscape hangs on the wall, and a sculpture of a playful cupid stands over the door. Steen's subsequent interpretations evolve from this composition,[13] from the other type,[14] or from both,[15] with dogs, new props, and in one case Steen himself with a herring coming out on stage. It is remarkable that in these popular pictures, which all have the same punch line (*minnepyn),* the story is always told differently; and the whole joke, each bit, is funny, not to mention decorative.

1. Peter C. Sutton, "Jan Steen, Comedy and Admonition," *Bulletin* [Philadelphia Museum of Art], vol. LXXVIII, nos. 337–38 (Winter 1982–Spring 1983), p. 21 and note 5; and J. B. Bedaux, "Minnekoorts-, zwangerschapsen doodverschijnselen op zeventiende-eeuwse schilderijen," *Antiek,* vol. x, no. 1 (June–July 1975), pp. 28–29, note 20, on the inscription, which Bedaux notes is taken from Propertius, *The Elegies.*

2. See E. de Jongh et al., *Tot Lering en Vermaak,* exh. cat., Rijksmuseum, Amsterdam, 1976, no. 8.

3. The same composition occurs on a much larger scale in the background of *The Physician's Visit,* Steen's panel in Apsley House; see C. M. Kauffmann, *Catalogue of Paintings in the Wellington Museum,* London, 1982, pp. 129–30, no. 163, in which the standing woman is assumed to be "the girl's mother," the brazier on the floor is "a curious dish," and the quack doctor's "wide hat and slashed sleeves" are considered on the authority of one Mrs. Ginsburg to be "part of the rather conservative professional dress of the 17th century." Sutton, p. 23, note 8, more excusably sees the painting in the background of the Taft picture as representing "a pair of unidentified lovers." The animal to the right of Adonis is one of his hounds, as is clear from Steen's source, one of Antonio Tempesta's series of engraved plates illustrating Ovid's *Metamorphoses,* which was published in book form by Pieter de Jode, Antwerp, 1606 (letter to the writer from E. J. Sluijter, Sept. 9, 1986; Sluijter reproduces the engraving as fig. 62 in his printed dissertation, *De "Heydensche Fabulen" in de Noordnederlandse Schilderkunst, circa 1590–1670,* Leiden, 1986).

4. Sutton, p. 24, note 10, thoroughly reviews the literature relevant to this paragraph and cites Dutch medical books published between 1589 and 1651. See also Bedaux, pp. 17–42.

5. Compare, for example, the portrait gallery of Franeker University, published by R. E. O. Ekkart, *Franeker professorportretten . . . 1585–1843,* Franeker, 1977; and discussed in Gary Schwartz, *The Dutch World of Painting,* exh. cat., Vancouver Art Gallery, 1986, pp. 106–11. Schwartz, nos. 60, 61, illustrates examples of academic dress in the middle of the seventeenth century and collar styles dating from 1641 and 1666.

6. On Steen's doctors, their dress, and the doctor type on the Dutch and Italian stage, see S. J. Gudlaugsson, *The Comedians in the Work of Jan Steen and His Contemporaries,* Soest, 1975, pp. 12–23, and Einar Petterson, "*Amans Amanti Medicus:* Die Ikonologie des Motivs *Der ärztliche Besuch,*" in H. Bock and T. W. Gaehtgens, eds., *Holländische Genremalerei im 17. Jahrhundert, Symposium Berlin 1984,* Berlin, 1987, pp. 193, 195, fig. 1.

7. Lyckle de Vries, "Jan Steen 'de kluchtschilder,'" Ph.D. diss., Rijksuniversiteit Groningen, 1977, p. 98 and no. 60; Karel Braun, *Alle tot nu toe bekende schilderijen van Jan Steen,* Rotterdam, 1980, no. 156, as 1662.

8. Here I am following De Vries, pp. 98–99.

9. Braun, nos. 154–56, 186, 194, 203, 219, 242, 243, and 289.

10. Braun, nos. 242 (Taft), 243 (Hermitage), and 243a (copy).

11. De Vries, p. 57, and letter of Aug. 4, 1986.

12. Braun, no. 241 and pl. 51.

13. Braun, no. 254.

14. Braun, no. 289, the three-figure composition in the Metropolitan Museum of Art, New York.

15. Braun, nos. 315–18 and 331.

Provenance Messrs. Smith (according to Smith; see Literature) (in 1842); William Theobald (1843–51; sale, Christie's, London, May 10, 1851); Octavius E. Coope, Rochetts, near Brentwood, Essex (sale, Christie's, London, May 6, 1910, p. 19, no. 71 [ill.], for £34 12s. to Sulley and Co. according to annotated cat. in the Metropolitan Museum of Art); [Scott and Fowles, New York, in 1910]; Taft collection, Nov. 2, 1910.

Exhibitions New York, Scott and Fowles, 1914, no. 7; Cincinnati Museum Association, 1935–36; Indianapolis, John Herron Art Museum, *Dutch Paintings, Etchings, Drawings, and Delftware of the Seventeenth Century,* Feb. 27–Apr. 11, 1937 (cat., no. 66 [ill.]); Dayton Art Institute, Ohio, *Old Masters from Midwestern Museums,* Mar. 15–Apr. 19, 1948 (cat., no. 5 [ill.]); Grand Rapids Art Gallery, Mich., 1948–49; Hartford, Conn., Wadsworth Atheneum, *Life in Seventeenth-Century Holland,* Nov. 21, 1950–Jan. 14, 1951 (cat., p. 19, no. 46), and *The Medicine Man: Medicine in Art,* Oct. 13–Dec. 12, 1954 (cat., p. 50, no. 290, pl. v); Kansas City, Mo., Nelson Gallery of Art and Atkins Museum, *Paintings of 17th-Century Dutch Interiors,* Dec. 1, 1967–Jan. 7, 1968 (cat., p. 38, no. 21, ill. p. 40).

Literature "Picture Sales of the Month," *The Art Journal* (1851), p. 174, as sold from the Theobald collection, at Christie's, for 56 gns.; John Smith, *A Catalogue Raisonné of the Works of the Most Eminent Dutch, Flemish, and French Painters,* vol. ix, Supplement, London, 1842, p. 478, no. 13; Tobias van Westrheene, *Jan Steen, Etude sur l'art en Hollande,* the Hague, 1856, p. 131, no. 141; Cornelis Hofstede de Groot, *A Catalogue Raisonné of the Works of the Most Eminent Dutch Painters of the Seventeenth Century,* vol. 1, London, 1908, pp. 58–59, no. 175; "Art Notes," *The Evening Post* [New York], Feb. 28, 1914, p. 7; Gustav Kobbe, "Noted Art Collectors Send Their Famous Old Masters for Loan Exhibition of Dutch Art in New York," *New York Herald,* Mar. 1, 1914; Royal Cortissoz, "Matters of Art," *New-York Tribune,* Mar. 1, 1914; Maurice W. Brockwell, *A Catalogue of Paintings in the Collection of Mr. and Mrs. Charles P. Taft,* New York, 1920, no. 10; W. G. Menzies, "The Present State of the Picture Market," *Apollo,* vol. xxi (Jan.–June 1935), p. 38, referring to the Taft painting's sale in 1910, for £3,412, as the highest price for Steen before 1919; E. Trautscholdt, in Thieme-Becker, vol. xxxi, p. 511, no. 175; "Master Painters of the Dutch School Presented in Midwestern Exhibition," *The Art Digest* (Mar. 15, 1937), p. 12; *Catalogue of the Taft Museum,* Cincinnati, 1939 and 1958, no. 127 (ill.); Baruch D. Kirschenbaum, *The Religious and Historical Paintings of Jan Steen,* New York and Montclair, N.J., 1977, p. 98, fig. 123; Lyckle de Vries, "Jan Steen 'de kluchtschilder,'" Ph.D. diss., Rijksuniversiteit Groningen, 1977, pp. 57, 99, 163, no. 112; Karel Braun, *Alle tot nu toe bekende schilderijen van Jan Steen,* Rotterdam, 1980, pp. 120–21, no. 242, and detail (of the book on the floor) on p. 10; Peter C. Sutton, "Jan Steen, Comedy and Admonition," *Bulletin* [Philadelphia Museum of Art], vol. LXXVIII, nos. 337–38 (Winter 1982–Spring 1983), p. 23, notes 4, 8; Peter C. Sutton et al., *Masters of Seventeenth-Century Dutch Genre Painting,* exh. cat., Philadelphia Museum of Art, 1984, p. 314, notes 1, 4; Einar Petterson, "*Amans Amanti Medicus:* Die Ikonologie des Motivs *Der ärztliche Besuch,*" in H. Bock and T. W. Gaehtgens, eds., *Holländische Genremalerei im 17. Jahrhundert, Symposium Berlin 1984,* Berlin, 1987, pp. 193, 195, fig. 1; Mary Frances Wack, *Lovesickness in the Middle Ages: The Viaticum and Its Commentaries,* Philadelphia, 1990, p. 139, ill. p. 138.

1931.396

Pieter de Hooch
Rotterdam 1629–1684 Amsterdam

Baptized in Rotterdam on November 20, 1629, Pieter Hendricksz. de Hooch was the son of a midwife and a master bricklayer, Hendrick de Hooch (the form De Hoogh, used by the artist in his mature years, is now orthographically unacceptable).[1] Houbraken, the first author to mention the painter, refers to him as having been "for some time" a pupil, along with fellow Rotterdamer Jacob Ochtervelt, of the Haarlem landscapist

Nicolaes Berchem.[2] However, in the same passage Houbraken described De Hooch, "who was excellent in the painting of interior views" (*kamergezigten*), as "following" (*Hem volgt)* the older Rotterdam artist Ludolf de Jongh (1616–1679), himself a specialist in *Moderne Kamerstukken*.[3] Yet another local genre painter with whom De Hooch was closely linked was the Delft artist Hendrick van der Burch, whom Sutton has shown was most probably the brother of the woman, Jannetge van der Burch, to whom De Hooch was betrothed in 1654. The couple had seven children. Although still a Rotterdam resident when he became engaged, De Hooch was inscribed in the painters' guild of Delft on September 20, 1655. He paid dues the following two years, and his first dated paintings, of 1658, include details of domestic and other architecture that derive from buildings in Delft.[4] Around 1660–61 the artist moved to Amsterdam, as had several important painters from Delft and Leiden (De Witte and Metsu among them) during the preceding years.[5] The new capital did not offer De Hooch's family more than a mean existence, to judge from their various addresses during the 1660s.[6] Nothing is known of their life after the birth of their last child in 1672, the year in which the French invasion and the fall of the stadholder Johan de Witt caused an economic depression.

The pictures painted by De Hooch during the 1670s (to follow Sutton's careful chronology) are on the whole inferior to those of the 1660s but include works as fine as *A Musical Party in a Courtyard* (1677, London, National Gallery). The paintings dating from the early 1680s seem to be uniformly mediocre in execution and, in conception, follow formulas unreflectingly. De Hooch died in the *Dolhuys* (madhouse) and was buried on March 24, 1684.

The artist was closely associated with Vermeer in Delft, and his best works show a comparable predilection (although not a similar talent) for describing effects of light and space. To a remarkable extent these interests offset De Hooch's modest ability as a figure painter; warm colors and restful compositions create a sense of well-being about the homely and almost always innocent situations in which De Hooch's inarticulate characters find themselves.[7] The painter was a good if not exceptional student of contemporary artistic trends, such as the guardroom scenes of De Jongh, Gerard ter Borch, Gerbrand van den Eeckhout, and Jacob van Loo;[8] of the architectural interests of the Delft School;[9] and of what has been described as the "South Holland tradition" of genre painting.[10] However, his reputation has rested on what he accomplished intuitively. The comfortable environments he affectionately described and his sympathy for everyday existence have earned De Hooch his reputation as Holland's quintessential painter of domestic life.

1. In this respect and others the biography by Neil Maclaren, *The Dutch School,* National Gallery Catalogues, London, 1960, pp. 183–84, is uncharacteristically dated. See Peter C. Sutton, *Pieter de Hooch,* Oxford, 1980, pp. 9–10, "The Life of the Artist."

2. Arnold Houbraken, *De Groote Schouburgh der Nederlantsche Konstschilders en Schilderessen,* vol. II, Amsterdam, 1719, pp. 34–35.

3. See Roland E. Fleischer, "Ludolf de Jongh and the Early Work of Pieter de Hooch," *Oud Holland,* vol. XCII (1978), pp. 49–67; and Susan D. Kuretsky, *The Paintings of Jacob Ochtervelt, 1634–1682,* Montclair, N.J., 1979, p. 4.

4. Sutton, p. 10 and nos. 35, 36; see also nos. 20–22, 33, 34.

5. Both of the bits of evidence cited by Maclaren, p. 184, to place De Hooch in Delft in 1660 and in Amsterdam before Sept. 1663, are entirely circumstantial. There is no reason to assume that a picture with "Delft features" dated 166(?) was painted in Delft, as Emanuel de Witte's contemporary "Delft" pictures, painted in Amsterdam, make clear. The first indisputable evidence of Amsterdam residency would appear to be that given at the death of a child on June 2, 1663, although the baptismal notices of April 15, 1661, and January 5, 1663, and perhaps that of April 4, 1660, suggest that De Hooch and his wife lived in Amsterdam earlier: Sutton, p. 147, document nos. 33, 36, 38, 40.

6. Sutton, p. 10.

7. Sutton, chap. VI, for some sensible remarks on the "Iconographic Issues."

8. Sutton, p. 14.

9. Christopher Brown, *Carel Fabritius,* Oxford, 1981, chap. III, and Walter Liedtke, *Architectural Painting in Delft,* Doornspijk, 1982, pp. 20–21, on the "Delft School"; also, for De Hooch, Walter Liedtke, "Hendrick van Vliet and the Delft School," *Museum News* [Toledo Museum of Art] (1979), pp. 40–52.

10. Walter Liedtke, "Toward a History of Dutch Genre Painting, II: The South Holland Tradition," in *The Age of Rembrandt: Studies in Seventeenth-Century Dutch Painting,* vol. III, Papers in Art History from the Pennsylvania State University, eds. Roland Fleischer and Susan Scott Munshower, University Park, Pa., 1988, pp. 95–131.

❧

Pieter de Hooch

A Woman with a Cittern and a Singing Couple at a Table

ca. 1667
Oil on canvas, 70.8 x 57.9 cm (27⅞ x 22¾ in.)
Signed (on the footstool): *P. de Ho[   ]*

A young woman in a fashionable and, for the period, daring dress of red and gold satin stands with one foot on a stool and plays a cittern. In the background a man and a woman, the latter in modest middle-class attire, sit at a carpet-covered table and sing, following songbooks. The man keeps meter with his raised hand. The fabric-covered walls, the stately fireplace, and the marble floor indicate that the setting is a very grand house in the city.

This mature picture was painted by De Hooch in Amsterdam during the mid-to-late 1660s. The recent cleaning (1986) at the Intermuseum Laboratory, Oberlin, Ohio, now allows a more reliable and distinctly higher estimate of the work. The man's stockings (he does not wear boots or any other attribute of a "cavalier") that had been overpainted in green are now again brown, as is most of his attire. Newly restored subtleties of light and atmosphere temper the strong impression made by the yellow, gold, and reds of the woman's dress, the man's cloak, and the table carpet; a visual core of color is centered within the tonal setting of a shadowy drawing room. Before these discreet qualities were retrieved the painting had an artificial and oddly French flavor as well as one discordant note: a poorly painted window to the left, which had been added over the striped cloth hung on the two visible walls.[1]

1931.395

This naïve attempt to make the painting seem more characteristic of De Hooch (or so it seems) struck a blow against the artist's most long-standing strength, his ability to suggest interior space through the interplay of sunlight and shadows. The effect here (despite the tiled floor that might too simply be associated with Delft) reveals an affinity with the work of Gerard ter Borch, as does the understated subject. Indeed, the figures — a seated and gesturing gentleman, an elegantly posed and lovely

young woman, a retiring woman to the rear, and even a dog to the right — are surprisingly reminiscent of Ter Borch's most celebrated picture, the so-called *Parental Admonition* of about 1654 (fig. 1).[2] This is so even though Ter Borch's man is not speaking or keeping time with his upraised hand; and Ter Borch's woman, with her sinuous silhouette and satin dress, is facing away from the viewer, which exquisitely enhances her beauty and the flow of her thoughts in the viewer's imagination.

That De Hooch stands up so well in this comparison might be taken as an index of how carefully he considered Ter Borch's composition and perhaps others by the same artist, such as two approximately contemporary Music Lessons, one in Bradford, England, and the other in the National Gallery, London.[3] Each of Ter Borch's three paintings, like De Hooch's, is about a man's amorous intentions, a young woman's less than wholehearted response, and (in three of the pictures) another figure ambivalently playing a supporting role. In all four paintings a dog serves as a conventional symbol of Lust, that harsh, Calvinist concept that could be called animal magnetism: love that holds no attraction for the specifically human soul. And music, at least the kind printed in songbooks like those depicted here, was considered by many contemporary writers to be but a sensual distraction, although it was also a common and usually innocent pastime of Amsterdam society.[4]

Differing opinions were probably held, too, about the meaning of pictures like this one. For most contemporary viewers the

Fig. 1 Gerard ter Borch, *Gallant Conversation* (known as *The Parental Admonition*), ca. 1654. Oil on canvas, 71 x 73 cm (28 x 28¾ in.). Amsterdam, Rijksmuseum-Stichting.

Fig. 2 Attributed to Eglon van der Neer, *A Woman with a Cittern and a Man Smoking at a Table*. Oil on panel, 39.5 x 30 cm (15½ x 11¾ in.). Photograph courtesy of Brod Gallery, London (1970).

painting's appeal was likely enhanced by its slight ambiguity. It is, on the one hand, a model, a modish ideal of fine homes and figures draped in fashionable fabrics — the kind of high life one might expect to find in the high-ceilinged houses on the Herengracht. On the other hand, it is a glimpse of sensual pleasure, caught as if through a keyhole, that quickens the eavesdropper's pulse even as it earns his or her disapproval. Fifty years earlier in the Netherlands the picture's moralistic message would have been obvious. Fifty years later it probably would have been overlooked.

The painting over the fireplace is a calm marine view of the Van de Cappelle type; three boats are visible, sketched in black and brown. Some seascapes suggest stormy emotions or absent lovers when they are found in domestic interiors, but here the image is barely readable and a decorator's idea.

The painting was dated to the early 1670s by Valentiner; Sutton placed it earlier, about 1667–70. Among the most similar pictures in De Hooch's oeuvre are *Council Chamber in the Town Hall, Amsterdam* (Lugano, Thyssen-Bornemisza Collection), dated by Sutton about 1664–66, in which the dog and a few other motifs might be compared, and, with closer respect to composition and subject, *Musical Party on a Terrace* of about 1667 (New York, private collection) and *Two Women and a Man Making Music*, dated 1667 (Hampton Court).[5] One is particularly struck by the young woman's frontal and precisely balanced pose in the Taft picture; she could easily join the two women in profile in the New York painting and the seated woman in the queen's picture to form a quartet in relief on a Wedgwood vase or in a marble panel by De Hooch's contemporary Artus Quellinus. These comparisons underscore the care with which the Taft painting's composition was conceived (infrared reflectography reveals no changes in the course of the work) and tend to support a date early in the period proposed by Sutton, or about 1667.

A panel bearing the signature of Eglon van der Neer may have been based on the Taft picture or on some intermediary work (fig. 2).[6]

1. Peter C. Sutton, *Pieter de Hooch*, Oxford, 1980, pl. 81, for the painting's previous state. Sutton's title is *A Woman with a Mandolin and a Couple at a Table Singing*, but Lawrence Libin, curator of musical instruments at the Metropolitan Museum, writes "no, not a mandolin, but a cittern" (memo to the writer).

2. S. J. Gudlaugsson, *Gerard ter Borch*, The Hague, 1959–60, vol. II, p. 116, no. 110, feels that the *Parental Admonition* was known to De Hooch because of the woman turned away from the viewer in a picture dated 1667 at Hampton Court (Sutton, no. 77, pl. 80, placed — for good reason in view of its numerous similarities — very close to the Taft painting). Walter Liedtke, "Hendrick van Vliet and the Delft School," *Museum News* [Toledo Museum of Art] (1979), pp. 40–52, suggests that Ter Borch's picture or some record of it was already known in Delft during the mid-1650s.

3. Gudlaugsson, nos. 220, 221, reproduced in vol. I, pp. 354–55, and dated about 1667–68. He states in his catalogue entries that the London picture must have been known in or around Amsterdam by 1673 (vol. II, p. 202); he lists numerous copies of the London and especially the Bradford painting (pp. 202–4). One should also compare the Taft picture to Gudlaugsson, no. 187, *Musical Company* of about 1660–62 at Polesden Lacey, Surrey (discussed unconvincingly in *The Treasure Houses of Britain*, exh. cat., National Gallery of Art, Washington, D.C., 1985, p. 364, no. 293).

4. One of several sources on this subject is D. J. Balfoort, *Het Muziekleven in Nederland in de 17de en 18de Eeuw*, 1st ed., 1938, the Hague, 1981. In his diary entries of the 1660s Samuel Pepys often mentions practicing any one of several stringed and wind instruments he kept at home for pleasure (see, for example, R. Latham, ed., *The Shorter Pepys*, Berkeley and Los Angeles, 1985, pp. 16–18, 22, 25, 51, 52, 65, 97).

5. Sutton, nos. 76, 77, pls. 79, 80 (see note 2 above). No. 76 was in the Guterman sale at Sotheby's, New York, Jan. 14, 1988, no. 21.

6. Brod Gallery, London (1970), which kindly supplied a photograph of the Van der Neer to the Taft Museum. There are two figures, a seated man who is smoking and a standing frontal woman with a lute. The execution and form of the signature appear to be consistent with Van der Neer's *Portrait of a Man and a Woman in an Interior* in the Museum of Fine Arts, Boston. The panel (39.5 x 30 cm) must be approximately contemporary to De Hooch's and is not necessarily directly related, but if it is, one would not for a moment be inclined to place it earlier than the Taft picture.

Provenance [Arthur Ruck, London, in Oct. 1920 (see Sutton, under no. 78)]; [Scott and Fowles, New York, 1924]; Taft collection, Dec. 1, 1924.

Literature Clotilde Brière-Misme, "Tableaux inédits ou peu connus de Pieter de Hooch," pt. III, *Gazette des beaux-arts*, vol. LXIX, no. 16 (Nov. 1927), p. 276 and note 14 as *La Mandoliniste*, with an English dealer in 1920; William R. Valentiner, *Pieter de Hooch, des Meisters Gemälde (Klassiker der Kunst)*, Berlin and Leipzig, 1929, pp. 135 (ill.), 285, as about 1675; *Catalogue of the Taft Museum*, Cincinnati, 1939 and 1958, no. 130; Peter C. Sutton, *Pieter de Hooch*, Oxford, 1980, p. 100, no. 78, pl. 81.

1931.395

Anthony van Dyck
Antwerp 1599–1641 London

Van Dyck, the son of a silk merchant, was born in Antwerp on March 22, 1599. At the age of ten he became a pupil of Hendrick van Balen, the dean of the painters' guild. Van Dyck had his own shop and pupils by about 1615, although he did not become a master of the guild until 1618. During the period 1618–20 Van Dyck was Rubens's most important assistant, and at the same time he turned out a considerable number of independent works.

Van Dyck entered the service of James I in London by November 1620 and in February 1621 received permission to travel for eight months. He returned to Antwerp and left for Italy sometime later in the year. He traveled extensively in Italy but was most active in Genoa, where he became the best portrait painter active south of the Alps during this decade. The Genoese portraits in full length and other formats and the religious pictures of the Italian period demonstrate the profound impression made by Titian's example on the still youthful Van Dyck. He returned to Antwerp probably in the autumn of 1627 and, apart from two visits to the Hague, worked mainly in his native city until he moved to London in 1632 (by April 1). On July 5 he was named principal painter and knighted by Charles I. Another period of residence in the southern Netherlands, from early 1634 to sometime before June 1635, was followed by five comparatively settled years in London. Between October 1640 and his death in London on December 9, 1641, Van Dyck was in Antwerp, Paris, London, the Hague, and Paris again.

Van Dyck painted a large number of religious and mythological pictures, but the sheer number of his portraits, the importance of his sitters, and his virtual definition of cosmopolitan elegance in this aristocratic age (Van Dyck never painted a subject that suggested it was otherwise) have identified him with courtly society and with a tradition of English portraiture extending from his busy studio, from Lely and from Kneller to Reynolds and especially to Gainsborough.[1]

1. For a more extensive version of this biography, see Walter Liedtke, *Flemish Paintings in the Metropolitan Museum of Art*, vol. 1, New York, 1984, pp. 41–42. See also the author's "Anthony van Dyck," *The Metropolitan Museum of Art Bulletin*, vol. XLII, no. 3 (Winter 1984–85), and the literature cited there on p. 48.

1931.447

Imitator of Van Dyck

Portrait of an Italian Noblewoman (previously identified as Paolina Adorno, Marchesa di Brignole Sale)

ca. 1900
Oil on canvas, 227.4 x 149.3 cm (89½ x 58¾ in.)

The painting is not well known from the literature on Van Dyck, although two recent catalogues, both by Erik Larsen, accept the work as "definitely by van Dyck" and as "one of his more important realizations" of the Genoese period.[1] Other Van Dyck scholars have verbally considered the painting to be a workshop product, although there is no evidence that Van Dyck had studio assistants capable of carrying out such a project during his Italian years. The present writer, together with a scholar of Van Dyck's Genoese portraits and a conservator who examined the painting at the Metropolitan Museum, maintains emphatically that it is approximately one hundred years old and shows clear signs of fraudulent intent.[2]

The painting first surfaced in 1905, the year in which the Tafts bought it, during what may be regarded as the first, largest, and most speculative wave of Van Dyck acquisitions in America. A recent survey by the writer found that of some 250 supposed Van Dycks in America (almost all of them portraits), a surprisingly high number to begin with, about forty percent are generally accepted by current scholars as paintings by or in part by Van Dyck himself. These statistics actually compare favorably with those that pertain to the decoration of English country homes, which was the principal model for American purchasers of works by Van Dyck and similar portraits during the late nineteenth and early twentieth centuries. For example, of the sixty-two portraits and thirteen history paintings attributed to Van Dyck in Norfolk County collections and sale catalogues, "the actual number of autograph works included within such statistics is extremely small."[3]

In old photographs and still today the Taft portrait makes a splendid impression in its usual setting, one reminiscent of full-length portraits by Van Dyck as seen in the baronial residences

of Frick, Morgan, and Widener. A very different impression is gained by examining the picture in broad daylight and with the help of radiographs. With the exception of the head, which is carefully executed in a manner smoother than Van Dyck's, the entire canvas is painted in a superficial technique that achieves Van Dyck–like effects while paying little heed to the artist's technical procedures. The lady's right arm, for example, is a two-dimensional exercise in shimmering striations that encourage critical eyes to pass over the complete lack of organic form, of consistent light and shade, and of knowledge regarding garment construction in seventeenth-century Italy. An X radiograph of the head reveals that this area alone was prepared with a patch of lead white (no preliminary drawing is visible).[4] A radiograph of the left hand and the dog, both of which are implausible enough on the surface, reveals nothing at all, including no trace of lead white in the hand, an all-but-unthinkable circumstance in a flesh part by Van Dyck or any comparable painter of the period. Throughout the picture one finds the beguiling benefits of studying paintings by Van Dyck (such as the vertical streak of light on the pier to the left and the soft curls framing the face) combined with technical shorthands seemingly modern and certainly alien to the artist, such as the black strokes throughout the ruff and the curved lines to the right of the cheek and chin. Finally, there are passages that appear to be well preserved but give the impression of wear and age: in the skirt and architecture to the lower left, for example, unusually fluid effects of scumbling, evidently in consort with scraping and a judicious selection of what might be called undertones, achieves a reassuring look of moderate abrasion at a viewing distance of more than a foot or two. In summary, the various areas of examination tell a consistent story, which is that this charming but strangely static, weightless, and awkward figure, wearing a dress one size too small, was conceived by a clever forger, probably not long before the painting first became known.

Conservators and scholars who have considerable experience with Genoese Van Dycks are familiar with this type of imitation, which they generally ascribe to capable restorers or conservative portraitists active in Italy during the second half of the nineteenth century. The skill evident here, especially in the face (which may be by a better hand than the rest of the picture), and the forger's obvious familiarity with Van Dyck's Genoese portraits, suggest that he himself was active in or around Genoa. Details of costume such as the skirt (even the pattern of highlights on it), the collar, the cuffs, and the feather in the hair; the form of the chair; and the approximate features of the face recall one Van Dyck portrait in particular, that of Paola Adorno, Marchesa di Brignole Sale, in the Palazzo Rosso, Genoa.

According to Fairfax Murray's letter of 1905, which is the only known evidence for the painting's earlier provenance, "the Marquis Durazzo purchased [the Taft picture] from the Brignole family [at] the Palace in the Via Garibaldi, Genoa," and the subject is supposed to be "the elder sister of Paolina Adorno, whose picture is now in the Red (Brignole) Palace." Fairfax Murray goes on to say that getting the right Genoese name is difficult because of the numerous intermarriages among the great Italian families, but that he "will see about this when I am in Paris or Italy." The subject was described as "a Lady of Rank" by Valentiner in 1914, but six years later she became Paolina Adorno in Brockwell's catalogue; he cited other supposed portraits of the same marchesa, and "the facts . . . set out in a letter written in 1905 by C. Fairfax Murray and now in the possession of Mr. and Mrs. Charles P. Taft."[5] Larsen rightly rejects the identification with Paola (Paolina) Adorno, which would be a moot point were it not for the possible connection with the Palazzo Rosso picture mentioned above.

Fairfax Murray has not been identified previously in the context of the present picture as a London dealer and partner of Agnew's, whose sticker is glued to the stretcher (next to Scott and Fowles's); Fairfax Murray wrote the letter of 1905 to Mr. Thompson at Agnew's. He was resentful of Bernard Berenson's rise as a connoisseur of Italian paintings, particularly since Berenson and his wife, Mary, had criticized Fairfax Murray's client, J. P. Morgan, for his gullibility in buying forgeries.[6] Mary also wrote to a friend in 1908 that Berenson hesitated to catalogue Peter Widener's collection, since it included "worthless school things [purchased] for vast sums" from Fairfax Murray.[7] This is sufficient circumstantial evidence to cast doubt on the reliability of Fairfax Murray's details of provenance, which are unsupported by any known reference in Genoese archives or by any reference to the Taft picture dating from before 1905.[8]

Although these conclusions may be disappointing, they provide an unusually clear view of the hazards that American collectors faced in the old-master market around the turn of the century. For Valentiner, the first connoisseur of northern European painting accessible to the Tafts, this painting was a typical Van Dyck of the Genoese period, and the *Singing Youth* by a nineteenth-century imitator of Frans Hals (see 1962.6, p. 146) was a work by the master worthy of repeated publication and exhibition. The "Hals" was never doubted in print before the 1970s, and the present picture seems never to have been questioned in a publication until now. It must be admitted that Van Dyck connoisseurship is a difficult discipline and that this Genoese portrait is an especially impressive example of what it is.

1. Erik Larsen, *L'Opera completa di Van Dyck, 1613–1626*, Milan, 1980, p. 108, no. 321; Larsen, *The Paintings of Anthony van Dyck*, vol. II, Freren, Ger., 1988, p. 133, no. 325, quoted here in the text. Larsen's catalogues are notoriously unreliable; about half of the thirty color plates, for example, are of pictures in private collections that most scholars would reject.

2. I am grateful to Susan Barnes and to the Metropolitan Museum's conservator, Gisela Helmkampf, for their extensive comments and examination of the painting in New York in Feb. 1989.

3. A. Moore, *Dutch and Flemish Paintings in Norfolk*, exh. cat., Norwich Castle Museum, London, 1988, p. 89, speaking of paintings attributed to Van Dyck that were not among the twenty catalogued by D. Singh, *Portraits in Norfolk Houses*, n.p., 1927.

4. It is possible that the patch of lead white screens a first, thinly painted head that was judged unsatisfactory; this would explain the use of "priming" in this area only.

5. Maurice W. Brockwell, *A Catalogue of Paintings in the Collection of Mr. and Mrs. Charles P. Taft*, New York, 1920, p. 53.

6. Ernest Samuels, *Bernard Berenson: The Making of a Connoisseur*, Cambridge, Mass., and London, 1979, p. 422. Fairfax Murray, in turn, gave Berenson credit for the sale of a supposed Leonardo to the American collector Theodore Davis. It was said to have been painted by an acquaintance of an old Milanese restorer, Luigi Cavenaghi, according to Meryle Secrest, *Being Bernard Berenson*, New York, 1979, p. 205, and the letters of Jan. 1904, cited on p. 435.

7. Samuels, p. 62, quoting from a letter to Hannah Whitall Smith dated June 28, 1908. See also p. 7, mentioning scandal stories about Fairfax Murray told by Hofstede de Groot.

8. This, according to Susan Barnes, Dallas Museum of Art, but there is little on the Brignole Sales in any case. Larsen, 1988, under no. 325, lists a book by Head, 1879, as illustrating the Taft picture, but Head's engraved reproduction is of the portrait of Paola Adorno in the Palazzo Rosso, Genoa.

Provenance Said by Fairfax Murray to have come from the Brignole Sale family in Genoa (see text above); [Agnew's, London (and Fairfax Murray?), in 1905]; [Scott and Fowles, New York, in 1905]; Taft collection, Nov. 25, 1905.

Literature William R. Valentiner, *The Art of the Low Countries*, Garden City, N.Y., 1914, pp. 208, 239, no. 24, ill. opp. p. 212, as by Van Dyck; *Ladies' Home Journal* (May 1917), pp. 5 (color ill), 59; Maurice W. Brockwell, *A Catalogue of Paintings in the Collection of Mr. and Mrs. Charles P. Taft*, New York, 1920, pp. 51–53, no. 14; *Catalogue of the Taft Museum*, 1939 and 1958, no. 472 (ill.); *The Frick Collection: An Illustrated Catalogue*, vol. I, New York, 1968, p. 176, doubting that the subject is Paola Adorno; Erik Larsen, *L'Opera completa di Van Dyck, 1613–1626*, Milan, 1980, p. 108, no. 321 (ill.), as "without doubt the work of Van Dyck," to be dated between 1621 and about 1625; Erik Larsen, *The Paintings of Anthony van Dyck*, vol. II, Freren, Ger., 1988, p. 133, no. 325 (ill.), as "definitely by van Dyck," and "in fact, one of his more important realizations."

1931.447

Eighteenth- and Nineteenth-Century English Paintings

Kenneth Paul Bendiner

Thomas Gainsborough
Sudbury, Suffolk 1727–1788 London

Thomas Gainsborough was the son of a prosperous Suffolk cloth merchant.[1] He studied art in London from 1740 to 1748 as an assistant to the French rococo graphic artist Hubert Gravelot. In 1746 Gainsborough married Margaret Burr. Before 1750 he established himself as an independent portrait painter, first at Sudbury and then at Ipswich. He was always attracted to landscape painting, and his early scenes of the English countryside are strongly indebted to seventeenth-century Dutch landscape traditions, especially to the works of Jacob van Ruisdael and Jan Wynants. Nevertheless, portraiture remained Gainsborough's necessary means of support, and he traveled through the Midlands in 1758 painting portraits. In 1759 he settled in the fashionable resort of Bath, where his somewhat stiff and blocky Ipswich manner gave way to a style that was more elegant and delicate. His portrait career flourished in Bath, and his renown spread.

From 1761 on Gainsborough sent ambitious full-length portraits to the annual London exhibitions of the Society of Artists of Great Britain. Beginning in 1763 he sent his more personal landscapes, which were untopographical, pastoral, and sometimes expressive of picturesque taste. Although still residing in Bath in 1768, Gainsborough was invited and agreed to become a founding member of the Royal Academy in London. In 1774 he moved to the capital despite several disputes with his fellow academicians over the hanging of his pictures. As a result of these disputes, he refused to exhibit at the Royal Academy from 1773 to 1777 and again from 1784 to 1788. He prospered nevertheless and received his first royal portrait commission in 1777.

Gainsborough's style became more diffused and fluent during the 1780s; fragile, narrow brushstrokes create a soft atmosphere for the figures and settings. His full-length portraits of this time sometimes display novel experiments in figural action, old-master allusions, and theatricality. During the same decade Gainsborough expanded his subject matter and produced picturesque seascapes and large-scale genre scenes called "fancy pictures." Some of these peasant paintings reflect charming French rococo shepherd subjects or the happy beggar boys of Murillo, but others display figures in disturbing psychological

states with hints of sadness and violence. In this late period of diversification, he also created a peep-show box with lighted transparencies inside (ca. 1783, London, Victoria and Albert Museum).

As a result of his disagreements with the Royal Academy and to present his paintings in a favorable position, not surrounded by highly colored pictures, Gainsborough exhibited his works yearly at his studio in Schomberg House, Pall Mall, from 1784 until his death in 1788. He had one pupil and assistant, his nephew, Gainsborough Dupont. Gainsborough never traveled abroad but is known to have toured the English Lake District in 1783.

1. On Gainsborough, see Philip Thicknesse, *A Sketch of the Life and Paintings of Thomas Gainsborough, Esq.*, London, 1788; Walter Armstrong, *Gainsborough and His Place in English Art*, 1st ed., London, 1899, rev. ed., London, 1904; William T. Whitley, *Thomas Gainsborough*, London, 1915; Oliver Millar, *Thomas Gainsborough*, London, 1949; Ellis K. Waterhouse, "Preliminary Check List of Portraits by Thomas Gainsborough," *The Walpole Society, 1948–50*, vol. XXXIII (1953); Ellis K. Waterhouse, *Gainsborough*, London, 1958; Jack Lindsay, *Thomas Gainsborough: His Life and Art*, London, 1981; John Hayes, *The Landscape Paintings of Thomas Gainsborough*, 2 vols., London and Ithaca, N.Y., 1982.

Thomas Gainsborough

Wooded Landscape with Milkmaids, Rustic Lover, Herdsman, Cows, Dogs, Sheep, and Goats

ca. 1772–74
Oil on canvas, 121.9 x 148.7 cm (48 x 58½ in.)

A milkmaid with a pail on her head and two fighting dogs at her side stands in the foreground clearing. Behind her another milkmaid reclines with her rustic lover. Farther back in a forest glade stand cattle, sheep, goats, and a herdsman. A lively screen of trees runs across the canvas, and a small avenue opens into the light-filled distance at right of center.

The bucolic theme and peaceful mood of this landscape are found in many other Gainsborough scenes. The Taft painting is a particularly fine example that spawned copies and variations by several artists.[1] Typical of Gainsborough's work during the early 1770s, the foliage is painted with rhythmically ordered, feathery strokes. The pinkish underpainting and green-brown coloration are also representative of that decade. A painting of virtually the same subject with only a few alterations is in the Museum of Fine Arts, Boston. John Hayes, however, has attributed the Boston picture in all probability to Gainsborough's nephew, pupil, and copyist, Gainsborough Dupont.[2] Waterhouse, the chief Gainsborough scholar before Hayes, had considered both the Boston and the Taft paintings to be probably authentic.[3] But the slight crudities of drawing and the dark tone of the Boston canvas support Hayes's attribution. Other copies are in the Petworth House collection (Sussex, Eng.) and in a private collection in Buenos Aires.

1931.445

Gainsborough modified seventeenth-century Dutch landscape traditions, adding the delicacy, wistfulness, and pastoral sweetness of French rococo painting. In most cases his scenery was largely poetic invention, not descriptive. The Taft painting seems typically untopographical, containing such standard literary features as a pair of pastoral lovers. In line with the arcadian sensibility is the foreground milkmaid, who supports her pail in a classical fashion. The motif of the fighting dogs, which introduces a tinge of natural violence, is seen in other Gainsborough images and was raised to a subject of major proportions in a painting of 1783, *Two Shepherd Boys with Dogs Fighting* (London, Iveagh Bequest, Kenwood House). John Barrell has examined Gainsborough's pastoral figures with a Marxist's eye for class distinctions, changing attitudes toward agricultural labor during the eighteenth century, and the rural ideal in literature.[4] In contrast to some of Gainsborough's other rustics, those in the Taft painting do not seem particularly hardworking, sad eyed, impoverished, or family oriented. At the very least, they give an imaginary glamor to rural existence.

1. John Hayes, *The Landscape Paintings of Thomas Gainsborough*, vol. II, London and Ithaca, N.Y., 1982, no. 112.

2. Hayes, vol. II, no. 581. He identifies the Boston painting as sold at the Dupont sale of 1797; see Hayes, vol. I, p. 227.

3. Ellis K. Waterhouse, *Gainsborough*, London, 1958, nos. 919, 920.

4. John Barrell, *The Dark Side of the Landscape*, Cambridge, 1980, pp. 35–88.

Provenance Probably William W. Pearce; [sale, Phillips, London, Apr. 30–May 1, 1872, no. 354]; Miss Holland, London, 1910; Edgar, viscount d'Abernon of Esher (1857–1941); [Scott and Fowles, New York]; Taft collection, Nov. 13, 1923.

Exhibitions London, Royal Academy of Arts, 1910 (cat., no. 140); Cincinnati Art Museum, *Gainsborough*, May 1–31, 1931 (cat., no. 26, pl. 25, and detail ill. p. 8).

Literature William Martin Conway, *The Artistic Development of Reynolds and Gainsborough*, London, 1886, p. 81; Walter Armstrong, *Gainsborough and His Place in English Art*, London, 1904, p. 288; Walter H. Siple, "The Gainsborough Exhibition Held in May," *Bulletin of the Cincinnati Art Museum* (July 1931), p. 74; Walter Heil, "Die Gainsborough-Ausstellung in Cincinnati," *Pantheon* (Sept. 1931), pp. 70, 384; *Catalogue of the Taft Museum*, Cincinnati, 1939 and 1958, no. 473; Ellis K. Waterhouse, *Gainsborough*, London, 1958, no. 920; John Hayes, *The Landscape Paintings of Thomas Gainsborough*, vol. II, London and Ithaca, N.Y., 1982, no. 112.

1931.445

Thomas Gainsborough

Maria Walpole, Duchess of Gloucester

ca. 1779
Oil on canvas, 92.1 x 71.8 cm (36¼ x 28¼ in.)

The duchess of Gloucester looks up to the viewer's right as she rests her head on her hand in a gesture of thoughtfulness. Her powdered hair is piled high, and her low-cut bodice is draped with a string of pearls. She leans against a parapet with decorous ease. The somewhat abrupt truncation and severely triangular form of the centrally placed half-length figure suggest that the painting may have been cut down from a full-length portrait.[1] Gainsborough exhibited a full-length portrait of the duchess at the Royal Academy in 1779 (no. 98), and it has been proposed that this work is the painting in question.[2] The evidence, however, is not absolutely firm. As Ellis K. Waterhouse has stated, the Taft painting could just as easily be the portrait sold at Mrs. Gainsborough's sale in 1797 (no. 27) and bought by a Dr. Duval.[3]

1931.406

three daughters who were later depicted together by Reynolds in one of his finest group portraits (1781, Edinburgh, National Gallery of Scotland). Another Gainsborough portrait of the duchess, while she was still the countess Waldegrave (ca. 1765), is in the Los Angeles County Museum of Art.

1. Maurice W. Brockwell, "Gainsborough's Maria, Duchess of Gloucester," *Art in America*, vol. VII (Oct. 1919), p. 235.

2. Brockwell, p. 235; Ellis K. Waterhouse, "Preliminary Check List of Portraits by Thomas Gainsborough," *The Walpole Society, 1948–50*, vol. XXXIII (1953), p. 49; Waterhouse, *Gainsborough*, London, 1958, no. 319.

3. Waterhouse 1953, p. 49.

4. William T. Whitley, *Thomas Gainsborough*, London, 1915, p. 97.

Provenance Possibly Mrs. Gainsborough (sale, London, Apr. 10, 1797, no. 27, bt. Dr. Duval); duchess of Gloucester (1857); bequeathed to duke of Cambridge (sale, Christie's, London, June 11, 1904, no. 85; bt. Agnew, London); [Scott and Fowles, New York, 1905]; Taft collection, Feb. 6, 1905.

Exhibitions Possibly London, Royal Academy of Arts, 1779 (cat., no. 98); London, Agnew, 1904 (cat., no. 9); New York, Scott and Fowles, *Paintings from the C. P. Taft Collection*, Nov. 1909 (cat., no. 7); Cincinnati Art Museum, *Thomas Gainsborough*, May 1–31, 1931 (cat., no. 13, pl. 23); Cincinnati Art Museum, 1942.

Literature George W. Fulcher, *Life of Thomas Gainsborough*, London, 1856, p. 113; Ronald S. Gower, *Gainsborough*, London, 1903, p. 81 (wrongly identified as "Anne Luttrell, Duchess of Cumberland"); Walter Armstrong, *Gainsborough and His Place in English Art*, rev. ed., London, 1904, pp. 267–68; *Burlington Magazine*, vol. XVI (1910), p. 368; William T. Whitley, *Thomas Gainsborough*, London, 1915, p. 97; Maurice W. Brockwell, "Gainsborough's Maria, Duchess of Gloucester," *Art in America*, vol. VII (Oct. 1919), p. 235; Maurice W. Brockwell, *A Catalogue of Paintings in the Collection of Mr. and Mrs. Charles P. Taft*, New York, 1920, pp. xix–xx, no. 21; Esther Singleton, *Old World Masters in New World Collections*, New York, 1929, pp. 366–72 (ill.); *Catalogue of the Taft Museum*, Cincinnati, 1939 and 1958, no. 200; Ellis K. Waterhouse, "Preliminary Check List of Portraits by Thomas Gainsborough," *The Walpole Society, 1948–50*, vol. XXXIII (1953), p. 49; Ellis K. Waterhouse, *Gainsborough*, London, 1958, no. 319.

1931.406

The Taft picture has darkened with age, perhaps because bitumen or some other deteriorating substance was used to obtain rich and translucent shadows. Gainsborough may have experimented with such chiaroscuro materials in emulation of Sir Joshua Reynolds, whose direct rival he became after moving to London in 1777.

The duchess's meditative pose is a common device used in late-eighteenth-century portraiture to give intellectual dignity to the sitter. It was more popular in portraits of men, although Gainsborough frequently used it in portraits of women (e.g., *Duchess of Cumberland*, 1777, collection of H. M. Queen Elizabeth II).

Maria, duchess of Gloucester (1735–1807), was the illegitimate daughter of Sir Edward Walpole and Maria Clements. She was the niece of Horace Walpole, through whose influence she was married in 1759 to James, second earl Waldegrave (1715–1763), an important figure in politics and a key adviser to George II. Maria was considered a great beauty with extravagant tastes. After the earl's death she was courted by the duke of Portland. She secretly married, however, the duke of Gloucester, the king's brother. The royal family strongly disapproved of the match and in 1772 forced through Parliament the Royal Marriage Bill, which was intended to prevent further unions of royalty to illegitimate offspring. William Whitley has speculated that Gainsborough's disputes with the Royal Academy during the 1770s may have stemmed from an attempt on the organization's part to suppress his portrait of the duchess, which would have been offensive to the royal family.[4] As Countess Waldegrave, Maria gave birth to

Thomas Gainsborough

Edward and William Tomkinson

ca. 1784

Oil on canvas, 211.8 x 152.1 cm (83⅜ x 59⅞ in.)

This double portrait is an exceptionally charming example of Gainsborough's late work. The two boys, both about eleven years old, were cousins. Edward Tomkinson (1773–1819) is the fair-haired boy who poses elegantly, arms akimbo. He holds his hat indolently and gazes at the viewer. William Tomkinson (b. 1772), the dark-haired boy, sits on a grassy embankment with a book in one hand and a walking stick in the other. His hat is at his side, and he looks to the viewer's left. The many trees in the background and the rustic path suggest that the boys have been strolling through the woods. They are nevertheless dressed with great refinement, mindful of civilized society.

1931.412

Many of Gainsborough's models were people of modest social status and of no great historical consequence. Usually, very little is known about such figures, as is the case here. William was born in Manchester, the elder son of Edward Tomkinson of Bostock and subsequently Hankelow. The family assumed the name of Wettenhall in 1798. In 1797 William married Frances Nesham of Houghton-le-Spring, County Durham, and had five sons. Edward was the eldest son of Henry Tomkinson of Dorfold (1741–1822).[1] The painting descended through the family to Henry James Tollemache, who lent it to an exhibition at the Royal Academy in 1889. The painting subsequently came into the London art market and was eventually purchased by the Tafts.

This large and ambitious work is probably related to a picture that figured in Gainsborough's final dispute with the Royal Academy in 1784. Gainsborough had sent his paintings for exhibition to the Royal Academy that year, but when they were not hung to his satisfaction at the proper height or in proper circumstances, he removed them before the opening and never exhibited there again. A note in Gainsborough's handwriting is preserved in the Royal Academy, which gives a list and summary sketches of the works sent in 1784.[2] Included among the eight sketches is a rough drawing that seems to represent the Taft painting, except that the figures are accompanied by a dog seated at the lower right. This sketch is labeled "Two Boys with a Dog/Master Tomkinsons." Either the dog was later painted out

(although no trace is now visible) or the Taft painting is another version of the portrait sent to the academy in 1784. In style, the Taft picture is in keeping with Gainsborough's feathery late manner.

The postures, background, and accoutrements of the Tomkinson painting are all more or less standard features of Gainsborough's portraits from early in his career. In virtually all his outdoor portraits, except perhaps the portrait of Mr. and Mrs. Robert Andrews (ca. 1748, London, National Gallery), there is a separation between the figures and their settings. The landscapes — no matter how vast, dense, detailed, or elaborate — seem like backdrops rather than surrounding space. The people thereby remain superior to nature, although a tinge of artificiality results.

Gainsborough produced a number of double portraits of children or adolescents. The pictures of the artist's own daughters (1750s, London, National Gallery and Victoria and Albert Museum) are the most intimate and lively. But *Edward and William Tomkinson* ranks in freshness with such delightful images as *Mary and Elizabeth Linley* (ca. 1772, London, Dulwich College). One of the problems of composing a double portrait is relating the sitters to each other and to the viewer. Should the sitters respond to each other in some specific situation, act in unison, or engage the viewer individually? Gainsborough worked out several solutions over the course of his career. The Linley girls appear to study music, the artist's daughters to chase a butterfly as they run toward the viewer, and Mr. and Mrs. Andrews to glance at the viewer as they rest before going shooting. In the Taft painting the viewer is engaged by Edward's gaze alone. The boys share neither thought nor glance. Nonetheless, their unity is maintained by their physical closeness. Like the trees behind them, they seem to be the individual limbs of one plant. The implied narrative of a walk in the country, no matter how artificial, is the other effective means used to draw the figures into a comprehensible situation where group action, individuality, portrait conventions, and the spectator all come into play.

1. The genealogical information has been gathered from notes and letters in the files of the Taft Museum and from Maurice W. Brockwell, "Gainsborough's Portrait of the Tomkinson Boys," *Art in America*, vol. VII (Apr. 1919), pp. 116–21.

2. The note is described in William T. Whitley, *Thomas Gainsborough*, London, 1915, p. 213, and reproduced in Mary Woodall, ed., *The Letters of Thomas Gainsborough*, Greenwich, Conn., 1963, pl. 5, opp. p. 41.

Provenance Henry James Tollemache (1889); [Agnew, London]; [Ludwig Neumann, London]; [Agnew, London, 1906]; [Scott and Fowles, New York, 1907]; Taft collection, Feb. 11, 1907.

Exhibitions London, Royal Academy of Arts, *Deceased Masters of the British School*, 1889 (cat., no. 142); New York, Scott and Fowles, *Paintings from the C. P. Taft Collection*, Nov. 1909 (cat., no. 8); Cincinnati Art Museum, *Thomas Gainsborough*, May 1–31, 1931 (cat., no. 48, pl. 48, detail ill. p. 7).

Literature Walter Armstrong, *Gainsborough and His Place in English Art*, rev. ed., London, 1904, p. 280; Arthur Hoeber, "Some Pictures from the Collection of Mr. and Mrs. Charles P. Taft," vol. XXXIX, *International Studio* (1910), p. LXXI; William T. Whitley, *Thomas Gainsborough*, London, 1915, p. 213; Maurice W. Brockwell, "Gainsborough's Portrait of the Tomkinson Boys," *Art in America*, vol. VII (Apr. 1919), pp. 116–21; Maurice W. Brockwell, *A Catalogue of Paintings in the Collection of Mr. and*

Mrs. Charles P. Taft, New York, 1920, pp. xx, xxvi, no. 1; *Catalogue of the Taft Museum*, Cincinnati, 1939 and 1958, no. 478 (ill.); Ellis K. Waterhouse, "Preliminary Check List of Portraits by Thomas Gainsborough," *The Walpole Society, 1948–50*, vol. XXXIII (1953), p. 106; Ellis K. Waterhouse, *Gainsborough*, London, 1958, no. 667; Ruth Krueger Meyer, "The Taft Collection: The First Ten Years of Its Development," *The Taft Museum: A Cincinnati Legacy*, Cincinnati, 1988, p. 9 (ill.); David Torbet Johnson, "Taft Museum," *Ventura*, vol. IV, no. 16 (June–Aug. 1991), p. 134 (ill.).

1931.412

1931.397

Provenance Francis Bentham, Suffolk; [Scott and Fowles, New York]; Taft collection, Nov. 10, 1903.

Exhibition Cincinnati Art Museum, *Thomas Gainsborough*, May 1–31, 1931 (cat., no. 9, pl. 40).

Literature Walter Armstrong, *Gainsborough and His Place in English Art*, rev. ed., London, 1904, p. 264; Maurice W. Brockwell, *A Catalogue of Paintings in the Collection of Mr. and Mrs. Charles P. Taft*, New York, 1920, no. 63; *Catalogue of the Taft Museum*, Cincinnati, 1939 and 1958, no. 206; Ellis K. Waterhouse, "Preliminary Check List of Portraits by Thomas Gainsborough," *The Walpole Society, 1948–50*, vol. XXXIII (1953), p. 33.

1931.397

Imitator of Thomas Gainsborough

Portrait of an Unknown Man

Late eighteenth or early nineteenth century
Oil on panel, 15.6 x 12.2 cm (6⅛ x 4¾ in.)

Bought by the Tafts as a Gainsborough self-portrait, this miniature bust-length portrait of an unknown man has a checkered history of identification. After the Tafts' purchase, the sitter was identified as Francis, lord de Dunstanville (1757–1835), who appears in a half-length portrait by Gainsborough in the Corcoran Gallery of Art, Washington, D.C.[1] In 1953 Waterhouse doubted this identification and more importantly rejected the portrait as an authentic work by Gainsborough.[2] He also made it clear that this work painted in Gainsborough's style of the 1780s was not by the artist's nephew and pupil, Gainsborough Dupont. When Waterhouse's more complete and definitive catalogue of Gainsborough's paintings was published in 1958, the Taft miniature was not even mentioned.

Although Waterhouse gave no reason for his rejection of the Taft miniature, there is little reason to question his judgment. The uncertain boundaries of the left side of the head and of the shoulder at the right, the squiggling line representing the upper lip, the two-dimensional stock and unconvincing waistcoat lapel, and the heavy handling of light behind the head together make the portrait suspect. These problematic areas cannot all be accounted for by the small size of the picture, in which the artist's large-scale methods of painting might appear brusque.

This work could well be by a copyist of the late eighteenth or early nineteenth century, although no known work by Gainsborough corresponds to it. It could also be a forgery. One need only compare this work to the masterful *Edward and William Tomkinson* from the 1780s to perceive the weaknesses of this miniature portrait.

1. The painting was identified as a self-portrait by the dealer Stevenson Scott in a letter of Oct. 20, 1903 (Taft Museum files). By 1931 it was perceived to be a portrait of lord de Dunstanville, similar to paintings of that sitter in the Corcoran Gallery of Art, Washington, D.C., and in the collection of A. W. Ericson, New York (see *Gainsborough*, exh. cat., Cincinnati Art Museum, 1931, p. 23). According to the Taft Museum files, attempts were made to link this painting to portraits of lord de Dunstanville recorded in the Gainsborough literature, but none of these linkages is convincing.

2. Ellis K. Waterhouse, "Preliminary Check List of Portraits by Thomas Gainsborough," *The Walpole Society, 1948–50*, vol. XXXIII (1953), p. 33.

Joshua Reynolds

Plympton, Devonshire 1723–1792 London

Sir Joshua Reynolds was the third son and seventh child of Samuel Reynolds, an Anglican minister and master of Plympton Grammar School.[1] The artist's mother, Theophila Potter, was the daughter of a clergyman. He displayed early talents in art and in 1740 was apprenticed for four years to the London portrait painter Thomas Hudson. In 1743, before the end of his training, Reynolds established himself as an independent portraitist in Devonshire and London. In 1749 he enlarged his outlook and education by sailing to the Mediterranean with Commodore Augustus Keppel. In 1750 Reynolds arrived in Rome, where he assiduously studied the old masters and the classical remains and painted some Hogarthian caricatures. He returned to England by way of Florence, Bologna, Venice, and Paris in 1752. The portrait of Commodore Keppel (1753–54, London, National Maritime Museum) made Reynolds's name in the London art world; the striding figure of the commodore, dramatized by chiaroscuro and a stormy landscape, attracted praise and important sitters. Reynolds revived the glamor and grandeur of Van Dyck and quickly became the chief portraitist in England, showing greater range and more sophisticated allusion and wit than such rivals as Allan Ramsay.

Although he was not well received at court, Reynolds maintained a grand air in London society with a lavish house and studio in Leicester Fields (from 1760), opulent carriages, liveried servants, and influential friends. He associated with literary, theatrical, and political figures, rather than with artists. He began to publish his own writings on art in Dr. Samuel Johnson's *Idler* in 1759. With Johnson in 1764 he founded The Club for intellectual discussions and comradeship. Reynolds's devotion to professional associations and the elevation of the artist's position in society had its fullest manifestation in 1768 with the founding of the Royal Academy. He was elected its first president and from 1769 until 1790 delivered yearly discourses on art. These essays were collected and published and came to be regarded as the most reputable art theory in both Britain and America. Reynolds advocated idealization, generalization, history painting, and a worshipful attitude toward the great masters of the High Renaissance and baroque periods. Although Reynolds often made pictorial alldsions to the style and masterpieces of Guercino, Reni, the Carracci, Rembrandt, Raphael, Correggio, and Michelangelo, he only rarely strayed beyond the confines of portraiture. He dignified that genre by placing his sitters amid various old-master motifs, historical events, classical subjects, and literary conceits. His great production of varied portraits was made possible by a large number of assistants.

Reynolds traveled to Paris in 1768 and 1771. He toured the Lowlands in 1781 and 1785. He finally achieved royal recognition in 1784, when he became Painter in Ordinary to the King. He was elected alderman of the Borough of Plympton in 1772 and mayor of Plympton in 1783, when he was also awarded a doctorate of civil law by Oxford University. Reynolds's eyesight began to fail during the 1780s. He resigned as president of the Royal Academy in 1790. He was almost totally blind when he died of a liver tumor in 1792. Reynolds created some of the finest portrayals of how the English wanted to look. He elevated the profession and ambition of British artists and codified a tradition of art theory that was honored far into the nineteenth century.

1. On Reynolds, see Edmond Malone, ed., *The Works of Sir Joshua Reynolds,* 2 vols., London, 1797; James Northcote, *The Life of Sir Joshua Reynolds,* 2 vols., London, 1818; Charles R. Leslie and Tom Taylor, *The Life and Times of Sir Joshua Reynolds,* 2 vols., London, 1865; Algernon Graves and William V. Cronin, *A History of the Works of Sir Joshua Reynolds,* 4 vols., London, 1899–1901; Ellis K. Waterhouse, *Reynolds,* London, 1941; Ellis K. Waterhouse, "Reynolds' 'Sitter Book' for 1755," *The Walpole Society, 1966–68,* vol. XLI (1968), pp. 112–64; Malcolm Cormack, "The Ledgers of Sir Joshua Reynolds," *The Walpole Society, 1968–69,* vol. XLII (1970), pp. 105–69; Ellis K. Waterhouse, *Reynolds,* London, 1973; Nicholas Penny, ed., *Reynolds,* exh. cat., Royal Academy of Arts, London, 1986.

1931.491

Joshua Reynolds

Mrs. John Weyland and Her Son John

1776
Oil on canvas, 142.2 x 114 cm (56 x 44⅞ in.)

Mrs. Weyland sits informally on a stair or platform and holds a lively one-year-old boy on her knee. Both figures smile and gaze out at the viewer. A country landscape is seen through the window at the upper left, a curtain hangs at the right, and a pug stretches out at the feet of the pair. Mother and son crouch energetically with arms raised. Mrs. Weyland is dressed in a rich satin gown, and her blond son wears only a brief shift. Reynolds mentioned this picture in his notebook of 1775: "Lord Henry and Lady Charlotte Spencer. First *olio e poi colori con cera senza olio.* Mrs. Weyland *ditto*" (First "oil and then colors with wax without oil").[1] In March 1776 he recorded in his ledger a second payment of £105 for this painting.[2] The nubby paint texture, blond color, stable compositional triangle, and modestly darkened surroundings of *Mrs. Weyland and Her Son* are perfectly representative of Reynolds's style of the 1770s.

Elizabeth Johanna Nourse (d. 1822) was the daughter and coheiress of John Nourse of Woodeaton, Oxfordshire. She married John Weyland (1744–1825) of Woodrising, Norfolk, and Woodeaton, Oxfordshire, in 1772. Their son John, who appears in the painting, was born on December 4, 1774. The boy eventually became a lawyer and member of Parliament (1830–32) for Hindon and Wiltshire. He studied the English Poor Laws, and among his publications is *A Short Enquiry into the Policy, Humanity, and Effect of the Poor Laws* (London, 1807). He advocated less education and more hard work for the poor as a necessary incentive to industry. He married Elizabeth Keene of Richmond in 1799 and died without issue on May 8, 1854.[3]

Reynolds was a great pioneer in the portrayal of children, and he painted them with their mothers on numerous occasions. In his works children such as John Weyland squirm and bounce with a freedom and delight rare in earlier art. In paintings such as *Master Crewe as Henry VIII* (1776, private collection) and *The Strawberry Girl* (1773, London, Wallace Collection), Reynolds, like his Continental contemporaries Jean-Baptiste Greuze, François Boucher, and Carle van Loo, created sentimental images that are among the first pictures of "cute" children. The purported vessels of innocence became soft and cuddly and naughty. Although Reynolds often included allusions to the old masters and wittily mined the history of art for meaningful visual quotations, his mothers and children are not mere revisions of Renaissance and baroque madonnas. The intimacy, playfulness, and informality of many of these paintings reflect current issues concerning proper maternal affection, breast-feeding, the early education of children, and "natural" family relations.[4] Reynolds's portraits also reveal the late-eighteenth-century perception of children as interesting in their own right, not just as protoadults.

Mrs. Weyland and her son number among Reynolds's more informal pairs. Their position near the floor and their eye-level engagement with the viewer differentiate them from the standing pyramidal dignity of *The Countess of Spencer and Her Daughter* (1760–61, Althorp, earl Spencer). In the latter picture the figures in tender embrace form a figural grouping that is grave and towering. *Mrs. Weyland and Her Son* is also far different from *The Duchess of Devonshire and Her Daughter* (ca. 1786, Chatsworth), which displays lively gestures but is a magnificent baroque ensemble poised high above the spectator. Perhaps the quieter and more intimate *Duchess of Marlborough and Her Daughter* (1765, Blenheim Palace, duke of Marlborough) is most similar to the Taft painting. Even there, though, the mother is more decorous as she sits on a chair, and the setting is ennobled by a pair of stately columns that echo those in Titian's *Pesaro Madonna*.

1. Charles R. Leslie and Tom Taylor, *The Life and Times of Sir Joshua Reynolds*, vol. II, London, 1865, p. 172. Reynolds habitually noted his painting recipes and techniques in Italian, either to keep his experimental practices secret from his ordinary assistants or to give instruction to his chief studio assistant, Giuseppe Marchi, an Italian, whom Reynolds first had employed during the 1750s. See M. Kirby Talley, Jr., "Sir Joshua Reynolds's Practice and Studio," in Nicholas Penny, ed., *Reynolds*, exh. cat., Royal Academy of Arts, London, 1986, p. 57.

2. Malcolm Cormack, "The Ledgers of Sir Joshua Reynolds," *The Walpole Society, 1968–70*, vol. XLII (1970), p. 166.

3. On John Weyland (1794–1854), see the *Dictionary of National Biography*.

4. On Reynolds's international connections and portrayal of children, see Robert Rosenblum, "Reynolds in an International Milieu," in Penny, ed., pp. 43–54.

Provenance Mark Ulick Weyland; [Lawrie and Co., London, 1903]; [Scott and Fowles, New York]; Taft collection, Oct. 22, 1904.

Exhibitions New York, Scott and Fowles, *Paintings in the C. P. Taft Collection*, Nov. 1909 (cat., no. 6); Columbus Gallery of Fine Arts, Ohio, *Sir Joshua Reynolds and His American Contemporaries*, Jan. 30–Mar. 2, 1958 (cat., no. 19).

Literature Charles R. Leslie and Tom Taylor, *The Life and Times of Sir Joshua Reynolds*, vol. II, London, 1865, pp. 172, 174; Walter Armstrong, *Sir Joshua Reynolds*, New York and London, 1905, p. 120; William Walton, "Exhibition in New York of Paintings from the Collection of Mr. and Mrs. Charles P. Taft," *Burlington Magazine*, vol. XVI (1910), p. 268; *Connoisseur* (1913), p. 153 (ill.); Maurice W. Brockwell, "Sir Joshua Reynolds's Portrait of Mrs. Weyland and Her Eldest Son," *Art in America*, vol. VII (Feb. 1919), pp. 63–69; Maurice W. Brockwell, *A Catalogue of Paintings in the Collection of Mr. and Mrs. Charles P. Taft*, New York, 1920, p. xix, no. 34; *Catalogue of the Taft Museum*, Cincinnati, 1939 and 1958, no. 231; Ellis K. Waterhouse, *Reynolds*, London, 1941, p. 181; Malcolm Cormack, "The Ledgers of Sir Joshua Reynolds," *The Walpole Society, 1968–70*, vol. XLII (1970), p. 166; Ruth Krueger Meyer, "The Taft Collection: The First Ten Years of Its Development," *The Taft Museum: A Cincinnati Legacy*, Cincinnati, 1988, p. 12 (ill.).

1931.491

&

Joshua Reynolds

Mrs. Stephen Payne-Gallwey (or Payne-Gallway) and Her Son Charles

1779
Oil on canvas, 76.2 x 63.5 cm (30 x 25 in.)

In this three-quarter-length portrait, Mrs. Payne-Gallwey is shown in profile facing left. Looking forward, she carries on her back a one- or two-year-old boy. The thrust of her figure from lower right to upper left suggests a walking motion and also ex-

1962.2

presses the weight of the child. Her dress is pink, and a white lace scarf is tied around her hair and under her chin. Her son Charles wears a straw hat. The mother holds her son's wrist with one hand extended across her breast. Her left hand apparently is placed behind her back to support the boy who clings to her with determination. A patch of light filtering through foliage can be seen in the left distance, but most of the picture space is in bituminous darkness.

Although darkening and deterioration of the surface have obscured many features, the areas of bright light still glow, and the fashionable beauty of Mrs. Payne-Gallwey is evident. Her long profile with hair piled high is similar to Reynolds's depictions of such contemporary beauties as Mrs. Lloyd (1776, private collection) and Lady Worsley (1780, earl of Harewood collection). The carefully calculated movement of Mrs. Payne-Gallwey is also similar to other portraits by Reynolds of women walking (e.g., *Mrs. Hale as Euphrosyne*, 1786, earl of Harewood collection; and *Mary, Countess of Bute*, ca. 1785, private collection). But the Taft portrait is unusual in implying ambulation in a less-than-full-length figure.

Although Reynolds painted numerous groupings of mothers with children in a great variety of postures and activities, the relationship portrayed here is particularly original. The work was titled *Pick-a-Back* in the nineteenth century. The piggyback ride is not seen elsewhere, even in such lively portraits by Reynolds as that of Lady Cockburn (1774, London, National Gallery), in which three sons squirm and climb about their seated mother. The intimate and playful action of Mrs. Payne-Gallwey suggests not only great affection but also the parental role as servant to the young and perhaps even an enthusiasm for the "natural" carrying techniques of Native Americans who were much admired in eighteenth-century England. Rembrandt had etched a beggar woman with a child on her back, but the low social position of Rembrandt's figures makes them an unlikely source of inspiration here, even though Reynolds frequently borrowed from the great Dutch master. The representation of a parent entering into the world of children's play, rather than the child taking on the responsibilities of the adult world, was an innovation of the eighteenth century that would be further elaborated during the next century. J.-A.-D. Ingres's depiction of Henry IV of France on all fours giving horseback rides to his children (1817, Paris, Petit Palais) is one later example of this implied homage to childhood.

Born in 1758, Philadelphia Payne-Gallwey apparently was the daughter of James Delancey, a lieutenant-governor of New York. In some accounts, however, she is identified as the daughter of Oliver de Lancey of New York, a supporter of the crown who lost his fortune in the American Revolution.[1] Her husband, Stephan Payne of Tofts Hall, Norfolk, assumed his mother's maiden name, Gallwey (or Gallway), by an act of Parliament in 1762. Mrs. Payne-Gallwey died in 1785. Mr. Payne-Gallwey appears at the left in Reynolds's first group portrait of the Dilettanti Society (1779, London, Society of Dilettanti). He is shown drinking wine amid these club men of antiquarian and convivial pursuits. He sat for Reynolds in 1777. His wife and son sat for the Taft picture in 1778, and the artist was paid seventy

pounds for it in 1779, the year the work was exhibited at the Royal Academy.[2] Charles Payne-Gallwey is said to have died in 1819.[3] The Taft painting was engraved by J. R. Smith in 1780 and by S. W. Reynolds about 1820.

1. She is said to be related to Lieutenant-Governor Delancey in William Roberts, "Mr. J. Pierpont Morgan's Pictures: The Early English School," *Connoisseur*, vol. XVI (Oct. 1906), p. 68. Her relation to Oliver de Lancey is noted in Thomas Humphry Ward and William Roberts, *Pictures in the Collection of J. Pierpont Morgan, Princes Gate and Dover House*, London, 1907, n.p.

2. On the Payne-Gallweys' sittings and payments, see Malcolm Cormack, "The Ledgers of Sir Joshua Reynolds," *The Walpole Society, 1968–70*, vol. XLII (1970), p. 153; Algernon Graves and William V. Cronin, *A History of the Works of Sir Joshua Reynolds*, London, 1899–1901, vol. I, pp. 343–44; Nicholas Penny, ed., *Reynolds*, exh. cat., Royal Academy of Arts, London, 1986, no. 109.

3. Ellis K. Waterhouse, *Reynolds*, London, 1941, p. 206.

Provenance Lord Monson (later lord Oxenbridge, by 1862), Gatton Park (sale, Christie's, London, May 22, 1888, no. 18); [Agnew, London]; J. P. Morgan, New York (by 1906); [Knoedler, New York]; Dr. and Mrs. William T. Semple, Cincinnati (Jan. 12, 1944); Louise Taft Semple bequest, 1962.

Exhibitions London, Royal Academy of Arts, 1779 (cat., no. 253); London, *International Exhibition*, 1862 (cat., no. 63); London, Royal Academy of Arts, *Exhibition of Works by Old Masters*, 1886 (cat., no. 41); London, Royal Academy of Arts, *Exhibition of Works by Old Masters*, 1895 (cat., no. 31); Paris, *Exposition Universelle*, British Pavilion, 1900 (cat., no. 51); London, Whitechapel Art Gallery, 1901 (cat., no. 261); Birmingham Museum and Art Gallery, *Loan Collection of Portraits*, 1903 (cat., no. 15 [ill.]); Berlin, Die Königliche Akademie der Künste, *Exhibition of English Old Masters*, 1908 (cat., no. 65 [ill.]); London, Agnew Galleries, Nov.–Dec. 1913 (cat., no. 19).

Literature *Engravings from the Works of Sir Joshua Reynolds*, London, ca. 1821, no. 87; William Cotton, *Sir Joshua Reynolds and His Works*, London, 1856, p. 29; Charles R. Leslie and Tom Taylor, *The Life and Times of Sir Joshua Reynolds*, vol. II, London, 1865, p. 224; *Engravings from the Works of Sir Joshua Reynolds*, vol. IV, London, 1865, no. 31; Frederic G. Stephens, *English Children as Painted by Sir Joshua Reynolds*, London, 1867, pp. 52–54, ill. opp. p. 54; F. S. Pulling, *Sir Joshua Reynolds*, London, 1886, p. 65; Algernon Graves and William V. Cronin, *A History of the Works of Sir Joshua Reynolds*, vol. I, London, 1899–1901, pp. 343–44; Ronald S. Gower, *Sir Joshua Reynolds: His Life and Art*, London, 1902, p. 86; Walter Armstrong, *Sir Joshua Reynolds*, London, 1905, p. 129; William Roberts, "Mr. J. Pierpont Morgan's Pictures: The Early English School," *Connoisseur* (Oct. 1906), pp. 67–68; John Lime, *Sir Joshua Reynolds*, London, 1906, p. 165; Thomas Humphry Ward and William Roberts, *Pictures in the Collection of J. Pierpont Morgan, Princes Gate and Dover House*, London, 1907, n.p.; R. H. Wilenski, *English Painting*, Boston and New York, 1933, pl. 58 opp. p. 123; Ellis K. Waterhouse, *Reynolds*, London, 1941, p. 206; Malcolm Cormack, "The Ledgers of Sir Joshua Reynolds," *The Walpole Society, 1968–70*, vol. XLII (1970), p. 153.

1962.2

Joshua Reynolds

Mrs. Mary Robinson

ca. 1784
Oil on panel, 75.9 x 62.5 cm (29⅞ x 24⅝ in.)

Mary Robinson was an actress, poet, and mistress of the Prince of Wales. She is portrayed half length and full face. Her hands

1931.440

Mary Robinson, née Darby (1758–1800), was born in Bristol, the daughter of an impoverished whaling captain. Her father became involved in fishery projects in America and abandoned the family for a long period. Mary attended numerous schools in Bristol and London until she was taken up by David Garrick and trained for the theater. In 1774 she married a clerk, Thomas Robinson. During the succeeding period, unattended by her husband, she received the attentions of various London rakes. Along with her husband, she was imprisoned for debt in 1775 and wrote verses while in jail. In 1776 she made her stage debut as Juliet and followed this success with numerous other parts. In 1778, while playing Perdita in *A Winter's Tale,* she attracted the attention of the Prince of Wales (later George IV) and eventually became his mistress. "Perdita," as she came to be known, had her last stage appearance in 1780. Her affair with the prince did not last long. She subsequently became the mistress of both the political leader Charles James Fox (who provided her with a five-hundred-pound yearly pension) and Colonel Banastre Tarleton, an English officer in the American Revolution. While still attached to Tarleton, she contracted an illness that left her lower limbs paralyzed. Thereafter, she devoted herself exclusively to literature. She died at Englefield Cottage, Surrey, in 1800, poor and crippled, and was survived by her daughter, Maria, or Mary, Elizabeth.

Among Mrs. Robinson's writings are two volumes of poems published in 1775, two more in 1791, *Angelina* (a novel of 1796), *A False Friend* (a domestic story of 1799), and *Lyrical Tales* of 1800. She also published *Effusions of Love* (n.d.), which she said were her correspondence with the Prince of Wales. Among her plays is *Nobody,* a controversial satire about women gamblers, which was produced in 1794. Her memoirs and poems were collected and published by her daughter in 1801 and 1806, respectively.[3]

1. Charles R. Leslie and Tom Taylor, *The Life and Times of Sir Joshua Reynolds,* vol. II, London, 1865, pp. 345, 361, 468; see also Nicholas Penny, ed., *Reynolds,* exh. cat., Royal Academy of Arts, London, 1986, no. 128; and J. Ingamells, *Wallace Collection: Catalogue of Pictures, I: British, German, Italian, and Spanish,* London, 1985, p. 45.

2. On the three portraits, see note 1. Ellis K. Waterhouse, *Reynolds,* London, 1941, p. 76, associates the Taft picture with the sittings of 1784 but states that the Wallace portrait could also have been the work of that year.

3. On Mary Robinson, see the *Dictionary of National Biography.*

Provenance Marchioness of Thomond, Reynolds's niece (1821); lord Wharncliffe (1835); John Smith (1841); H. A. J. Munro (1860); Mrs. Octavius E. Coope (1888; sale, Christie's, London, May 6, 1910, no. 54); [Scott and Fowles, New York]; Taft collection, Oct. 31, 1912.

Exhibitions London, British Institution, 1852 (cat., no. 167); London, Grosvenor Gallery, 1888 (cat., no. 81); New York, Knoedler Galleries, *Loan Exhibition to Honor Queen Elizabeth II,* May 4–23, 1953; Columbus Gallery of Fine Arts, Ohio, *Sir Joshua Reynolds and His American Contemporaries,* Jan. 30–Mar. 2, 1958 (cat., no. 27).

Literature Charles R. Leslie and Tom Taylor, *The Life and Times of Sir Joshua Reynolds,* vol. II, London, 1865, pp. 179, 345–46, 361, 468; Maurice W. Brockwell, *A Catalogue of Paintings in the Collection of Mr. and Mrs. Charles P. Taft,* New York, 1920, pp. xix, xxviii, no. 35; *Catalogue of the Taft Museum,* Cincinnati, 1939 and 1958, no. 205; Ellis K. Waterhouse, *Reynolds,* London, 1941, p. 76.

1931.440

are not visible. She wears a broad-brimmed, plumed hat, a ribbon around her neck, and a dark gown with a white fichu. A windswept landscape with the suggestion of a tree appears at the left, and a curtain occupies the remainder of the background. The rich and fluent paint handling, typical of Reynolds's style of the 1780s, animates this static frontal figure.

Although this portrait is primarily devoted to characterizing Mrs. Robinson as a sweet personality, charmingly petite within the pictorial space, Reynolds's mastery of the formal elements of picture making is also evident. The sitter's plumes, hair, and bodice form a carefully calculated spiral of active shapes circulating around the face. The head acts as the calm center of a gently swirling mass and is given three-dimensional structure by such subtle devices as the neck ribbon, which disappears behind the projecting chin.

In 1782 Mrs. Robinson had fourteen appointments with Reynolds, and in 1784 she sat for him again.[1] He eventually produced at least three portraits of this talented and beautiful woman: the Taft picture, a painting at Waddesdon Manor, Buckinghamshire; and a portrait in the Wallace Collection, London. All three are half-length figures. In the Waddesdon picture, Mrs. Robinson folds her hands at the waist and turns her head to three-quarter view; she wears a low-cut gown and the same hat as in the Taft painting. The Wallace picture presents the sitter in profile without a hat and with a melancholy expression. When engraved in 1787, the Wallace portrait was titled *Contemplation.* The Waddesdon Manor painting appears to be the most ambitious of the three and was probably the portrait of Mrs. Robinson exhibited at the Royal Academy in 1782 (no. 22).[2]

John Hoppner

London 1758–1810 London

John Hoppner was born in Whitechapel of German parents. His father was a surgeon in the retinue of King George II. His mother is said to have been a lady-in-waiting at the court of George III, and the king has often been suspected as Hoppner's actual father.[1] This story of royal paternity is questionable, although the artist himself never discouraged the rumor. His career prospered because of it, and he received exceptional help from the king. At an early age Hoppner was a chorister in the royal chapel, and George III gave him an allowance to study art. In 1775 he entered the Royal Academy schools, where he won the silver medal for life drawing in 1778 and the gold medal for painting in 1782. Hoppner first exhibited at the Royal Academy in 1780. He was appointed Portrait Painter to the Prince of Wales in 1789 and became an associate of the Royal Academy in 1792 and full academician in 1795. In 1782 he married Phoebe Wright, the youngest daughter of Mrs. Patience Wright, an American sculptor. From 1784 until his death he lived and worked at 18 Charles Street, St. James Square.

The patronage of the Prince of Wales and notables of the Whig party assured Hoppner's financial security and fashionable reputation. His chief rival, Sir Thomas Lawrence, however, was appointed Painter to the King in 1792, and modern critics have judged Lawrence far superior in bravura, elegance, and originality. Many of Hoppner's portraits closely follow those of Sir Joshua Reynolds, but in Hoppner's hands the Venetian pigment and noble demeanor become prosaic.

At his best, Hoppner added a sunny and unpretentious charm to the established formulas of eighteenth-century English portraiture. He would occasionally exaggerate the elongation and buttery paint of Lawrence, and such works are fascinating studies of distortion and of the mannerist opulence of Regency taste. Hoppner painted several mythological, historical, and Shakespearean subjects during the 1780s but devoted the rest of his career exclusively to portraiture, the only lucrative field of art in England. Like many other English painters, he visited Paris during the Peace of Amiens in 1802, but his style remained uninspired by modern foreign influences. Hoppner had some literary talent, writing scathing criticisms of his fellow academicians and in 1805 publishing a volume of poems, *Oriental Tales Translated into English Verse.*

1. On Hoppner, see H. P. K. Skipton, *John Hoppner,* London, 1905; Frank Rutter, ed., *Essays on Art by John Hoppner,* London, 1908; William McKay and William Roberts, *John Hoppner, R.A.,* London, 1909; William McKay and William Roberts, *Supplement and Index to "John Hoppner, R.A.,"* London, 1914.

1931.403

John Hoppner

Catherine Horneck Bunbury

ca. 1790
Oil on canvas, 76.2 x 63.8 cm (30 x 25⅛ in.)

Mrs. Bunbury is placed asymmetrically on the canvas, suggesting movement, as if the figure were walking across the pictorial space. Her cocked head adds further animation. Hoppner's chunky strokes of paint, squarish volumes, and coyly smiling figure are indebted to some of Reynolds's stylistic features of the 1770s. And, like Reynolds, on many occasions Hoppner gave his young women not only lively movement but also a hint of monumentality by setting them against a broad sky.

The subject of this painting has long been misidentified as Mrs. Mary Horneck Gwyn. The young woman in the mob cap portrayed here is actually Mrs. Gwyn's sister, Catherine Horneck Bunbury.[1] Hoppner painted both women, and engravings by John Young of Hoppner's two portraits were published as a pair in 1791. The engraved portrait of Catherine, labeled *Mrs. Bunbury,* clearly represents the Taft picture in reverse so that the pair of women would face each other. Catherine appears older in the engraving than in the Taft picture, and the latter may have been rejuvenated by some overpainting. Executed at the same time, Hoppner's portraits of the Horneck sisters also were exhibited as a pair at the Royal Academy in 1790.

Catherine Horneck (ca. 1754–1799) was the daughter of Kane William Horneck, a captain of engineers in the British Army, who resigned his post in Antigua in 1751 to become lieutenant-colonel in the Army of Sicily. Her mother, Hannah Mangles, married Horneck about 1749. The Horneck daughters, Catherine and Mary, became celebrated beauties in London, frequenting literary and artistic circles. They were especially close to Oliver Goldsmith, who traveled on the Continent with the Horneck family in 1770 and affectionately referred to Catherine as "Little Comedy" in several light verses.[2] Catherine married Henry Bunbury of Barton in 1771. Sir Joshua Reynolds was another good friend of the Hornecks and portrayed the daughters in a number of canvases. Catherine's sister-in-law appears in one of Reynolds's most famous works, *Lady Sarah Bunbury Sacrificing to the Graces* (1765, The Art Institute of Chicago). Apparently, Catherine Bunbury was more than an ordinary client to Hoppner as well, for she became the godmother of his child, Helen Clarence Hoppner, in 1791.

Although the apparent age of the sitter would suggest a date considerably earlier than 1790, the publication of the engraving in that year supports a similar date for the painting.

1. The misidentification was made by Maurice Brockwell in his catalogue of the Taft collection (1920); the catalogue raisonné of Hoppner's works by William McKay and William Roberts fails to mention the portrait of Mrs. Bunbury but does note the portrait of Mrs. Gwyn (*John Hoppner, R.A.,* London, 1909, p. 114). H. P. K. Skipton, *John Hoppner,* London, 1905, identified the Taft picture correctly (pp. 52–54), and the same author reproduced John Young's engravings of Hoppner's portraits of Catherine and Mary in "The Hornecks," *Connoisseur,* vol. XXVIII (1910), pp. 3–13. The correct identification of the Taft portrait was made most recently by John Human Wilson (letter to Taft Museum, 1986), and a letter in the Taft Museum files indicates that the dealers Scott and Fowles recognized in 1907 that the Hoppner painting represented Catherine rather than Mary.

2. On the Horneck family's friendship with Goldsmith, see Skipton 1910 and Arthur Lytton Sells, *Oliver Goldsmith: His Life and Works,* London, 1974.

Provenance Henry G. Marquand (1899, sale, Mendelssohn Hall, New York, Jan. 23, 1903, no. 36 [ill.]); [Seligmann, New York]; Taft collection, Jan. 23, 1903.

Exhibition London, Royal Academy of Arts, 1790 (cat., no. 190).

Literature H. P. K. Skipton, *John Hoppner,* London, 1905, pp. 32, 52–54; William McKay and William Roberts, *John Hoppner, R.A.,* London, 1909, p. 114; H. P. K. Skipton, "The Hornecks," *Connoisseur,* vol. XXVIII (1910), pp. 3–13; Maurice W. Brockwell, *A Catalogue of Paintings in the Collection of Mr. and Mrs. Charles P. Taft,* New York, 1920, p. xxii, no. 25; *Catalogue of the Taft Museum,* Cincinnati, 1939 and 1958, no. 203 (ill. in 1939 ed.).

1931.403

🐚

John Hoppner

Miss Agnes Coussmaker

ca. 1788
Oil on canvas, 76 x 63.5 cm (30 x 25 in.)

Miss Agnes Coussmaker is shown half length, standing somewhat rigidly before a landscape. She gazes at the viewer intently. Her hair and waist are bound with blue ribbons. Her slightly awkward posture gives her an air of innocence, which may, however, be unintentional. Hoppner's figures almost never have the grace, sophistication, or elegance evident in Sir Joshua

1931.405

Reynolds's portraits. Nevertheless, Reynolds inspired Hoppner on numerous occasions, and the rapid, animated brushstrokes of the Taft picture suggest that Hoppner looked closely at Reynolds's style of the 1780s.

The portrait of Miss Coussmaker may be dated about 1788 when the sitter was twenty years old. Agnes Katherine Coussmaker was the third daughter of John Coussmaker of Westwood, Guildford. The family was of Flemish descent and came to England in the seventeenth century. Agnes's mother, Elizabeth, was the daughter of William Newton of Baconthorpe, Norfolk. Miss Coussmaker married the Reverend W. K. Heath; she died in 1824. One of Reynolds's most lavish full-length portraits, dating from 1782, depicts another member of the family, Colonel George Kein Hayward Coussmaker (New York, The Metropolitan Museum of Art).[1]

1. Katharine Baetjer, *European Paintings in the Metropolitan Museum of Art,* vol. 1, New York, 1980, p. 154.

Provenance [Agnew, London, 1905]; [Scott and Fowles, New York]; Taft collection, Feb. 8, 1906.

Exhibitions London, Agnew, 1905 (cat., no. 16); New York, Scott and Fowles, *Paintings from the C. P. Taft Collection,* Nov. 1909 (cat., no. 9).

Literature William McKay and William Roberts, *John Hoppner, R.A.,* London, 1909, pp. 58, 332 (ill. opp. p. 58); *Burlington Magazine,* vol. XVI (1910), p. 368; *International Studio,* vol. XXXIX (1910), p. lxxiv; Maurice W. Brockwell, *A Catalogue of Paintings in the Collection of Mr. and Mrs. Charles P. Taft,* New York, 1920, pp. xxi, xxii, no. 22; *Catalogue of the Taft Museum,* Cincinnati, 1939 and 1958, no. 462; Ruth Krueger Meyer, "The Taft Collection: The First Ten Years of Its Development," *The Taft Museum: A Cincinnati Legacy,* Cincinnati, 1988, p. 9 (ill.).

1931.405

1931.470

John Hoppner

Mrs. Parkyns

1794
Oil on canvas, 76.2 x 63.8 cm (30 x 25⅛ in.)

Mrs. Parkyns, heavyset and forthright, is portrayed wearing a low-cut gown, necklace, shawl, and feathered hat. She holds a glove in her left hand. She stands beneath a large tree, and a wooded landscape appears behind her to the left. The Rubensian fullness, jewelry, and relatively rich costume are typical of a trend in fashion toward the end of the eighteenth century. The Taft painting was exhibited at the Royal Academy in 1794 and was engraved by Charles Wilkin in 1795. During the early years of the nineteenth century, both Hoppner and his rival Thomas Lawrence portrayed women wearing numerous bracelets, rings, necklaces, extravagant hats, and a multiplicity of bright garments. But Hoppner's painting of Mrs. Parkyns only hints at this later development in taste.

Elizabeth Anne James was the daughter of Sir William James, baronet of Eltham Park, Kent. In 1783 she married Thomas Boothby Parkyns, who became first baron Rancliffe in 1795. Lady Rancliffe died in 1797, leaving three children. She was godmother to Henry Parkyns Hoppner, the artist's son.

According to McKay and Roberts, a portrait of Mrs. Parkyns by Hoppner, showing the sitter in a pink dress, was sold in 1900. Also, a full-size copy of the Taft picture and a painting of Mr. Parkyns by Hoppner were copied by R. S. Spanton for Sir Horace

Rumbold, ambassador to Vienna and the Parkyns' grandson.[1] In 1920 Brockwell noted that a portrait of Mrs. Parkyns was in the Willys collection, Toledo, Ohio.[2]

1. William McKay and William Roberts, *John Hoppner, R.A.,* London, 1909, pp. 198–99, 337.
2. Maurice W. Brockwell, *A Catalogue of Paintings in the Collection of Mr. and Mrs. Charles P. Taft,* New York, 1920, pp. 133–40.

Provenance Miss Hawkesley, Bunny Park (the Parkyns family seat), Nottinghamshire (sale, Christie's, London, Feb. 24, 1910, no. 900); [Scott and Fowles, New York]; Taft collection, 1913.

Exhibitions London, Royal Academy of Arts, 1794 (cat., no. 155); London, British Institution, 1817 (cat., no. 43); New York, Scott and Fowles, 1913 (cat., no. 8).

Literature William McKay and William Roberts, *John Hoppner, R.A.,* London, 1909, pp. 198–99, 337; *Connoisseur,* vol. xxxvi (1913), ill. p. 125; Maurice W. Brockwell, *A Catalogue of Paintings in the Collection of Mr. and Mrs. Charles P. Taft,* New York, 1920, p. xxi, no. 36; *Catalogue of the Taft Museum,* Cincinnati, 1939 and 1958, no. 207.

1931.470

George Romney
Beckside, near Dalton-in-Furness, Lancashire 1734–1802
Kendal, Lancashire

George Romney was the second son of a Lancashire cabinet-maker, farmer, and builder.[1] He left the local school at the age of eleven to assist his father in the village of Upper Crocken. In 1755 he was apprenticed to Christopher Steele, an itinerant portrait painter with French training. Romney married his land-lady's daughter, Mary Abbott, in 1756 but joined Steele in York and Lancaster, leaving his wife in Kendal. She remained there with their children, separated from her husband until his last years.

Romney went into business on his own in 1757, painting provincial portraits and shop signs until moving to London in 1762. There, he won several competitions in history painting at the Society of Arts. In 1764 he traveled to Paris, where he was entertained by Joseph Vernet. After his return to London, his career as a portraitist gradually began to flourish, but Romney left England again in 1773 to travel to Rome with Ozias Humphries, the miniaturist. There, Romney copied works by Raphael and Michelangelo and studied ancient art. He visited Bologna, Parma, Venice, and Paris on his return trip to London in 1775.

With the assistance of several well-connected literary friends, especially William Hayley, Romney was able to regain a foothold in the London portrait market and soon attracted some of the most prestigious sitters. These same friends also encouraged the artist to attempt grandiose history paintings. Most of Romney's ambitious subject pictures, however, remained in the form of sketches and drawings.

As a portrait painter, Romney became a keen rival of Sir Joshua Reynolds during the 1770s; he never exhibited at the Royal Academy, where Reynolds reigned. Romney's portraits tend to be classically stable images with unemotional faces, weighty sculptural bodies, marblelike whiteness of tone, and dignified simplicity. Rhythmic curvilinear arrangements of limbs and draperies, especially in group portraits, enliven many of the portraits. Romney sought inspiration for his severe and spatially shallow likenesses in the relief sculpture of the ancients and in the paintings of the Italian High Renaissance. Like Reynolds, but with less animation, he occasionally attempted to aggrandize his sitters by painting them in the guise of gods or literary characters. With Reynolds and Gainsborough, Romney is considered one of the great English portraitists of the eighteenth century.

In 1782 Romney met Emma Hart, then the mistress of Charles Greville and later to become Lady Hamilton in 1791. During the years before she left England for Italy in 1786, Romney painted dozens of pictures of her. In these thematic portraits she appears in the roles of peasant girl, literary character, virtue, and saint. She obviously represented Romney's feminine ideal.

Although Romney was a very successful portrait painter with a studio on Cavendish Square, his desire to paint more elevated subjects increased during the 1790s, when he produced hundreds of drawings for such projects in the furiously dramatic manner of Henry Fuseli. Romney prepared grandiose pictures for Boydell's Shakespeare Gallery, a commercial venture financed by entrance fees to encourage high-minded art and celebrate national literature and patronage. Like many others during the 1790s, Romney began planning a Milton gallery along similar lines.

Romney was described by his contemporaries as nervous, shy, and suspicious. He suffered periods of depression, fitfulness, and megalomania that became more marked during the last decade of the century. He visited Paris in 1790, the Isle of Wight in 1794, and Stonehenge in 1796 and toured the north of England in 1798. He moved to Hampstead in 1797 and bought an estate at Kendal in 1799. During this time he concocted extravagant enterprises and conceived fantastic new subjects for pictures. He eventually returned to his wife at Kendal, succumbed to insanity, and died in 1802.

1. On Romney, see William Hayley, *The Life of George Romney,* Chichester, 1809; John Romney, *Memoirs of the Life and Works of George Romney,* London, 1830; Ronald S. Gower, *George Romney,* London, 1904; Humphrey Ward and William Roberts, *Romney: A Biographical and Critical Essay with a Catalogue of His Works,* 2 vols., London, 1904; Patricia Milne-Henderson, *The Drawings of George Romney,* exh. cat., Smith College Museum of Art, Northhampton, Mass., 1962; Gerhard Charles Rump, *George Romney,* 2 vols., Hildesheim and New York, 1974; Patricia Jaffe, *Drawings by George Romney from the Fitzwilliam Museum,* exh. cat., Fitzwilliam Museum, Cambridge, 1977.

George Romney

Mrs. John Johnson

ca. 1786
Oil on canvas, 75.6 x 63.5 cm (29¾ x 25 in.)

Mrs. John Johnson, a well-known work by Romney, is reproduced in the standard literature and is representative of his portrait style of the 1780s. Fluency of brushwork is balanced by strong

1931.404

volumes. The sculptural features of the head and the foreshortened hat are the most three-dimensional elements of the painting. The young woman is shown three-quarter length, sitting with her hands in her lap while she gazes steadily at the viewer with an impenetrable expression that is typical of Romney's sitters. The white tonality helps create an overall mood of delicate restraint.

Nothing definite is known about the sitter. Romney's diaries, published by Ward and Roberts in 1904, contain so many references to Mrs. Johnson, Johnston, Johnstone, Johns, and other variations of the name that exact identification is difficult. Ward and Roberts nevertheless specified that the Taft painting, which they illustrated, represents Mrs. Johnson, née Ponsonby, of Walton House (now Castlesteads), near Brampton, Cumberland, who married John Johnson on November 30, 1786, and who died on January 15, 1792.[1] They also noted that her husband's portrait, also by Romney, still hung at Castlesteads. They felt that the portraits probably should be identified with Romney's diary references to Mr. and Mrs. Johnson of Bloomsbury Square, whom Romney painted during 1786. The same diary source mentions that on April 5, 1792, Romney received forty-two pounds from a Mr. Lind for the portraits of Mr. and Mrs. Johnson.[2] A few years after the publication of Ward and Roberts's book, Arthur B. Chamberlain again reproduced the Taft painting, but identified the sitter as Miss Mary Johnson.[3] The reason for this change was not indicated. In the succeeding seventy-five years, no further information on the sitter has come to light.

The strong pyramidal figure filling the canvas firmly weights the lower edge of the picture; this portrait formula was frequently employed by Romney. For example, in the painting of Lady Caroline Price (1790, formerly New York, Newhouse Galleries) and the portrait of Mrs. Davenport (1782, Washington, D.C., National Gallery of Art), the same compositional strengths appear. The "classicism" of Romney does not consist solely of antiquarian allusion but incorporates a thorough taste for simple, stable pictorial structures, an air of detachment, and an avoidance of excessive detail and individuality. The character of the sitter may be left unexplored and animation hindered, but calm dignity is achieved.

1. See Humphrey Ward and William Roberts, *Romney: A Biographical and Critical Essay with a Catalogue of His Works*, vol. I, London, 1904, pp. 111ff.; Ward and Roberts, vol. II, p. 85, ill. opp. p. 85.

2. Ward and Roberts, vol. I, pp. 111ff.; Ward and Roberts, vol. II, p. 85.

3. Arthur B. Chamberlain, *George Romney*, New York, 1910, p. 337, pl. lxii, opp. p. 306.

Provenance Charles J. Wertheimer, London (in 1904); [Scott and Fowles, New York]; Taft collection, Jan. 4, 1910.

Exhibitions Berlin, Die Königliche Akademie der Künste, 1908, *Exhibition of English Old Masters* (cat., no. 82); New York, Scott and Fowles, 1913 (cat., no. 4).

Literature Humphrey Ward and William Roberts, *Romney: A Biographical and Critical Essay with a Catalogue of His Works*, London, 1904, vol. I, pp. 111ff., vol. II, p. 85, ill. opp. p. 85; Arthur B. Chamberlain, *George Romney*, New York, 1910, p. 337, ill. opp. p. 306; *Connoisseur*, vol. XXXVI (May 1913), pp. 13, 47 (ill.); Maurice W. Brockwell, *A Catalogue of Paintings in the Collection of Mr. and Mrs. Charles P. Taft*, New York, 1920, no. 24; *New York Times*, Jan. 1, 1933; *Catalogue of the Taft Museum*, Cincinnati, 1939 and 1958, no. 458 (pl. 25, 1939 ed.); Gerhard Charles Rump, *George Romney, 1734–1802*, Hildesheim and New York, 1974, vol. I, p. 171, vol. II, pl. 142.

1931.404

George Morland

London 1763–1804 London

George Morland was the son of Henry Robert Morland, a genre and portrait painter, restorer, and art dealer.[1] Morland's talents were apparent early. He exhibited at the Royal Academy at the age of ten and as his father's apprentice copied seventeenth-century Dutch genre scenes (which were then probably sold as originals). He was released from his father's severe control in 1784 and admitted to the Royal Academy schools the same year. He did not stay there, however, but came under the influence of unscrupulous dealers who catered to the young artist's taste for dissipation and exploited his popularity. Such circumstances recurred frequently throughout Morland's career, which was marked by debt, alcoholism, and association with underworld characters. Morland employed disreputable friends and chance acquaintances as middlemen in the selling of his pictures, thereby losing huge sums of money. He gained fame through his numerous engravings. Between 1788 and 1791, for example, approximately one hundred engravings after Morland's paintings were published.

In 1785 Morland moved to Margate; he also visited France briefly. In 1786 he returned to London, where he married Ann Ward, the sister of one of his engravers, William Ward. At the same time William Ward married Morland's sister, Maria. The two couples lived together briefly. Following the birth of a stillborn child around 1787, Morland left his wife more or less permanently but provided for her from time to time. His subsequent life was highly transient: he lived in Camden Town, Paddington, Kensington, Highgate, Lambeth, Hackney, East Sheen, the Isle of Wight, Yarmouth, and many other sites around London and in southern England. There are tales of his being arrested as a spy and being suspected of counterfeiting and of wild sprees in city and country. Morland lived with boxers, dressed as a jockey or in rags, maintained a menagerie, and spawned endless reports of mayhem and dissipation. There is no doubt that he was hounded by creditors throughout the country and that much of his itinerant life was spent in hiding. He was arrested for debt in 1799 and only freed from the resulting restrictions by a new bankruptcy law in 1801. Morland's constitution and art were greatly enfeebled by drink during his last few years. He was arrested for debt again in 1804 and died in a sponging house in Cold Bath Fields in the same year.[2]

Despite his undisciplined existence, Morland was prolific. He exhibited thirty-nine works at the Royal Academy and sometimes painted several pictures in a day. Although a decline is apparent during the late 1790s, he continued to produce works until his last days. His immense popularity generated many forgeries, copies, imitations, and misattributions during and after his life, making the study of Morland difficult. In addition, the artist's reported habit of producing potboilers in a few strokes and of leaving works incomplete, which dealers would then have finished by others, further complicates the assessment of his career and oeuvre.

During the 1780s Morland painted moralistic middle-class genre scenes very much in the manner of Francis Wheatley. In this sentimental vein he produced scenes from *The Vicar of Wakefield* and a painting condemning the slave trade. During the 1790s, influenced by seventeenth-century Dutch art, he began producing picturesque images of country folk. The works of Thomas Rowlandson and P. J. de Loutherbourg also inspired him. Cottage life, hunting, coaches, taverns, and barnyards became the staple subjects of his normally small canvases. Pictures of gypsy encampments and fishermen also appeared. During his last years Morland's visits to the Isle of Wight led him to paint a number of breezy coastal scenes peopled with smugglers and fisherfolk. These, like many other subjects by Morland, reflect his admiration for the landscapes and country pictures of Thomas Gainsborough. However, Morland's common people are more forthright and unprettified. The popularity of his works suggests changing attitudes toward the lower classes and alterations in the system of patronage.

1. On Morland, see J. Hassell, *Memoirs of the Life of the Late George Morland*, London, 1806; George Dawe, *The Life of George Morland*, London, 1807; Ralph Richardson, *George Morland*, London, 1895; Martin Hardie, "George Morland, I," *Connoisseur*, vol. IX (July 1904), pp. 153–63; Martin Hardie, "George Morland, II," *Connoisseur*, vol. IX (Aug. 1904), pp. 199–207; Walter Gilbey and E. D. Cuming, *George Morland: His Life and Works*, London, 1907; David Winter, *George Morland*, Stanford,

Calif., 1977; John Barrell, *The Dark Side of the Landscape*, Cambridge, 1980, pp. 89–130.

2. Under English law, debtors were kept at a sponging house, usually a bailiff's house, for one day to afford them the opportunity to compromise with their creditors.

𝔤

George Morland

Apple Gatherers

1791
Oil on canvas, 38.1 x 30.5 cm (15 x 12 in.)
Signed and dated lower right: *G. Morland 1791*

In this small painting, three children gather apples in the woods. A boy climbs a tree while one girl kneels to pick up fallen fruit and another stands to the right eating an apple. The boy's up-turned hat lies on the ground. Grasses and brambles abound, and most of the canvas is filled with brusquely painted foliage and branches. George Morland's style was forged, imitated, and copied widely during and after the artist's lifetime, and even his genuine works are sometimes weak and uninventive. However, the Taft painting is vigorous in execution and subject — a fine example of Morland's production. The swift, blunt brush-strokes, zigzagging branches, well-articulated limbs and gestures, muddy colors, and rustic childhood theme are both typical and authentic.

The painting was engraved by R. M. Meadows in 1795 and paired with *Gathering Wood*, another subject of country economy, likewise treated in an unprettified and unsentimental manner.[1] Morland transformed the peasant scenes of Thomas Gainsborough into more rudely honest images, untouched by pastoral poetry or homages to Murillo. Gainsborough's country children would never have devoured apples with such passion, climbed trees with such gracelessness, or possessed such truly childlike bodies.

Earlier, Morland had painted a scene of boys robbing an orchard (engraved by E. Scott in 1790), but the Taft picture depicts no such rollicking incident. There is no indication that the children are engaged in theft, as the apple tree seems to be a rough forest plant, not some well-pruned garden variety. The suggestion of subsistence living culled from woods and untended land is typical of Morland's work. He did not portray the labors of well-ordered agriculture. The people in his paintings are not polite figures in a harmonious universe, but hulking folk who, like the artist himself, scrounge for a living and often do wrong.

The pendant painting, *Gathering Wood*, also dated 1791, shows two of the same children picking up bundles of twigs in the forest.[2] A pair of gypsies appears in the distance, and the same sort of scrubby glade forms the setting. The two pictures, of course, are also linked by the activities depicted. Both represent autumnal labors, rude harvesting from raw nature in preparation for the coming winter. As in many other works by Morland, a vignette composition is employed. An asymmetric and rough-edged arrangement of trees and grasses frames the well-lighted

1931.381

protagonists, and a glimpse into the undistracting distance is presented behind the figures. In general, Morland's country scenes display the picturesque taste for patchy forms and textures, unevenness of composition and shape, and uncultivated landscape.

The Taft painting is just one of Morland's images of children at work. Although early in his career the artist had produced moralistic paintings commenting on contemporary life and portraying the horrors of the slave trade, there is no reason to believe that his pictures of laboring children were meant as social critique. The children's work seems more like play, and no contemporary writers found the imagery particularly barbed. John Barrell has recently interpreted Morland's figures as forceful social statements about a truculent lower class.[3] One may disagree with such readings, but at the very least it must be admitted that Morland's children differ from the sweet and clean children who appear in eighteenth-century portraits and from the graceful child shepherds who populate Gainsborough's bucolic scenes. Morland's children exhibit a tough and hearty realism that anticipates the coarse ragamuffins of Charles Dickens, Mark Twain, and a host of mid-nineteenth-century realistic writers and painters with social convictions.

1. Both engravings are in the collection of the British Museum, London.

2. The painting was formerly in the collection of Sir Walter Gilbey and is reproduced in color in Walter Gilbey and E. D. Cuming, *George Morland: His Life and Works*, London, 1907, p. 108.

3. John Barrell, *The Dark Side of the Landscape*, Cambridge, 1980, pp. 89–130.

Provenance [Scott and Fowles, New York]; Taft collection, Nov. 25, 1922.
Literature J. Hassell, *Memoirs of the Life of the Late George Morland*, London, 1806, pp. 98–100, 170–71; Walter Gilbey and E. D. Cuming, *George Morland: His Life and Works*, London, 1907, p. 108; George Williamson, *George Morland: His Life and Work*, London, 1907, p. 181; *Catalogue of the Taft Museum*, Cincinnati, 1939 and 1958, no. 80.

1931.381

Henry Raeburn

Stockbridge, near Edinburgh 1756–1823 Edinburgh

Henry Raeburn's biographers have presented conflicting descriptions of the artist's family, studies, and travels.[1] His father's profession is not known, and Raeburn was orphaned at an early age and placed under the care of his elder brother. The family was evidently not well-off, for Raeburn attended Heriot's Hospital grammar school in Edinburgh, a charitable institution. He was apprenticed around 1772 to an Edinburgh goldsmith and jeweler named James Galliland and is said to have begun painting miniatures at the same time. Raeburn apparently studied under John Runciman, and he may have been a pupil of David Martin, whose paintings, it is claimed, Raeburn copied. But, in fact, nothing about his training is certain. By 1780 he had married Ann Edgar, the wealthy and propertied widow of a certain James Leslie of Deanhaugh, called Count Leslie, and by 1782 Raeburn had established himself as a portrait painter in the Scottish capital. In 1784 Raeburn traveled to London, made contact with Sir Joshua Reynolds, and journeyed on to Rome, probably on Reynolds's advice. He returned to Edinburgh in 1786 and thereafter became the most fashionable portrait painter in Scotland.[2]

After Raeburn's experience on the Continent and his familiarity with art in London, his sitters began to appear in relaxed postures, and his paintings began to display powerful lighting effects. However, most of the basic elements of his distinctive style had already been formed by 1782, the year of his earliest portrait. His style essentially varied little throughout his career. With a square brush, he emphasized broad shapes of nearly geometric simplicity. The strongly angled planes of color set against dark backgrounds give stability and gravity to his sitters, who are frequently thrust close to the viewer. Raeburn's portraits, like those of George Romney, display a sculptural severity. In his work of the early nineteenth century, dark shadows often dominate his paintings and accessories are minimized. His later works are slightly softer with more diffused lighting, but stylistic consistency rather than change or development marks Raeburn's career.

Through a disastrous business investment, Raeburn became bankrupt in 1808. He visited London in 1810 to explore the possibility of practicing portraiture there to recoup his losses. One serious competitor, John Hoppner, had just died; but Thomas Lawrence, with a more dashing and elegant style, dominated the field in London, so Raeburn returned to Scotland. He traveled to London again in 1812 when he became an associate of the Royal Academy, in 1813, and lastly in 1815 when he was elected full academician. He first exhibited in London in 1792 and sent portraits to the Royal Academy every year from 1810 to 1823. In 1812 Raeburn became president of the Society of Artists of Edinburgh and in 1822 was knighted during the visit of George IV to Scotland. In 1823 he was appointed King's Limner for Scotland.

Raeburn was a sportsman, gardener, and father of two children. He was a prominent and gregarious figure in Edinburgh society and fit neatly into that illustrious period of Scottish culture of the late eighteenth and early nineteenth centuries. During that time, scholarship, science, education, literature, cultivated society, landscape architecture, and eminent building flourished, and Edinburgh was known as the Athens of the North. Raeburn has not received a great deal of scholarly attention in recent decades, but his reputation has not been obscured. The grandly simple power of his flat, faceted style makes Raeburn acceptable to twentieth-century taste.

1. On Raeburn, see Andrew Duncan, *A Tribute of Regard to the Memory of Sir Henry Raeburn*, Edinburgh, 1824; Allan Cunningham, *The Lives of the Most Eminent British Painters*, London, 1879; Walter Armstrong, *Sir Henry Raeburn*, with a catalogue by J. L. Caw, Paris, 1902; D. Baxandal, *Raeburn Bicentenary Exhibition*, exh. cat., National Gallery of Scotland, Edinburgh, 1956; Kenneth Garlick, "Sir Henry Raeburn," in *Encyclopedia of World Art*, New York, 1966; Frederick Cummings and Allen Staley, *Romantic Art in Britain: Paintings and Drawings, 1760–1860*, exh. cat., Philadelphia Museum of Art, 1968; David Irwin and Francina Irwin, *Scottish Painters at Home and Abroad, 1700–1900*, London, 1975; Richard Dorment, *British Painting in the Philadelphia Museum of Art*, London, 1986; Duncan Macmillan, *Scottish Art, 1460–1990*, Edinburgh, 1990, chap. VIII. The last three works represent the most carefully researched material on Raeburn's life.

2. The Irwins (see note 1) claim the year of Raeburn's departure for London and Rome as 1784; most other sources assert that Raeburn left Edinburgh in 1785 and returned in 1787.

Henry Raeburn

Edward Satchwell Fraser, Jr.

1803
Oil on canvas, 75.6 x 62.9 cm (29¾ x 24¾ in.)

This half-length portrait features a teenage boy in a tartan jacket, holding his arms akimbo. With confident posture and demeanor, he has the forthrightness typical of Raeburn's sitters. The pyramidal composition, large square brushstrokes, angular garments, and crisp shadows exemplify the artist's geometric style. Raeburn's enthusiasm for bold, plain shapes and masses can be interpreted as part of a general trend of the neoclassical period. The astringent and sculptural portraits of George Romney display a similar taste but lack the Scottish painter's fondness for richly shadowed settings. Although Raeburn was the chief portraitist of Scotland, tartan garments are not common in his paintings and usually appear only when the sitter is in military dress. The sitter's costume, while not unknown, was not part of current fashion and suggests his pride in nationality and pedigree. The Scottish plaids are nationalistic symbols that at one point during the eighteenth century were banned by the English overlords, fearful of the rebellious spirit they represented.

1931.425

This portrait of Edward Satchwell Fraser, Jr., is part of a series of works by Raeburn depicting members of the Fraser family of Reelig. The portraits were executed between 1800 and 1816. The eldest member of the family to be painted by Raeburn was Edward Satchwell Fraser, Sr. (1751–1835). The Taft picture represents one of his sons, Edward Satchwell Fraser, Jr. *Burke's Landed Gentry* notes that the Fraser family seat is at Reelig, or Easter Moniack, in Inverness-shire and that Edward Satchwell Fraser, Sr., was an aide-de-camp to General Simon during the American Revolution. He and his wife, Jane Fraser of Balnain, had five sons and one daughter. Edward, Jr., their third child, was born on April 26, 1786; he died unmarried and without issue on the island of St. Helena on April 25, 1813. Brockwell has noted that Edward Satchwell Fraser, Jr., served in the East India Company. Other members of the Fraser family had strong connections with India. Brockwell also indicated that this picture was one of nine Fraser portraits from the Reelig household that were sold by Phillip Affleck Fraser in 1897.[1] Phillip Affleck Fraser was the grandson of Jane Ann Catherine Fraser, the sister of Edward Satchwell Fraser, Jr. A label on the back of the painting dates the work 1803. Since Raeburn kept no ledgers, diaries, or account books, there is no documentary proof of the date, yet nothing in the style of the portrait or the apparent age of the sitter would challenge it.

1. Maurice W. Brockwell, *A Catalogue of Paintings in the Collection of Mr. and Mrs. Charles P. Taft*, New York, 1920, pp. 168–71. Walter Armstrong (*Sir Henry Raeburn*, with a catalogue by J. L. Caw, Paris, 1902, p. 119) lists only eight portraits of the Fraser family of Reelig sold in 1897: Alexander Charles Fraser (1789–1816), Edward S. Fraser (1751–1835), E. S. Fraser (1786–1813), George John Fraser (1800–1842), James Baillie Fraser (1783–1856), Jane A. C. Fraser (1797–1880), Jane Fraser Tytler (wife of James Baillie Fraser; see the following entry), and William Fraser (1784–

1835). Information on the Frasers has been confused by entries in the *Dictionary of National Biography* on James Baillie Fraser and William Fraser. There, the name Satchwell is spelled Satchell, and the dates and orders of birth given the sons of Edward Satchwell Fraser, Sr., are sometimes questionable. *Burke's Landed Gentry* is a more reliable source.

Provenance Philip Affleck Fraser (sale, Christie's, London, Oct. 7, 1897, no. 27); [Scott and Fowles, New York, 1906]; Taft collection, Oct. 17, 1906.

Exhibition New York, Scott and Fowles, *Paintings from the Collection of C. P. Taft*, Nov. 1909 (cat., no. 10).

Literature Walter Armstrong, *Sir Henry Raeburn*, with a catalogue by J. L. Caw, Paris, 1902, p. 119; William Walton, "Exhibition in New York of Paintings from the Collection of Mr. and Mrs. Charles P. Taft," *Burlington Magazine*, vol. XVI (1910), p. 368; Arthur Hoeber, "Some Pictures from the Collection of Mr. and Mrs. Charles P. Taft," *International Studio*, vol. XXXIX (1910), p. lxxiv; *Putnam's Magazine*, vol. VII (Feb. 1910), p. 525; J. Greig, *Raeburn*, London, 1911, p. 45; *Connoisseur*, vol. XXXVI (1913), pp. 163, 188 (ill.); Maurice W. Brockwell, *A Catalogue of Paintings in the Collection of Mr. and Mrs. Charles P. Taft*, New York, 1920, p. xx, no. 59; *Catalogue of the Taft Museum*, Cincinnati, 1939 and 1958, no. 230 (ill. in 1958 ed.).

1931.425

Henry Raeburn

Jane Fraser Tytler

ca. 1810
Oil on canvas, 76.5 x 63.5 cm (30⅛ x 25 in.)

This portrait of Jane Fraser Tytler presumably was painted before her marriage, since she was married in the year of Raeburn's death. Her clothes and hairstyle indicate that the painting should probably be dated about 1810. The undetailed handling of the

1931.424

lower portion of the portrait also suggests a date after 1808, when Raeburn, hard pressed for money after his bankruptcy, worked quickly and often treated everything but the heads of his portraits in a generalized manner. Nevertheless, the painting is a good example of Raeburn's softer style, featuring diffused lighting. The paint strokes and long-necked anatomy somewhat resemble the style of Thomas Lawrence, whose domination of London portraiture in 1810 persuaded Raeburn to stay in Edinburgh.

Jane Fraser Tytler (d. 1861) was the daughter of Alexander Fraser Tytler, Lord Woodhouselee (1747–1813). Her father was a distinguished Scottish lawyer who became professor of universal history at the University of Edinburgh and judge advocate of Scotland. He published poetry and several general books on history. Jane's sister, Ann Fraser Tytler, was a well-known writer of children's books, including *Leila on the Island* (1839). In 1823 Jane married the famous Asian traveler James Baillie Fraser of Reelig (1783–1856). He was one of the first Europeans to visit the Himalayas. He also traveled extensively in Persia and Mesopotamia, publishing illustrated descriptions of his journeys as well as romantic fiction on oriental themes. He acted as official guide for the Persian princes who visited England in 1835–36. Although a great deal is known about her relatives, little about Jane Fraser Tytler has come to light. Raeburn painted her father in 1804 and several members of her husband's family between 1800 and 1816.[1]

1. See the listing of Fraser portraits in note 1 of the preceding entry.

Provenance Phillip Affleck Fraser (sale, Christie's, London, Oct. 7, 1897, no. 33); [Scott and Fowles, New York, 1906]; Taft collection, Oct. 17, 1906.

Exhibitions New York, Scott and Fowles, *Paintings from the Collection of C. P. Taft*, Nov. 1909 (cat., no. 11); Omaha, Nebr., Joslyn Art Museum, *Twenty-fifth Anniversary Exhibition*, Nov. 29, 1956–Jan. 1, 1957.

Literature Walter Armstrong, *Sir Henry Raeburn*, with a catalogue by J. L. Caw, Paris, 1902, p. 119; William Walton, "Exhibition in New York of Paintings from the Collection of Mr. and Mrs. Charles P. Taft," *Burlington Magazine*, vol. XVI (1910), p. 368; Maurice W. Brockwell, *A Catalogue of Paintings in the Collection of Mr. and Mrs. Charles P. Taft*, New York, 1920, p. xx, no. 56; W. G. Menzies, "The Present State of the Picture Market," *Apollo*, vol. XXI, no. 121 (Jan. 1935), p. 38; *Catalogue of the Taft Museum*, Cincinnati, 1939 and 1958, no. 232 (ill. in 1939 ed.).

1931.424

Joseph Mallord William Turner

London 1775–1851 London

Turner's first signed drawings date from 1786, when he was living with an uncle at Brentford, Middlesex.[1] In 1789 he became a student at the Royal Academy schools and also studied under the architectural watercolorist Thomas Malton. He exhibited his first watercolor at the Royal Academy in 1790 and his first oil in 1796. From 1791 on Turner made frequent sketching tours throughout England, Wales, and Scotland. Many of his landscape drawings and watercolors were engraved for a variety of topographical, poetic, and historical publications. With his friend Thomas Girtin during the last years of the eighteenth century, Turner began to give new grandeur and poetry to the depiction of specific places. This development was encouraged by Dr. Thomas Monro, who from 1794 to 1797 employed Turner and Girtin to copy the moody topographical watercolors of John Robert Cozens. Turner was elected associate of the Royal Academy in 1799 and full academician in 1802. In the latter year, like many other British artists, Turner took the opportunity provided by the brief Peace of Amiens to visit the Louvre, but unlike his fellow painters, he also visited the Alps, which subsequently became an important subject in his art.

In 1804 Turner built a gallery next to his house in London and showed work there for many years. He nevertheless remained loyally attached to the Royal Academy and its annual exhibitions; that institution was always the center of his career. Between 1807 and 1819 Turner published a series of landscape engravings that displayed the breadth and power of his art, which he called the *Liber Studiorum* in imitation of Claude Lorrain's *Liber Veritatis*. By thus associating himself with the great landscape tradition of the seventeenth century, he signaled his ambition to rise above the status of a modest topographical draftsman. In 1817 he toured the Rhine and in 1819, Italy. From 1821 to 1845 he made numerous trips abroad, visiting France, Italy, Austria, Holland, Germany, and Switzerland. During his first Italian trip he began to compose his images in terms of color rather than light and dark contrasts. He continued this coloristic exploration, with increasing intensity, until the end of his life.

Turner bequeathed the remains of his studio to the British nation with the stipulation that two of his works should hang next to paintings by Claude Lorrain in the National Gallery. After much controversy over which works were finished and acceptable, over nineteen thousand oils, watercolors, and drawings entered the national collections in 1856.

Little is known of Turner's private life. His father, a barber and wigmaker, encouraged his career. Turner's mother was institutionalized for insanity. Turner became a reclusive bachelor, secretive, careless in dress, somewhat miserly, and not polite. He worked sporadically and inconclusively on a long pessimistic poem, *The Fallacies of Hope*, often appending its verses to his exhibited paintings.

Turner was the most renowned British landscape painter in the first half of the nineteenth century. He attracted the attention of critics, collectors, and artists as early as 1794, acquiring such patrons as William Beckford and Lord Egremont. Turner's spectacular manipulation of color and pigment was often controversial, and during the 1830s he was harshly criticized. However, he remained financially secure, retaining admirers, collectors, and imitators throughout his long career. During the 1840s he was avidly defended by John Ruskin. Turner is one of the very few English painters to be considered a great artist beyond the confines of Britain.

1. On Turner, see Walter Thornbury, *The Life of J. M. W. Turner*, 2 vols., London, 1862; Walter Armstrong, *Turner*, 2 vols., London, 1902; A. J. Finberg, *The Life and Work of J. M. W. Turner*, 2d ed., London, 1961; A. J. Finberg, *The National Gallery: A Complete Inventory of the Drawings of the Turner Bequest*, 2d ed., New York, 1961; Lawrence Gowing, *Turner: Imagination and Reality*, exh. cat., Museum of Modern Art, New York,

1931.459

1966; Jack Lindsay, *J. M. W. Turner: His Life and Work*, London, 1966; John Gage, *Colour in Turner: Poetry and Truth*, London, 1969; Graham Reynolds, *Turner*, London, 1969; Andrew Wilton, *J. M. W. Turner: His Art and Life*, New York, 1979; John Gage, ed., *Collected Correspondence of J. M. W. Turner*, Oxford, 1980; Andrew Wilton, *Turner and the Sublime*, exh. cat., Yale Center for British Art, New Haven, 1980; Martin Butlin and Evelyn Joll, *The Paintings of J. M. W. Turner*, 2 vols., rev. ed., New Haven and London, 1984; John Gage, *J. M. W. Turner: "A Wonderful Range of Mind,"* New Haven and London, 1987; Andrew Wilton, *Turner in His Time*, London, 1987; Eric Shanes, *Turner's Human Landscape*, London, 1990; Kathleen Nicholson, *Turner's Classical Landscapes: Myth and Meaning*, Princeton, N.J., 1990.

J. M. W. Turner

The Trout Stream

1809

Oil on canvas, 91.5 x 122 cm (36 x 48 in.)

Signed lower right: J M W T

In this large oil the river Dee flows swiftly toward Corwen Bridge in the middle distance. Fishermen cast and reel in their lines and count their catch in the sandy foreground and shallows while harvesters work in the left distance. A high hill rises at the left. Swirling clouds darken the sky. The spray of pebbles in the foreground, the string of active figures, and the weather make this Welsh scene highly dynamic.

Wales had attracted Turner from the earliest years of his career. It was a region favored by advocates of picturesque taste. Although Turner often portrayed its rough and barren terrain, here the land appears civilized and relatively hospitable. Angling is not a rare subject in Turner's art but is minor compared to the depictions of commercial fishing. The artist's contemporary figures more frequently engage in labor than in pleasure, but when they do entertain themselves, as is the case here, they set a tone of ease and delight.

Turner apparently visited the Dee just before or after staying at nearby Tabley House, Cheshire, during the summer of 1808.[1] He was at Tabley to portray Sir John Leicester's estate in two major paintings (Butlin and Joll, no. 98, Victoria University of Manchester, on loan to Whitworth Art Gallery, Manchester, and no. 99, Tate Gallery and National Trust, Petworth House). A rough drawing for the Taft painting is in one of Turner's Tabley sketchbooks among other scenes of the same countryside.[2] The painter and diarist Joseph Farington noted in 1809 that *The Trout Stream* had been criticized by the watercolorist Thomas Hearne in July of that year as not being worth the two hundred guineas that Lord Essex had paid for it.[3] Hearne's low opinion has not held sway over time. The picture was included in such prestigious nineteenth-century celebrations as the Manchester art treasures exhibition of 1857 and is today admired as a major work by the artist.

The dark, sandy colors of *The Trout Stream*, as well as the strong silhouettes and the seventeenth-century landscape formula of coulisses receding along a river into the distance, are common features of Turner's work during the first decade of the nineteenth century. The cloud pattern with its incipient vortical form is similar to that in such works as *Iveagh Seapiece* (1803–4, London, Iveagh Bequest, Kenwood House; Butlin and Joll, no. 144) and *The Pilot Boat* (1809, Ottawa, National Gallery of Canada; Butlin and Joll, no. 85). During this period Turner also frequently placed a bridge in the right middle distance as a stabilizing element in his compositions.[4]

The Trout Stream was exhibited in 1809 at Turner's private gallery along with such notable works as *Thomson's Aeolian Harp* (Manchester, City Art Galleries; Butlin and Joll, no. 86). Turner evidently considered the works he exhibited at the Royal Academy, however, to be his most ambitious public showpieces. The three paintings he exhibited there in 1809 were all very different from *The Trout Stream*: the two views of Tabley depict a single site at different times of the day and in different weather conditions and moods. The pair displayed not only Turner's prestigious commission in the field of house portraiture but also his ability to create two radically diverse images of one subject. Turner's third Royal Academy contribution of 1809 was *The Garreteer's Petition* (London, Tate Gallery; Butlin and Joll, no. 100), a Rembrandtesque reprise of William Hogarth's *Distressed Poet*, a barbed genre scene recalling an earlier British master.

The Trout Stream is not a spectacular cadenza meant to attract public acclaim for its social reference, tour-de-force exhibition of skill, or nationalistic sentiment. It does, however, represent Turner's more private taste in mood, human activity, and natural scenery.

1. Martin Butlin and Evelyn Joll, *The Paintings of J. M. W. Turner*, rev. ed., New Haven and London, 1984, no. 92.

2. London, British Museum, Turner Bequest, "Tabley Sketchbook no. 2," Sketchbook CIV, p. 28 verso.

3. Joseph Farington, *Diary*, July 5 and 7, 1809; Butlin and Joll, no. 92.

4. For example, Butlin and Joll, nos. 107 (*Dorchester Mead*, 1810, London, Tate Gallery) and 46 (*Bonneville, Savoy*, 1803, New York, Newhouse Galleries).

Provenance George, fifth earl of Essex, Cassiobury Park (from 1809; sale, Christie's, London, July 22, 1893, no. 46; bt. A. Nattali for Abel Buckley, Glasgow; Arthur Sanderson (by 1902; sold to Agnew, London, 1905); [Scott and Fowles, New York]; Taft collection, Nov. 25, 1905.

Exhibitions London, Turner's gallery, 1809 (cat., no. 13); Manchester, *Art Treasures of the United Kingdom*, 1857 (cat., no. 621); London, Royal Academy of Arts, 1878 (cat., no. 134), and 1895 (cat., no. 8); Corporation of London, Art Gallery, Guildhall, and Corporation of Birmingham Museum and Art Gallery, *Loan Collection of Pictures and Drawings by J. M. W. Turner*, 1899 (cat., no. 12); Glasgow, Kelvingrove Park, Fine Art Section, *International Exhibition*, 1901 (cat., no. 98); Art Gallery of Toronto, *Great Paintings in Aid of Allied Merchant Seamen*, Feb. 4–Mar. 12, 1944; Boston, Museum of Fine Arts, *Paintings, Drawings, and Prints by J. M. W. Turner, John Constable, and R. P. Bonington*, Mar. 19–Apr. 28, 1946 (cat., no. 3 [ill.]); Art Gallery of Toronto, *Paintings by J. M. W. Turner*, Oct. 6–Nov. 18, 1951 (cat., no. 4).

Literature Walter Armstrong, *Turner*, vol. I, London, 1902, pp. 59, 233 (ill. opp. p. 58); D. S. MacColl, *Nineteenth-Century Art*, Glasgow, 1902, p. 69, p. 66 (ill.); Maurice W. Brockwell, *A Catalogue of Paintings in the Collection of Mr. and Mrs. Charles P. Taft*, New York, 1920, p. xxvii, no. 26; *Bulletin of the Cincinnati Art Museum*, vol. IV, no. 1 (Jan. 1933), p. 14 (ill.); *Catalogue of the Taft Museum*, Cincinnati, 1939 and 1958, no. 105 (ill. in 1939 ed.); A. J. Finberg, *Life of J. M. W. Turner*, 2d ed., London, 1961, pp. 151, 156, 471, no. 140; John Gage, ed., *Collected Correspondence of J. M. W. Turner*, Oxford, 1980, p. 253; Martin Butlin and Evelyn Joll, *The Paintings of J. M. W. Turner*, rev. ed., New Haven and London, 1984, vol. I, no. 92, vol. II, pl. 102; John Gage, *J. M. W. Turner: "A Wonderful Range of Mind,"* New Haven and London, 1987, p. 73, pl. 99; Eric Shanes, *Turner's Human Landscape*, London, 1990, p. 264, fig. 164.

1931.459

J. M. W. Turner

Europa and the Bull

ca. 1840–50
Oil on canvas, 91.1 x 121.6 cm (35⅞ x 47⅞ in.)

Europa and the Bull is an unfinished painting belonging to a group of eleven incomplete canvases by Turner. Like eight others in the series, it is based on a mezzotint engraving in the *Liber Studiorum* (published 1807–19).[1] The dating of the group is imprecise, because the pictures are in such an amorphous state that many telling stylistic features are absent. Most scholars agree, however, that the works fall very late in the artist's career, probably 1840–50.[2] Turner is unlikely to have sold any unfinished works, so four of this group of paintings were left in the artist's studio at his death and were bequeathed to the British nation along with the rest of his estate. Mysteriously, seven of these works, including the Taft picture, disappeared from Turner's studio at some unknown date and eventually entered the art market. There has been much speculation but little hard information about how such a dispersal could have occurred.[3]

Europa and the Bull is based on the frontispiece to the edition of the *Liber Studiorum* first published in 1812. The print, however, sets the scene within a scrolled frame, surrounded by medieval arches, a fragment of a classical cornice, a peahen, dead fish, lily pads, and marsh plants; a classical seaport occupies the background.[4] The subject is taken from the Greek myth (and Ovid's *Metamorphoses*), in which Zeus falls in love with Europa, daughter of the king of Tyre. The god turns himself into a white bull to entice Europa, who is playing at the seashore, to ride on his back. Once mounted, the beautiful bull carries her into the sea and takes her to Crete, where she bears Zeus two or three children, including King Minos. The bull becomes the constellation Taurus.

In Turner's reworking of the frontispiece in the Taft painting, nearly everything has become nebulous. Europa is now only dimly seen on the white bull entering the sea in the right distance. The city in the left background has disappeared in a haze of light. Europa's companions on the shore are, however, clearly represented in the center of the painting; they gesticulate wildly at the surprise abduction. The distraught friends are a feature of some classical retellings of the myth and also appear in Titian's famous depiction of the story (Boston, Isabella Stewart Gardner Museum). Turner might have seen the Titian when it was in London in 1798–99 and again in 1816.[5]

The Taft image is in a state of gestation with swaths of effulgent color suggesting land, sea, air, and figures. Kathleen Nicholson has described this as "the chaos of creation in progress: paint and brushwork becoming a story about powers of transformation and generation. The actual handling is not so much gestural as charged with narrative significance."[6] Eric Shanes has perceived that the theme of Europa and the Bull, chosen originally to introduce the engraved exposition of Turner's oeuvre, refers to one of the essential aims of Turner's art as a whole: the representation of the difference between appearance and real-

1931.442

ity.[7] Shanes considers Turner's probable literary source, Joseph Addison's translation of parts of Ovid's *Metamorphoses* in volume seven of Robert Anderson's *A Complete Edition of the Poets of Great Britain,* and concludes that in the Taft painting we witness the revelation to Europa that the bull, which has dissolved in the blazing sun, is actually a god, with "glowing features, and celestial light."[8] Turner's art, it is claimed, similarly reveals the essentials of nature that lie behind the rude world of appearances. In contrast, earlier commentators had interpreted the *Liber Studiorum* frontispiece as a *vanitas* image; the maritime empire of Tyre, like Europa, is raped and removed from its position of glory.[9] The weeds and architectural debris that decorate the 1812 frontispiece suggest decay, and the peahen (in addition to its association with Juno) perhaps symbolizes the pride that had been Tyre's. All these surroundings, in fairness to Shanes's interpretation, have been excised from the Taft painting, and we may see, as both Shanes and Nicholson imply, a transformation of theme in the Taft canvas. It is difficult to remain entirely earthbound in the face of Turner's magnificently open-ended late pictures.

Turner's unfinished canvases are sometimes celebrated as protoimpressionist works, freely painted and nearly abstract in their presentation of subject. These loose and evocative visions of colored space, however, are far more emotional than any impressionist image and represent more than mere manipulation of form without regard for perceptual reality. They were almost certainly meant to be worked up more fully. On a number of occasions Turner took such nebulous pictures to the Royal Academy on varnishing day, just prior to the opening of the annual exhibition, and completed the works there and then in a dazzling display of skill and imagination, transforming indefinite masses into specific portrayals. According to his contemporaries, it was as if the primordial chaos of the universe had congealed into recognizable reality before their eyes.[10]

Turner often depicted classical subjects in his landscapes, for they could then be considered history paintings, the most high-minded and ambitious category of art, according to Sir Joshua Reynolds and many other art theorists both earlier and later. Landscape per se was of a lesser order than images drawn from the Bible, serious literature, ennobling history, or classical myth. In the eighteenth century Richard Wilson had similarly aggrandized his landscapes with stories of antiquity, and Turner, from the outset of his career, obviously intended to add to this tradition. Around 1798 he painted *Aeneas and the Sibyl* (London, Tate Gallery; Butlin and Joll, no. 34), and he first exhibited a classical subject, *Jason,* in 1802 (London, Tate Gallery; Butlin and Joll, no. 19). Classical themes were more than a superficial gloss used to elevate an ordinary scene of nature. Classical mythological narratives often give moral force to Turner's paintings, create moods of romantic melancholy or elation, and express the artist's world view. The tale of Europa and the Bull gives meaning to the bloody sunset colors, receding spaces, and distant figures. It speaks directly of abandonment, loss, lust, rape, and deceit.

1. The others in the series to which *Europa and the Bull* belongs are all roughly similar in size, color, state of incompletion, and paint handling. The group is discussed at length in Martin Butlin and Evelyn Joll, *The Paintings of J. M. W. Turner*, rev. ed., vol. I, New Haven and London, 1984, pp. 298–99, nos. 509–19. *Europa and the Bull* (no. 514) is the only one with a classical subject. Turner's renewed interest in the *Liber Studiorum* late in his life is indicated by his ordering fifteen new sets of the publication in 1845 (see J. Pye and J. L. Roget, *Notes and Memoranda Respecting the "Liber Studiorum,"* London, 1879, p. 71, note).

2. The dating problems are discussed in Butlin and Joll, vol. I, pp. 298–99. The series was previously thought to have been painted earlier. In the first edition of Butlin and Joll (1977), the group was dated 1835–40. The manufacturer's stamp on some of the canvases, however, indicates a date during the 1840s. Eric Shanes, in a review of Butlin and Joll in *Turner Studies*, vol. I, no. 1 (1981), pp. 45–46, and in "The True Subject of a Major Painting by Turner Identified," *Burlington Magazine*, vol. CXXVI (1984), pp. 284–88, dates the group 1845 and later. John Gage, in *J. M. W. Turner*, exh. cat., Grand Palais, Paris, 1983, pp. 149–51, dates the group 1845. Butlin and Joll now date nos. 509–19 ca. 1840–50 in their authoritative revised edition.

3. Butlin and Joll, vol. I, pp. 298–99.

4. W. G. Rawlinson, *Turner's "Liber Studiorum": A Description and a Catalogue*, rev. ed., London, 1906, no. 1.

5. On the London exhibition of Titian's *Rape of Europa*, see Butlin and Joll, no. 514.

6. Kathleen Nicholson, *Turner's Classical Landscapes: Myth and Meaning*, Princeton, N.J., 1990, p. 192.

7. Eric Shanes, *Turner's Human Landscape*, London, 1990, pp. 291–93.

8. Shanes 1990, pp. 291–94.

9. This was the view of John Ruskin and the Reverend Stopford Brooke; see Shanes 1990, p. 291.

10. See the description by E. V. Rippingille in *Art Journal* (1860), p. 100.

Provenance Rev. Thomas Prater (sale, Christie's, London, May 6, 1871, no. 127); Walter R. Cassels (1871, sale, Christie's, London, June 30, 1906, no. 63); [Colnaghi, London]; [Scott and Fowles, New York]; Taft collection, Feb. 11, 1907.

Exhibitions Corporation of London, Art Gallery, Guildhall, *Loan Collection of Pictures and Drawings by J. M. W. Turner*, 1899 (cat., no. 25); Art Gallery of Toronto, *Great Paintings in Aid of Allied Merchant Seamen*, Feb. 4–Mar. 12, 1944; Boston, Museum of Fine Arts, *Paintings, Drawings, and Prints by J. M. W. Turner, John Constable, and R. P. Bonington*, Mar. 19–Apr. 28, 1946; Bloomfield Hills, Mich., Cranbrook Academy of Art, *Light and the Painter*, Sept. 5–28, 1952 (cat., no. 40).

Literature Walter Armstrong, *Turner*, vol. I, London, 1902, p. 221; *Connoisseur*, vol. XV (1906), p. 262; Maurice W. Brockwell, *A Catalogue of Paintings in the Collection of Mr. and Mrs. Charles P. Taft*, New York, 1920, p. xxviii, no. 8; *Catalogue of the Taft Museum*, Cincinnati, 1939 and 1958, no. 162; Michael Kitson, "Nouvelles Précisions sur le 'paysage' de Turner," *La Revue du Louvre*, no. 2 (1971), pp. 89–94, fig. 4; Eric Shanes, "The True Subject of a Major Painting by Turner Identified," *Burlington Magazine*, vol. CXXVI (1984), pp. 284–88; Martin Butlin and Evelyn Joll, *The Paintings of J. M. W. Turner*, rev. ed., New Haven and London, 1984, vol. I, no. 514, vol. II, pl. 516; Kathleen Nicholson, "Style as Meaning: Turner's Late Mythological Landscapes," *Turner Studies*, vol. VIII, no. 2 (Winter 1988), pp. 51–53, fig. 12; Kathleen Nicholson, *Turner's Classical Landscapes: Myth and Meaning*, Princeton, N.J., 1990, p. 192; Eric Shanes, *Turner's Human Landscape*, London, 1990, pp. 291–93.

1931.442

ᏇᎧ

Copyist or forger of J. M. W. Turner

Old London Bridge

Nineteenth century
Oil on canvas, 102 x 125.7 cm (40⅛ x 49½ in.)
Inscribed and dated on a buoy in the left foreground: *Port of London 1825*

Evelyn Joll has rightly declared this painting to be not by Turner. It is a weak copy of a Turner watercolor in the Victoria and Albert Museum, London (1824), or of E. Goodall's engraving after that watercolor published in 1827.[1]

1. Martin Butlin and Evelyn Joll, *The Paintings of J. M. W. Turner*, rev. ed., New Haven and London, 1984, no. 553; Andrew Wilton, *J. M. W. Turner: His Art and Life*, New York, 1979, no. 514, illustrates the watercolor in question.

Provenance [Bt. from Dalton by Agnew in 1872]; John Heugh, Holmewood (1872; sale, Christie's, London, Apr. 24, 1874, no. 186); bt. Agnew for H. W. F. Bolckow, Marton Hall, Middlesborough (sale, Christie's, London, May 5, 1888, no. 68; bt. Colnaghi); Taft collection, 1910.

Exhibitions London, Royal Academy of Arts, 1885 (cat., no. 194); Art Gallery of Toronto, *Great Paintings in Aid of Allied Merchant Seamen*, Feb. 4–Mar. 12, 1944; Boston, Museum of Fine Arts, *Paintings, Drawings, and Prints by J. M. W. Turner, John Constable, and R. P. Bonington*, Mar. 19–Apr. 28, 1946; Art Gallery of Toronto [also Ottawa], *Paintings by J. M. W. Turner*, Oct. 6–Dec. 31, 1951 (cat., no. 7); Indianapolis, John Herron Art Museum [also Dayton, Ohio], *Turner in America*, Nov. 6, 1955–Jan. 25, 1956 (cat., no. 20 [ill.]).

Literature *Art Journal* (1888), p. 342; Walter Armstrong, *Turner*, vol. I, London, 1902, p. 224; Maurice W. Brockwell, *A Catalogue of Paintings in the Collection of Mr. and Mrs. Charles P. Taft*, New York, 1920, p. xxvii, no. 7; *Catalogue of the Taft Museum*, Cincinnati, 1939 and 1958, no. 505; Martin Butlin and Evelyn Joll, *The Paintings of J. M. W. Turner*, rev. ed., New Haven and London, 1984, vol. I, no. 553, vol. II, pl. 545.

1931.444

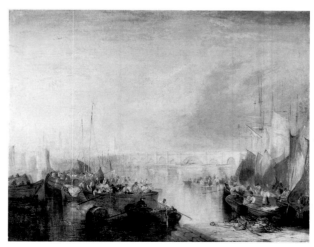

1931.444

1931.388

J. M. W. Turner

Château de Rinkenberg, on the Lac de Brienz, Switzerland

1809
Watercolor on paper, 281 x 394 mm (11⅟₁₆ x 15½ in.)
Signed and dated lower right: *J M W Turner RA PP 1809*

Since the Napoleonic Wars prevented most of the English from touring Europe, Turner, like many other British artists, took the opportunity offered by the Peace of Amiens (1802) to visit the Continent. He used his sketches from that journey, especially those of the Alps, for years afterward as the basis of many works, including the *Château de Rinkenberg*. Sketches for the watercolor appear in Turner's Grenoble Sketchbook (London, Tate Gallery, Turner Bequest, Sketchbook LXXIV, p. 46) and in the Rhine, Strasbourg, and Oxford Sketchbook (Sketchbook LXXVII, pp. 17a, 23a). The final watercolor is polished and carefully organized: boats and architecture balance one another and animate the mountains, lake, and shadow. The broad, flat shapes bear a mild resemblance to the works of Turner's friend Thomas Girtin, but the tiny trees in the distance are depicted in a more unusual manner with small dots and vertical strokes. This technique gives the impression of both great distance and infinite detail. The watercolor is clearly related to Turner's other placid

water views of around 1809, such as *Tabley: Calm Morning* (1809, Petworth House; Butlin and Joll, no. 99).

The Taft watercolor presents a contrast between the old building, shadowy, empty, and in ruins, and the modern fishing boats, enlivened by figures and productive activity. Both fishing craft and decayed architecture had been staples of Turner's subject matter from early in his career. The contrast between the two elements is also typical, representing the passage of time. The lakes of Switzerland became a favored subject again late in Turner's career when he portrayed the region with ecstatic colors, huge rippling lines, and palpable atmosphere. He made eight watercolors of the Lake of Brienz.[1] The lake is located in the canton of Bern and lies in the center of Switzerland close to Interlaken and Thun. In the Taft watercolor the viewer is looking southwest, with the town of Brienz behind. The twelfth-century Castle of Ringgenberg (called Rinkenberg by Turner), which became a church in the seventeenth century, is the romantic focus of the scene. Vying with the distant mountains in height and thrust, it towers above the waters like the more famous castles along the Rhine. Turner perpetually contrasted manufactured and natural grandeur in this way.

Switzerland only became a popular resort destination for English tourists toward the middle of the nineteenth century. This novel attraction developed not only from the general increase in enthusiasm for spectacular natural scenery but also from Turner's numerous Swiss views.

The letters *PP* attached to Turner's signature on the Taft watercolor stand for "Professor of Perspective," a post at the Royal Academy to which he was elected in 1807 and of which he was evidently very proud.

1. See Andrew Wilton, *J. M. W. Turner: His Art and Life,* New York, 1979, nos. 374, 386, 388 (the Taft watercolor), 391, 1506, 1518, 1562, 1563. On the *Château de Rinkenberg,* see also Eric Shanes, *J. M. W. Turner: The Foundations of Genius,* exh. cat., Taft Museum, Cincinnati, 1986, no. 27.

Provenance Walter Fawkes, Farnley Hall; John Ruskin (sale, Apr. 15, 1869, no. 40; bt. Agnew); John Heugh (sale, Apr. 24, 1874, no. 90; bt. Agnew); T. S. Kennedy, Park Hill, Wetherby, Yorkshire (sale, Christie's, London, May 18, 1895, no. 92; bt. H. Quilter); [Scott and Fowles, New York]; Taft collection, Nov. 25, 1905.

Exhibitions London, Grosvenor Place, 1819 (cat., no. 32); Boston, Museum of Fine Arts, *Paintings, Drawings, and Prints by J. M. W. Turner, John Constable, and R. P. Bonington,* Mar. 19–Apr. 28, 1946; Art Gallery of Toronto [also Ottawa], *Paintings by J. M. W. Turner,* Oct. 6–Dec. 31, 1951 (cat., no. 41); Cincinnati, Taft Museum, *J. M. W. Turner: The Foundations of Genius,* Sept. 18–Nov. 2, 1986 (cat. by Eric Shanes, no. 27 [color pl.]).

Literature Walter Armstrong, *Turner,* vol. 1, London, 1902, p. 244; Maurice W. Brockwell, *A Catalogue of Paintings in the Collection of Mr. and Mrs. Charles P. Taft,* New York, 1920, p. xxvii, no. 87; *Catalogue of the Taft Museum,* Cincinnati, 1939 and 1958, no. 161; Andrew Wilton, *J. M. W. Turner: His Art and Life,* New York, 1979, p. 92, fig. 87, no. 388.

1931.388

❧

J. M. W. Turner

Mer de Glace, in the Valley of Chamouni, Switzerland

ca. 1815
Watercolor on paper, 280 x 394 mm (11 x 15½ in.)

Turner's friend and patron Walter Fawkes owned three watercolors depicting this site in Chamonix (called Chamouni by Turner), and the Taft watercolor is one of these. The other two are in the Yale Center for British Art, New Haven (Wilton, no. 365), and the National Museum of Wales, Cardiff (Wilton, no. 376).[1] One of the three watercolors was exhibited at the Royal Academy in 1803 (no. 396) as *Glacier and Source of the Arveiron, Going up to the Mer de Glace,* but there has been disagreement as to which of the works is the 1803 picture. In 1980 David Hill argued that the watercolor at Cardiff is the 1803 watercolor, noting that it is the only one that actually presents the source of the Arveiron, the foot of the glacier, with any degree of emphasis; it is also the only one that places the Mer de Glace above the viewer (in accord with the title phrase, "Going up to the Mer de Glace").[2] Both the Taft and New Haven watercolors, in contrast, concentrate on foreground trees rather than the glacier, and the great sheet of ice, furthermore, lies beneath the viewer's gaze. In 1979 Andrew Wilton had favored the New Haven watercolor as the 1803 work, but Eric Shanes has sided with Hill and noted additionally that the depiction of trees in the New Haven watercolor can be safely associated with Turner's style of 1809–15.[3] He has also dated the Taft watercolor 1815 and with good reason, for it is closely related to the New Haven watercolor in its stormy weather, prominent trees, and emotionalism, all of which suggest a similar date of execution.[4] Both present the Alps as ferocious and overwhelming. Although the Taft watercolor includes wind-torn firs, swirling clouds, flashes of sunlight, spiraling gorges, scurrying goatherds, and destabilizing compositional diagonals, it is, in fact, less theatrical, less artificial, than the New Haven watercolor, which displays many of these same motifs but with greater exaggeration. In comparison, the Taft scene is calm and realistic. The diverse meteorological conditions that meet and clash in the Taft watercolor are careful studies of nature as well as stage props and symbols of the force of nature.

1931.389

All three Fawkes watercolors stem from Turner's trip to the Alps in 1802, when he visited Chamonix and made numerous sketches (London, Tate Gallery, Turner Bequest, St. Gothard and Mont Blanc Sketchbook LXXV).[5] That initial tour, which was in part inspired by the mountain landscapes of the Alsatian painter Philip James de Loutherbourg, was of seminal importance in Turner's career and generated many of his Alpine scenes for decades. Turner added naturalistic light, air, and weather to De Loutherbourg's sensational subject matter.

The Mer de Glace, one of the largest glaciers in the Alps, is located on the north face of Mont Blanc, and the town of Chamonix lies below. The area obviously impressed Turner, for he returned to the subject repeatedly over more than a decade. In addition to the three Fawkes pictures, watercolors of the valley of Chamonix are in the Courtauld Institute, London (Wilton, no. 371), and the Whitworth Art Gallery, Manchester (Wilton, no. 387). The importance of the site presumably lay not merely in its appearance but in its position next to the highest peak in Europe. Chamonix represented Alpine gigantism and power at their supreme pitch.

The scraping and blotting evident in the Taft watercolor are techniques that Turner and Thomas Girtin developed during the last years of the eighteenth century to give greater force and manipulability to the medium and to make the effects of watercolor rival those of oil paint.

1. Andrew Wilton, *J. M. W. Turner: His Art and Life*, New York, 1979.

2. David Hill, *Turner in Yorkshire*, exh. cat., York City Art Gallery, 1980, p. 62.

3. Eric Shanes, *Turner's Human Landscape*, London, 1990, pp. 189, 364, notes 28, 29.

4. Eric Shanes, *J. M. W. Turner: The Foundations of Genius*, exh. cat., Taft Museum, Cincinnati, 1986, no. 28.

5. Wilton, no. 389, suggests that the Taft watercolor may be based on a specific drawing in the St. Gothard and Mont Blanc Sketchbook, p. 20.

Provenance Walter Fawkes, Farnley Hall (sale, Christie's, London, 1890, no. 47); Humphrey Roberts; [Scott and Fowles, New York]; Taft collection, Nov. 25, 1905.

Exhibitions London, Grosvenor Place, 1819 (cat., no. 24); Leeds, 1839 (cat., no. 60 or 65); Boston, Museum of Fine Arts, *Paintings, Drawings, and Prints by J. M. W. Turner, John Constable, and R. P. Bonington*, Mar. 19–Apr. 28, 1946; Art Gallery of Toronto [also Ottawa], *J. M. W. Turner*, Oct. 6–Dec. 31, 1951 (cat., no. 39); St. Louis, Washington University Art Gallery, *The Beautiful, the Sublime, and the Picturesque: British Influences on American Landscape Painting*, Feb. 18–Apr. 8, 1984; Cincinnati, Taft Museum, *J. M. W. Turner: The Foundations of Genius*, Sept. 18–Nov. 2, 1986 (cat. by Eric Shanes, no. 28 [color pl.]).

Literature Walter Armstrong, *Turner*, vol. 1, London, 1902, p. 246 (as *Chamonix: Mer de Glace*); Maurice W. Brockwell, *A Catalogue of Paintings in the Collection of Mr. and Mrs. Charles P. Taft*, New York, 1920, p. xxvii, no. 89; *Catalogue of the Taft Museum*, Cincinnati, 1939 and 1958, no. 164; Andrew Wilton, *J. M. W. Turner: His Art and Life*, New York, 1979, no. 389.

1931.389

J. M. W. Turner

Weissenthurm and the Hoche Monument

1817
Watercolor on paper, 197 x 311 mm (7¾ x 12½ in.)

In this haunting view of Germany, Turner portrays a battleground and the cenotaph to a French general. The major architectural form is the watchtower at Weissenthurm, a village on the Rhine about ten miles above Coblenz. At the far right is an obelisk that commemorates General Lazar Hoche, who valiantly led his troops against the Austrians in 1797. He crossed the Rhine and defeated the enemy at Neuweid, just across the river from Weissenthurm and just to the left of the territory represented in Turner's watercolor. Hoche died of natural causes at Wetzlar immediately following the Neuweid victory, and the monument was erected shortly thereafter. Turner frequently alluded to French Revolutionary events and to the Napoleonic Wars in his landscapes, and most often his attitude toward the French seems

1962.8

unfriendly. The death-tinged reference to French military glory may be a comment on the final defeat of the French in 1815, two years before this watercolor was executed. On Turner's Continental tour of 1817, from which the Taft watercolor stems, the artist also visited the field of Waterloo, and certainly Napoleonic battles were of interest to him. The Hoche obelisk could, however, be an incidental feature of no political significance. In any event, the monument plays a more general symbolic role, as a reminder of death, which so often in Turner's art is the only permanent result of valor and human history. The cenotaph also adds to the melancholy quiet of the scene. The meandering river flowing slowly into blue, misty nothingness and the eerie light produce an elegiac mood similar to that found in Caspar David Friedrich's contemporary works.

Eric Shanes refers to this image as a sunrise, but the placement of the light source so far to the south in Turner's landscape suggests that what is actually shown is a moonrise.[1] For a romantic landscapist, Turner depicted surprisingly few moonlit views. The most notable example in oil is *Keelmen Heaving Coals by Night* (1835, Washington, D.C., National Gallery of Art).[2] But like many other works by Turner, *Weissenthurm and the Hoche Monument,* with its central river, framing silhouettes, and soft atmosphere, is basically derived from Claude. Turner represented Weissenthurm in two other watercolors, an untraced work of 1817 and a distant view of about 1820.[3]

1. Eric Shanes, *J. M. W. Turner: The Foundations of Genius,* exh. cat., Taft Museum, Cincinnati, 1986, no. 35.

2. Martin Butlin and Evelyn Joll, *The Paintings of J. M. W. Turner,* 2 vols., rev. ed., New Haven and London, no. 360.

3. Andrew Wilton, *J. M. W. Turner: His Art and Life,* New York, 1979, nos. 661, 689.

Provenance Walter Fawkes, Farnley Hall; [Agnew, London, 1912]; Sir Algernon Firth; Mrs. Dewar; D. V. Shaw-Kennedy; C. R. N. Routh; [Agnew, 1954]; Jane Taft Ingalls, Cleveland (July 30, 1954); Jane Taft Ingalls bequest, 1962.

Exhibitions London, Burlington House, *Exhibition of Old Masters,* 1889

(cat., no. 63); London, Agnew, *Turner, Cox, and de Wint,* 1924 (cat. by A. P. Oppe, no. 24, pl. 5); London, Agnew, *Centenary Loan Exhibition of Water-Colours by J. M. W. Turner, R.A.,* 1951 (cat., no. 55); Cincinnati, Taft Museum, *J. M. W. Turner: The Foundations of Genius,* Sept. 18–Nov. 2, 1986 (cat. by Eric Shanes, no. 35 [color pl.]).

Literature Walter Armstrong, *Turner,* vol. 1, London, 1902, p. 284; Andrew Wilton, *J. M. W. Turner: His Art and Life,* New York, 1979, no. 660.

1962.8

J. M. W. Turner

Folkestone, Kent

ca. 1822
Watercolor on paper, 150 x 242 mm (5⅞ x 9⁹⁄₁₆ in.)

This bright watercolor depicts a scene on the southern coast of England with smugglers in the foreground. A dynamic line of chalk cliffs stretches into the distance toward Dover. The church of Saints Nary and Eanswyth stands in the middle ground atop the Folkestone bluff called Lees, and figures appear below on the beach. Shanes has noted that the residents of Folkestone, located close to France, earned their livelihood from smuggling and that here and in three other watercolors Turner portrayed the various stages of smuggling.[1]

In the first picture (1822, London, Tate Gallery, Turner Bequest, inv. no. CCVIII-Y) the smugglers hide kegs of gin under water. In the second (1824, private collection; Wilton, no. 509) the kegs are retrieved at twilight. The third image is the Taft watercolor, which shows the kegs being buried inland. In the final picture (ca. 1830, New Haven, Yale Center for British Art; Wilton, no. 826) the merchandise is found and confiscated by customs officers. The varying dates of the watercolors suggest that they were not conceived as a coherent series but perhaps as a repeated reflection on the acts and vicissitudes of illegal trade.

1931.385

During the 1820s and 1830s artists throughout Europe depicted brigands, outlaws, poachers, and smugglers. The subject, although harking back to Salvator Rosa, is particularly associated with the romantic interest in rebelliousness, outsider status, secretiveness, adventure, and high emotion. Nothing in the Taft watercolor indicates that Turner disapproved of smuggling, and romantic writers as well as artists often glorified the outlaw. In England Charles Eastlake, William Allan, Edwin Landseer, John Frederick Lewis, and many others portrayed glamorous folk of the underworld.

The Taft watercolor was engraved in 1826 by R. Wallis for a series titled *Picturesque Views on the Southern Coast of England.* Turner's other smuggling scenes were made to illustrate other topographical publications: *Marine Views* and *Picturesque Views in England and Wales.*[2] Drawings for *Folkestone, Kent* are in the Folkestone Sketchbook (London, Tate Gallery, Turner Bequest, inv. no. CXCVIII-17v).

The costumes and gestures of the smugglers, who possess the rotund and awkward proportions typical of Turner's figures, are repeated in many other works by him (e.g., *St. Mawes, Cornwall,* ca. 1822, New Haven, Yale Center for British Art; Wilton, no. 473). The dramatic cusp-shaped shadow (possibly of a cloud) that falls across the landscape is balanced by the sunny expanse of land in the distance, giving a rhythmic buoyancy to the composition.

1. Eric Shanes, *J. M. W. Turner: The Foundations of Genius,* exh. cat., Cincinnati, Taft Museum, 1986, no. 40. For other references, see Andrew Wilton, *J. M. W. Turner: His Art and Life,* New York, 1979.

2. Shanes, no. 40.

Provenance John Ruskin; given by Ruskin to Sir John Simeon; Humphrey Roberts; [Agnew, London, 1904]; [Scott and Fowles, New York]; Taft collection, Nov. 25, 1905.

Exhibitions Boston, Museum of Fine Arts, *Paintings, Drawings, and Prints by J. M. W. Turner, John Constable, and R. P. Bonington,* Mar. 19–Apr. 28, 1946; Art Gallery of Toronto [also Ottawa], *J. M. W. Turner,* Oct. 6–Dec. 31, 1951 (cat., no. 48); Cincinnati, Taft Museum, *J. M. W. Turner: The Foundations of Genius,* Sept. 18–Nov. 2, 1986 (cat. by Eric Shanes, no. 40 [color pl.]).

Literature Walter Armstrong, *Turner,* vol. 1, London, 1902, p. 254; W. G. Rawlinson, *The Engraved Work of Turner,* London, 1908 and 1913, no. 123, vol. 1, pp. xxix–xxxv, vol. 11, p. 66; Maurice W. Brockwell, *A Catalogue of Paintings in the Collection of Mr. and Mrs. Charles P. Taft,* New York, 1920, p. xxvii, no. 84; *Catalogue of the Taft Museum,* Cincinnati, 1939 and 1958, no. 166; Andrew Wilton, *J. M. W. Turner: His Art and Life,* New York, 1979, no. 480; Eric Shanes, *Turner's Rivers, Harbours, and Coasts,* London, 1981, p. 44.

1931.385

ৡ

J. M. W. Turner

Jedburgh Abbey

ca. 1832
Watercolor on paper, 94 x 159 mm (3¹¹⁄₁₆ x 6¼ in.)

The twelfth-century Scottish abbey, roofless and crumbling, appears in the central distance rising above modern buildings, the Jed River, and washerwomen in the foreground. The abbey's orange tinge and its mighty architecture and size set it apart from its surroundings. The clouds and light that seem to radiate from the Romanesque ruin further glorify it. Turner often placed grandiose, decrepit relics amid humdrum modern scenes to suggest decline and the sad march of history.

This watercolor was made to be engraved as an illustration for Sir Walter Scott's *Poetical Works* (London, 1834). The publisher Robert Cadell commissioned Turner in 1831, and the artist eventually produced twenty-four illustrations for the publication after visiting Scotland and Sir Walter Scott. *Jedburgh Abbey* was engraved by R. Brandard in 1833 for the frontispiece of volume 2, which includes *The Minstrelsy of the Scottish Border.*[1]

In 1118 the future King David I of Scotland founded an Augustinian priory at Jedburgh, elevating it to the status of abbey in 1147. Located in the much-disputed border region ten miles from England, this building was burned in 1523 and ruined again in 1544. The abbey was suppressed in 1559 and purchased

1931.383

in 1637 by the third earl of Lothian. The National Monuments Commission took over the building in 1913.

Turner depicted medieval buildings from his earliest years as an artist. Among his first mature romantic essays in watercolor are images of ruined Romanesque structures — gloomy, majestic, and huge. In a fairly late work such as *Jedburgh Abbey*, a Piranesian tone is still present. Although atmosphere and suggestion now outweigh architectural delineation, Turner's watercolor remains precise and specific.

Turner executed numerous drawings for book publishers, remuneratively wedding his taste for landscape to the mass production of illustrated books during the nineteenth century. Most frequently, the artist and the publisher were satisfied with the contemporary depiction of a site mentioned in the text. Narrative scenes and action were not required in illustrations; landscape by itself conveyed sufficient drama and meaning. Turner's interest in such subjects as Jedburgh Abbey, however, was not solely a matter of producing potboilers for the publishers. For his own satisfaction, he painted the works in color, exploring chromatic atmosphere even though the images would be reproduced in black and white, and indeed, the translation of Turner's vivid illustrations into mezzotint engravings is usually disappointing.

1. See Gerald Finley, *Landscapes of Memory: Turner as Illustrator to Scott*, London, 1980, pp. 125, 159, 246. The pencil sketch for *Jedburgh Abbey* (London, British Museum, Turner Bequest, Sketchbook CCLXVII) is reproduced in Finley, fig. 51.

Provenance Robert Cadell, London (1832); Henry Cooke; [Agnew, London, 1858]; T. Rought; John Feetham, Oakfields, Weybridge (sale, Christie's, London, May 27, 1895, no. 111; bt. H. Quilter); [Agnew, London, 1904]; [Scott and Fowles, New York]; Taft collection, Nov. 25, 1905.

Exhibitions London, Moon, Boys and Graves Gallery, 1832, 1833; London, Agnew, Feb. 1904; Cincinnati, Taft Museum, *J. M. W. Turner: The Foundations of Genius*, Sept. 18–Nov. 2, 1986 (cat. by Eric Shanes, no. 45 [color pl.]).

Literature Walter Armstrong, *Turner*, vol. I, London, 1902, p. 259; W. G. Rawlinson, *The Engraved Work of J. M. W. Turner*, London, 1908 and 1913, no. 495, vol. I, p. lvii, vol. II, p. 278; Maurice W. Brockwell, *A Catalogue of Paintings in the Collection of Mr. and Mrs. Charles P. Taft*, New York, 1920, p. xxviii, no. 90; *Catalogue of the Taft Museum*, Cincinnati, 1939 and 1958, no. 186; Andrew Wilton, *J. M. W. Turner: His Art and Life*, New York, 1979, no. 1072; Gerald Finley, *Landscapes of Memory: Turner as Illustrator to Scott*, London, 1980, pp. 125–27, fig. 52; Luke Herrmann, *Turner Prints: The Engraved Work of J. M. W. Turner*, Oxford, 1990, p. 197.

1931.383

J. M. W. Turner

Johnny Armstrong's Tower

ca. 1832
Watercolor on paper, 282 x 206 mm (11¹⁄₁₆ x 8⅛ in.)
Inscribed: *Border Minstrel / vol / Johnny Armstrongs / Tower*

This vignette was made to illustrate Sir Walter Scott's *Poetical Works* (London, 1834)[1] and was engraved by E. Goodall as the title page for volume 2, which includes *The Minstrelsy of the*

1931.386

Scottish Border. Before making sketches for the Scott illustrations, Turner visited the author's home in Scotland, Abbotsford, in 1831, when Scott was terminally ill.[2]

Beyond the tower in the distance rise hills, and a coach-and-four crosses a bridge in the foreground. An armored knight with crossbow stands behind the semiarchitectural frame at the left; a Scotsman with kilt and musket stands at the right. The entire image represents the complexity of title-page illustration during the early nineteenth century. Several levels of reality, time, scale, and style coexist on the sheet. Left unclear is whether the colored landscape is meant to represent a page with a watercolor drawing or the landscape itself. Angled viewpoints and symmetrical planar arrangements are presented simultaneously. What sort of space lies behind the purported page or plaque in the center of the composition? The artificial ornament of a title page and the representation of the landscape are weighted equally, while the modern, medieval, and more recent past are shown side by side. The lateral figures evoke not only the themes of Scott's novels but also the writer's rich collection of armor, weaponry, and national costume.[3] The figures were not engraved in the octavo edition of Scott's poems.

Turner frequently employed the vignette format for his illustrations; the scene blurs out asymmetrically at the edges, forming a generally ovoid compositional shape. This organizational device was commonplace during the first sixty years of the nineteenth century, although in Turner's case the vignette composition also may have been attractive for its vortical implications. Many of the artist's paintings spiral into depth or contain great sweeping curves that are similar in some ways to a vignette.

Johnny Armstrong was a famous Scottish outlaw-hero and clan chief of the early sixteenth century who raided the border areas of England. He was Laird of Gilnockie and was hanged along with thirty-six of his followers in 1529. His tower, also known as Hollows Tower and Gilnockie Tower, is outside Langholm on the Esk River. It is today a private house. In Turner's watercolor the tower is roofless but stands powerfully and shines brightly in a landscape that ripples with energy. Gerald Finley sees the speeding carriage as a *vanitas* motif, referring to Scott's death.[4] Turner made sketches of the tower in Sketchbook CCLXVI (London, Tate Gallery, Turner Bequest).

1. On this commission, see the preceding entry on *Jedburgh Abbey* (1931.383), which was made for the same volume. On *Johnny Armstrong's Tower*, see Eric Shanes, *J. M. W. Turner: The Foundations of Genius*, exh. cat., Taft Museum, Cincinnati, 1986, no. 46.

2. On Turner's visit to Abbotsford and his illustrations for Scott, see Gerald Finley, *Landscapes of Memory: Turner as Illustrator to Scott*, London, 1980.

3. On Scott's collection, see Clive Wainwright, *The Romantic Interior: The British Collector at Home*, New Haven, 1989, pp. 147–207.

4. Finley, p. 159.

Provenance Robert Cadell; H. A. J. Munro, Novar (sale, Christie's, London, June 2, 1877, no. 2; bt. Gibbs); Lady Ashburton; [Scott and Fowles, New York]; Taft collection, Nov. 25, 1905.

Exhibitions London, Moon, Boys and Graves Gallery, 1832, 1833; Indianapolis, John Herron Art Museum [also Dayton, Ohio], *Turner in America*, Nov. 6, 1955–Jan. 25, 1956 (cat., no. 25 [ill.]); Cincinnati, Taft Museum, *J. M. W. Turner: The Foundations of Genius*, Sept. 18–Nov. 2, 1986 (cat. by Eric Shanes, no. 46 [color pl.]).

Literature *The Times* [London], June 1 and 4, 1877; Walter Armstrong, *Turner*, vol. I, London, 1902, p. 259; W. G. Rawlinson, *The Engraved Work of Turner*, London, 1908 and 1913, no. 496, vol. I, pp. xxix–xxxv, vol. II, p. 278; Maurice W. Brockwell, *A Catalogue of Paintings in the Collection of Mr. and Mrs. Charles P. Taft*, New York, 1920, pp. xxvii–xxviii, no. 86; *Catalogue of the Taft Museum*, Cincinnati, 1939 and 1958, no. 160; Andrew Wilton, *J. M. W. Turner: His Art and Life*, New York, 1979, no. 1073; Gerald Finley, *Landscapes of Memory: Turner as Illustrator to Scott*, London, 1980, pp. 159–60, fig. 66.

1931.386

J. M. W. Turner

The Death of Lycidas — "Vision of the Guarded Mount"

ca. 1834
Watercolor on paper, 199 x 148 mm (7 13/16 x 5 13/16 in.)

Turner made this vignette to illustrate John Milton's *Poetical Works* (London, 1835); it was engraved for that publication by W. Miller. In the watercolor great waves roar, seamen cling to masts, strange lights flash amid swirling winds, and a lone man sinks into the deep at the lower edge of the vignette. High above this turmoil a tiny winged figure stands on the tower of Saint

1931.384

Michael's Mount, Cornwall. The greatest blaze of light surrounds this smallest figure. The watercolor previously was titled *Saint Michael's Mount*, but Shanes has recently found that in the publication of 1835 the image is titled *The Death of Lycidas — "Vision of the Guarded Mount."*[1] He also points out that Turner's work specifically illustrates lines 161–63 of *Lycidas:*

> Where the great vision of the guarded mount
> Looks towards Namacos and Bayona's hold;
> Look homeward angel. . . .

Shanes ties the image to the explanations of Sir Egerton Brydges, which accompany the Milton publication of 1835. Brydges remarked that Milton's lines portray the angel Saint Michael looking toward Spain from atop Saint Michael's Mount in Cornwall. The angel is instructed to look homeward to the Cornish coast where the corpse of shipwrecked Lycidas is floating. In the watercolor the dead body of Lycidas is at the bottom of the picture.

Turner's figure of Saint Michael, indistinct yet all ablaze, may be indebted to Francis Danby's painting of one of the Angels of Revelation, exhibited at the Royal Academy in 1829 (New York, collection of Robert Rosenblum).[2] Danby's dark but glowing figure surrounded by clouds and rays of light stands frontally with outstretched arms in the center of the painting. Artists such as Danby and John Martin derived much of their spectacular art from Turner's early visions of grand catastrophe, but Turner could also have been stimulated by these younger men.

The taste for Miltonic subjects in art reached its high point during the late eighteenth and early nineteenth centuries.

Among others, Henry Fuseli, William Blake, and George Romney produced scores of images. Despite the efforts of John Martin and other artists during the 1820s, this enthusiasm began to wane. Some scenes from *Comus* were executed to try out mural techniques during the 1840s, but by midcentury Milton had become a duly revered but unfashionable poet, fit only for the schoolroom. Although Milton's stern, otherworldly dramas were attractive to romantic artists, Turner included, the advent of realism toward the middle of the century caused appreciation of both Milton and Turner to fall sharply.

1. Eric Shanes, *J. M. W. Turner: The Foundations of Genius*, exh. cat., Taft Museum, Cincinnati, 1986, no. 47.

2. The Danby painting is reproduced and discussed in Frederick Cummings and Allen Staley, *Romantic Art in Britain: Paintings and Drawings, 1760–1860*, exh. cat., Detroit Institute of Arts, 1968, no. 161.

Provenance H. A. J. Munro, Novar (sale, Christie's, London, June 2, 1877, no. 31; bt. Bromley); George Gurney (sale, Christie's, London, Mar. 17, 1883, no. 198; bt. in); sale, Christie's, London, July 11, 1903, no. 42; bt. Agnew; [Scott and Fowles, New York]; Taft collection, Nov. 25, 1905.

Exhibitions London, Royal Academy of Arts, 1892 (cat., no. 59); London, Agnew, Feb. 1904; Cincinnati, Taft Museum, *J. M. W. Turner: The Foundations of Genius*, Sept. 18–Nov. 2, 1986 (cat. by Eric Shanes, no. 47 [color pl.]).

Literature Walter Armstrong, *Turner*, vol. I, London, 1902, p. 266; W. G. Rawlinson, *The Engraved Work of J. M. W. Turner*, London, 1908 and 1913, no. 603, vol. I, p. lviii, vol. II, p. 314; Maurice W. Brockwell, *A Catalogue of Paintings in the Collection of Mr. and Mrs. Charles P. Taft*, New York, 1920, p. xxviii, no. 94; *Catalogue of the Taft Museum*, Cincinnati, 1939 and 1958, no. 165; Andrew Wilton, *J. M. W. Turner: His Art and Life*, New York, 1979, no. 1269.

1931.384

J. M. W. Turner

Lake Nemi

ca. 1835
Watercolor, pencil, and bodycolor, sheet 267 x 221 mm (10½ x 8¹¹⁄₁₆ in.), comp. 185 x 145 mm (7⁵⁄₁₆ x 5¹¹⁄₁₆ in.)

Lake Nemi was visited by virtually every tourist to Italy and was painted by J. R. Cozens, Richard Wilson, and innumerable other English artists. Turner himself visited Lake Nemi, located just south of Rome, in 1819 and probably again in 1828. Travel guides from the eighteenth and nineteenth centuries nearly all recommend a visit to Nemi, proclaiming the idyllic beauty of the place as representative of classical harmony in nature. In Turner's watercolor the classical architectural fragments in the foreground allude to that association. The Claudean trees, placidity, and sunniness of this view of the small round lake also contribute to the mood of ease and contentment. The figures who lounge about the foreground are in contemporary Italian peasant costume, which was much admired by tourists and was depicted frequently by genre painters such as Thomas Uwins and John Frederick Lewis. A great part of Turner's art is devoted to the Claudean ideal of peace and harmony and evokes an ancient

1931.387

golden age (even when the figures wear modern dress). *Lake Nemi* belongs to that strain in Turner's work that stands in opposition to his visions of nature's threat and fury.

This watercolor was probably made to illustrate a book of poems by a certain Dr. Broadley, which was to be published privately around 1844. It is one of six such designs, but the volume was never published. The engraving by E. Goodall was only published after Turner's death when it was used to illustrate a work titled *Art and Song* in 1867.[1]

Turner had previously depicted Lake Nemi: he began, but left incomplete, a large oil of the subject in 1828 (London, Tate Gallery; Butlin and Joll, no. 304), and drawings of the site are in the Vatican Fragments and sketchbooks of 1819.[2] During the 1840s Turner also produced a large watercolor of Lake Nemi, now in the British Museum (Wilton, no. 1381).[3] Other watercolor views of the lake are in the collection of Christopher Lennox-Boyd, London (Wilton, no. 711); a private collection (Wilton, no. 1560); and the South African National Museum, Cape Town (Wilton, no. 1561). In its general features the Taft watercolor is related to such pastoral Italian paintings as *Childe Harold's Pilgrimage* (1831, London, Tate Gallery; Butlin and Joll, no. 342).

1. On the book of poems by Dr. Broadley and Goodall's engraving, see W. G. Rawlinson, *The Engraved Work of J. M. W. Turner*, London, 1908 and 1913, vol. I, no. 638, vol. II, pp. 322, 325. See also Eric Shanes, *J. M. W. Turner: The Foundations of Genius*, exh. cat., Taft Museum, Cincinnati, 1986, no. 52.

2. See Martin Butlin and Evelyn Joll, *The Paintings of J. M. W. Turner*, rev. ed., New Haven and London, 1984, no. 304, which notes the sketches and drawings related to the unfinished oil of Lake Nemi.

3. Andrew Wilton, *J. M. W. Turner: His Art and Life*, New York, 1979.

Provenance Edward Fordham (sale, Christie's, London, Apr. 30, 1904, no. 48; bt. McLean); [Scott and Fowles, New York]; Taft collection, Oct. 24, 1904.

Exhibitions Indianapolis, John Herron Art Museum [also Dayton, Ohio], *Turner in America,* Nov. 6, 1955–Jan. 25, 1956 (cat., no. 26); New York, Otto Gerson Gallery, *Joseph Mallord William Turner: Watercolors and Drawings,* Nov. 9–Dec. 10, 1960 (cat., no. 24); Cincinnati, Taft Museum, *J. M. W. Turner: The Foundations of Genius,* Sept. 18–Nov. 2, 1986 (cat. by Eric Shanes, no. 52 [color pl.]).

Literature Walter Armstrong, *Turner,* vol. I, London, 1902, p. 268; W. G. Rawlinson, *The Engraved Work of J. M. W. Turner,* 1908 and 1913, no. 638, vol. II, pp. 322, 325; Maurice W. Brockwell, *A Catalogue of Paintings in the Collection of Mr. and Mrs. Charles P. Taft,* New York, 1920, p. xxvii, no. 93; *Catalogue of the Taft Museum,* Cincinnati, 1939 and 1958, no. 163; Andrew Wilton, *J. M. W. Turner: His Art and Life,* New York, 1979, no. 1311.

1931.387

J. M. W. Turner

The Whale on Shore

ca. 1837
Watercolor on paper, 100 x 143 mm (4 x 5⅝ in.)

Robert K. Wallace and Eric Shanes recently explained this previously puzzling watercolor by Turner.[1] They discovered that Turner made this work to be engraved as an illustration to *Landscape: Historical Illustrations of Scotland and the Waverley Novels.* The book was published by Fisher and Son, London, in two volumes in 1836 and 1837. The Reverend G. N. Wright wrote the book's letterpress. Seven of Turner's illustrations appear in the book, but not *The Whale on Shore.* That particular subject was illustrated in volume 2, page 38, by a little-known artist named Harden Sidney Melville (act. 1837–81). Although the Taft water-color evidently portrays the same scene, for some reason Melville's design was published instead of Turner's.

The passage illustrated is from Sir Walter Scott's novel *The Pirate* and describes a beached whale at Burgh Westra in Orkney. Scott related how the animal was washed over a sandbar into a creek. The local inhabitants attacked the helpless whale under the direction of a Udaller (a freehold tenant of land in the Orkneys) who wore a bearskin cap and sea boots. The islanders bound the tail with a cable and anchor and then harpooned and shot the beast, which roared and spouted brine and blood. In dying, the whale broke the cable and overturned a boat with its tail. The thrashing tail, anchor, cable, weapons, clothes, boats, and sandbar of Scott's description are all included in Turner's dramatic representation of the whale's final moments.

Turner made three watercolor vignettes of whaling subjects during the 1830s at about the same time as the Taft picture, but they are unrelated to it.[2] Turner is known to have read Thomas Beal's *Natural History of the Sperm Whale* (London, 1835, 2d ed., 1839), and whaling became increasingly interesting to him during the mid-1840s. He exhibited two oils on whaling themes in 1845 and two more in 1846.[3] In addition to the inherent violence, danger, and gigantism of the subject, Turner was probably interested in attracting a patron from the whaling industry.[4]

1. Eric Shanes, *J. M. W. Turner: The Foundations of Genius,* exh. cat., Taft Museum, Cincinnati, 1986, no. 54, who discusses his joint research with Robert K. Wallace.

2. Andrew Wilton, *J. M. W. Turner: His Art and Life,* New York, 1979, nos. 1308–10.

3. See Martin Butlin and Evelyn Joll, *The Paintings of J. M. W. Turner,* 2 vols., rev. ed., New Haven and London, 1984, nos. 414, 415, 423, 426; Barry Venning, "Turner's Whaling Subjects," *Burlington Magazine,* vol. CXXVII (Feb. 1985), pp. 75–81; John Gage, *Turner and Watercolours,* exh. cat., Arts Council of Great Britain traveling exhibition, 1974, p. 189.

4. Venning, pp. 75–81.

1931.382

Provenance John Feetham, Oakfields, Weybridge (sale, Christie's, London, May 27, 1895, no. 112; bt. H. Quilter); [Scott and Fowles, New York, 1903]; Taft collection, Sept. 24, 1903.

Exhibitions New York, Otto Gerson Gallery, *Joseph Mallord William Turner: Watercolors and Drawings*, Nov. 9–Dec. 10, 1960 (cat., no. 26 [ill.]); Cincinnati, Taft Museum, *J. M. W. Turner: The Foundations of Genius*, Sept. 18–Nov. 2, 1986 (cat. by Eric Shanes, no. 54 [ill.]).

Literature Maurice W. Brockwell, *A Catalogue of Paintings in the Collection of Mr. and Mrs. Charles P. Taft*, New York, 1920, p. xxix, no. 95; *Catalogue of the Taft Museum*, Cincinnati, 1939 and 1958, no. 184; Andrew Wilton, *J. M. W. Turner: His Art and Life*, New York, 1979, no. 1307; Barry Venning, "Turner's Whaling Subjects," *Burlington Magazine*, vol. cxxvii (Feb. 1985), pp. 75–81.

1931.382

J. M. W. Turner

Lake of Thun

ca. 1845–51
Watercolor on paper, 369 x 541 mm (14½ x 21⅝₁₆ in.)

Although there is no doubt that this watercolor is a late work by Turner, there has been some disagreement about its exact date. Wilton suggests that it is among the artist's last works, about 1850–51.[1] Shanes, however, claims that Turner had given up watercolor painting by 1848 and therefore dates the Taft picture about 1845.[2] Like other watercolors of Swiss sites from the mid-1840s, the present example is soft, filmy, and suffused with yellow light and features a complex architectural platform in the foreground. As an additional basis for the date of 1845, Shanes points out that the figures in quasi-historical costume here are nowhere present in works from the very end of Turner's career.

Perhaps the most significant question raised by both Shanes and Wilton concerns the subject. There is no good reason, they claim, for calling the view Lake Thun; no specific features of that site are represented. Furthermore, Shanes notes that the figures may allude to some historical or literary narrative. The characters in the scene point, gesture, and look across the water, but the action or event represented is uncertain. Without further information, however, the traditional title, *Lake of Thun*, will be retained.

Although Turner was trained as an architectural draftsman and became professor of perspective at the Royal Academy, in many late works such as the *Lake of Thun*, the delineation of firm architectural forms is curiously confused. The platform in the foreground is spatially unclear; levels and scale change suddenly, edges and corners disappear or warp, and shadows provide no clue to the three-dimensional configuration of the plateau. This amorphous portrayal allows the foreground architecture to melt easily into the enveloping light and perhaps more importantly adds a sense of movement and instability to even the hard, constructed elements of the scene. This sense of fluctuating, unbound energy is present throughout Turner's late works.

1. Andrew Wilton, *J. M. W. Turner: His Art and Life*, New York, 1979, no. 1567, and pp. 246–48.

2. Eric Shanes, *J. M. W. Turner: The Foundations of Genius*, exh. cat., Cincinnati, Taft Museum, 1986, no. 57.

Provenance General Rawdon; William Quilter, Norwood, Lincoln (sale, Christie's, London, Apr. 9, 1875, no. 237; bt. in); sale, Christie's, London, May 18, 1889, no. 97 (bt. Agnew, London); Joseph Ruston, Monks Manor, Lincoln (sale, Christie's, London, July 4, 1913, no. 106; bt. Agnew, London); [Scott and Fowles, New York]; Taft collection, Dec. 22, 1914.

Exhibitions Leeds, *National Exhibition of Works of Art*, 1868 (cat., no. 2064); London, Old Water-Colour Society, 1870 (cat., no. 227); London, Royal Academy of Arts, 1873 (cat., no. 377); Cincinnati Art Museum,

1931.390

1935–36; Boston, Museum of Fine Arts, *Paintings, Drawings, and Prints by J. M. W. Turner, John Constable, and R. P. Bonington,* Mar. 19–Apr. 28, 1946 (cat., no. 46); Bloomfield Hills, Mich., Cranbrook Academy of Art, *Light and the Painter,* Sept. 5–28, 1952 (cat., no. 39); Art Institute of Zanesville, Ohio, *Masterpieces from Ohio Museums,* Apr. 11–May 9, 1954; Indianapolis, John Herron Art Museum [also Dayton, Ohio], *Turner in America,* Nov. 6, 1955–Jan. 25, 1956 (cat., no. 48 [ill.]); New York, Otto Gerson Gallery, *Joseph Mallord William Turner: Watercolors and Drawings,* Nov. 9–Dec. 10, 1960 (cat., no. 37 [ill.]); Grand Rapids Art Museum, Mich., Feb. 7–28, 1965; Cincinnati, Taft Museum, *J. M. W. Turner: The Foundations of Genius,* Sept. 18–Nov. 2, 1986 (cat. by Eric Shanes, no. 57 [color pl.]).

Literature Walter Armstrong, *Turner,* vol. 1, London, 1902, p. 280; Maurice W. Brockwell, *A Catalogue of Paintings in the Collection of Mr. and Mrs. Charles P. Taft,* New York, 1920, p. xxviii, no. 88; *Catalogue of the Taft Museum,* Cincinnati, 1939 and 1958, no. 159; Andrew Wilton, *J. M. W. Turner: His Art and Life,* New York, 1979, pp. 246–48, fig. 258, no. 1567.

1931.390

Thomas Lawrence

Bristol 1769–1830 London

Thomas Lawrence, something of a child prodigy, was encouraged at an early age by his innkeeper father to recite literature and to make portrait drawings for the hotel guests, first in Bristol and then at Devizes.[1] His only formal study was at a private school in Bristol for a short time. The father was a ne'er-do-well entrepreneur, and after his failure as an innkeeper in 1779, his son became the major financial support of the family, working as a portraitist in pastel and pencil at Oxford and from 1780 at Bath. At Bath Lawrence not only came into contact with fashionable society but also saw private art collections and numerous engravings after the old masters. He made copies after Guido Reni, Rubens, and the Carracci. In 1785 he won a prize from the Society of Arts of London for a copy after Raphael's *Transfiguration.* His first recorded oil painting dates from 1786. In 1787 he settled in London, where he received some advice from Sir Joshua Reynolds and spent three months at the Royal Academy schools. However, Lawrence had already begun to exhibit at the Royal Academy and by 1788 was well known. By 1790 Lawrence was receiving royal portrait commissions and was highly successful at the Royal Academy exhibitions. In 1791, through the direct influence of the king, Lawrence was made associate of the academy at the age of twenty-one. In 1794 he was elected full academician. In achieving this position, he defeated John Hoppner, his chief rival in portraiture and the Prince of Wales's painter. Lawrence was made Painter in Ordinary to the King immediately after Reynolds's death in 1792.

Lawrence based his style on that of Reynolds's late work, but he elongated figures, dramatized settings, and created gestures, glances, and postures of exaggerated elegance, confidence, sentiment, and action. He produced monumental portraits of figures standing on tiptoe who smile and gesticulate before gigantic skyscapes. He painted fluently with lavish strokes of pigment and glittering highlights. The mannered power of these dashing portraits has long been interpreted as the epitome of Regency taste, meretricious and theatrical.

Lawrence attracted commissions from the greatest people of his era, becoming the Prince Regent's chief portraitist in 1814. At royal command he painted the allied leaders of the Napoleonic Wars for the Waterloo Chamber at Windsor Castle. From 1818 to 1820 he traveled on the Continent to carry out this project, staying at Aix-la-Chapelle, Vienna, and Rome and acting as ambassador and courtier as well as portraitist. His only previous journey abroad had been a brief visit to Paris in 1814; he traveled there once again in 1825 to complete the Waterloo commission. On his return to England in 1820, Lawrence was elected president of the Royal Academy.

During the Regency period, Lawrence was a handsome and respected figure, friend of actors and aristocrats, and purported lover of several fashionable women. He was suspected of being the paramour of the Prince Regent's wife, Caroline, but was exonerated of this charge by an investigation of 1806. Lawrence was knighted in 1815. He established an international reputation, was made a member of most of the art academies of Europe, never lacked for sitters, and from the 1790s onward employed several assistants.

Despite his success, Lawrence suffered financial ruin several times and was forced to make unhappy arrangements with bankers. His insolvency stemmed largely from his unceasing purchase of old-master drawings. His collection, one of the finest ever formed, was dispersed after his death. During his early career Lawrence occasionally attempted history paintings, most notably a Miltonian subject of 1797 influenced by James Barry and Henry Fuseli. He recognized, however, that his talents lay in portraiture, and he continued the eighteenth-century portrait tradition of Reynolds, Gainsborough, and Romney. Lawrence's dynamic, bravura pictures, however, are so rhapsodic and dazzling that he is justly considered one of the great masters of nineteenth-century romanticism.

1. On Lawrence, see D. E. Williams, *The Life and Correspondence of Sir Thomas Lawrence,* 2 vols., London, 1831; R. S. Gower, *Sir Thomas Lawrence,* London, 1900; Walter Armstrong, *Lawrence,* London, 1913; G. S. Layard, *Sir Thomas Lawrence's Letterbag,* London, 1926; Kenneth Garlick, *Sir Thomas Lawrence,* London, 1954; Kenneth Garlick, "A Catalogue of the Paintings, Drawings, and Pastels of Sir Thomas Lawrence," *The Walpole Society,* 1962–64, vol. XXXIX (1964).

Follower of Thomas Lawrence

Jane Bell Livesay

ca. 1810
Pencil and chalk on paper, 216 x 187 mm (8½ x 7⅜ in.)

This handsome young woman, seated in profile with folded arms, is drawn in the manner of Lawrence but is not by the master himself. Garlick deliberately excluded this work from his catalogue of the artist's oeuvre.[1] Although this early-nineteenth-century drawing is very delicate and subtle, the contours do not swell and flow, the eyes are not emphasized, and the drawing of the body is somewhat hesitant: it is a fine work, but not by

1931.380

Lawrence. Nothing is known of the sitter, who was identified as Jane Bell Livesay in an inscription on an earlier frame. There is also no known authentic work by Lawrence that corresponds to this drawing. The dress of the sitter, as well as the style of the furniture, dates the drawing to around 1810.

1. Kenneth Garlick, "A Catalogue of the Paintings, Drawings, and Pastels of Sir Thomas Lawrence," *The Walpole Society, 1962–64*, vol. XXXIX (1964). He was certainly aware of this drawing because he cited Josephine Galbraith's article, noted below, in which this work is illustrated.

Provenance Sale, Christie's, London, Mar. 16, 1908 (according to Armstrong; see Literature); [Scott and Fowles, New York]; gift of Scott and Fowles to the Tafts, Nov. 2, 1910.

Literature Walter Armstrong, *Sir Thomas Lawrence*, London, 1913, p. 185; Josephine C. Galbraith, "Two Drawings by Sir Thomas Lawrence in the Taft Collection," *Bulletin of the Cincinnati Art Museum*, vol. VI, no. 2 (Apr. 1935), pp. 35–43, ill. p. 37; *Catalogue of the Taft Museum*, Cincinnati, 1939 and 1958, no. 42.

1931.380

❧

Copyist after Thomas Lawrence

The Ladies Maryborough

Nineteenth century
Pencil and chalk on paper, 175 x 238 mm (6⅞ x 9⅜ in.)

This drawing portrays the three daughters of William Wellesley, baron Maryborough, third earl of Mornington. At the left is Mary Charlotte Anne (d. 1845), who married Sir Charles Bagot in 1806. In the center is Emily Harriet (d. 1881), who in 1814 married Lord Fitzroy Somerset, first baron Raglan, commander of British forces in the Crimean War. At the right is Priscilla Anne (1793–1879), who married John, lord Burghersh, earl of Westmorland, in 1811. The three women were nieces of the duke of Wellington.

Kenneth Garlick, the chief authority on Lawrence, has concluded that the Taft drawing is the work of a copyist.[1] Lawrence's original drawing of 1814 (Lord Raglan, Centilla Court, Usk, Wales) shows the three sisters full length, seated on the ground. It was engraved by J. Thomson in 1827. The Taft drawing presents just the heads of the sisters as they appear in the original work. One must agree with Garlick that the Taft drawing is not

1931.379

by Lawrence: it is somewhat hard and lacking in fluency in the outlines and shows patchlike shading. The copyist remains unnamed. Lawrence himself made a copy for the duke of Wellington (Stratfield Saye, Wellington Collection), and other copies of the heads of the three ladies Maryborough by unknown hands are known. One was sold at Sotheby's, London, on June 30, 1920; another was sold at Christie's, London, on February 12, 1926. At Stratfield Saye, the Wellington country estate, there is a receipt dated 1818 for a copy of Lawrence's drawing by Mary Smirke. Which copy was made by Smirke has yet to be discovered.

Lawrence had many assistants during his career, including George Henry Harlow and John Frederick Lewis, and the production of replicas was a standard part of any successful portraitist's studio. Lawrence was dedicated to draftsmanship, owned a magnificent collection of old-master drawings, and prepared his richly painted portraits with careful drawing on canvas. His highly finished drawings were often copied by both amateurs and professionals.

1. See Kenneth Garlick, "A Catalogue of the Paintings, Drawings, and Pastels of Sir Thomas Lawrence," *The Walpole Society, 1962–64,* vol. XXXIX (1964), p. 219. The information given above on other copies has been gathered from Garlick, pp. 218–19.

Provenance E. J. Edward, London; [Scott and Fowles, New York]; Taft collection, Mar. 18, 1914.

Exhibition London, Edward Gallery, and New York, Scott and Fowles, *Sixty Drawings by Sir Thomas Lawrence,* 1913 (cat. by C. Reginald Grundy, no. 41).

Literature C. Reginald Grundy, "The Drawings of Sir Thomas Lawrence," *Connoisseur,* vol. XXX (May–Aug. 1911), p. 237; Maurice W. Brockwell, *A Catalogue of Paintings in the Collection of Mr. and Mrs. Charles P. Taft,* New York, 1920, no. 58; Josephine Galbraith, "Two Drawings by Sir Thomas Lawrence in the Taft Collection," *Bulletin of the Cincinnati Art Museum,* vol. VI, no. 2 (Apr. 1935), pp. 35–43, ill. p. 39; *Catalogue of the Taft Museum,* Cincinnati, 1939 and 1958, no. 38.

1931.379

Frederick Waters Watts

Bath? 1800–1872 Hampstead

F. W. Watts was a prolific landscape painter whose small-scale works were often confused with those of John Constable during Constable's lifetime and have continued to be misattributed to the present time. The fullest and most reliable information on the artist was recently published by Ian Fleming-Williams and Leslie Parris.[1] Watts was born on October 7, 1800, apparently in Bath, but he spent his entire working life in Hampstead, where Constable also lived. Watts's father was at one time in the Royal Navy, and Watts's mother was a daughter of Ambrose Eyre, M.A., rector of Levrington, Isle of Ely. This maternal grandfather was the nephew of Edmund Keene, bishop of Ely. Watts can probably be identified with a certain William Watts, who is recorded as being a student at the Royal Academy schools in London in 1817 and who won silver medals there in 1819, 1820, and 1821.

Watts exhibited 76 works at the Royal Academy between 1821 and 1860, 108 works at the British Institution between 1823 and 1862, and 71 works at the Society of British Artists between 1825 and 1838. These paintings were almost entirely landscapes, from whose titles some account of Watts's presumed sketching tours can be deduced. He probably visited Wales during the early 1820s, Hampshire around 1829, and Derbyshire and Devon during the 1830s. He must also have visited France (two Rouen subjects are recorded) and Scotland. A great many of his pictures also depict the area near his home in Hampstead. Watts's earlier works often have topographical titles, whereas he showed more general subjects in his later years (e.g., *A Water-Mill).* In a letter of 1859 Watts noted that he rarely portrayed specific places but instead invented his own compositions based on various sketches and motifs.[2]

Although there is no evidence that Watts studied under Constable or even knew him personally, he is known to have made copies of paintings by Constable, as well as copies of works by earlier landscapists such as Meyndert Hobbema. Watts must have known Constable's large finished canvases exhibited at the Royal Academy, for a number of Watts's works are close variations of authentic paintings by Constable. Among the numerous works by Watts misattributed to Constable are a painting acquired by the Louvre in 1873 and one acquired by the Metropolitan Museum of Art in New York in 1897. During Constable's lifetime one of his works was sold at auction for a pittance because it was believed to be by Watts.

Watts produced many sketches in addition to finished paintings, although he apparently was inactive as a painter during the last ten years of his life. He married twice, had three daughters by his first wife, and was survived by his second wife, Julia Watts.

1. Ian Fleming-Williams and Leslie Parris, *The Discovery of Constable,* London, 1984, pp. 205–11.

2. Letter published in Leslie Parris, Ian Fleming-Williams, and Conal Shields, *Constable: Paintings, Watercolours, and Drawings,* exh. cat., Tate Gallery, London, 1976, no. 348.

Frederick Waters Watts

Landscape with Canal

ca. 1820–60
Oil on canvas, 60.6 x 88.9 cm (23⅞ x 35 in.)
Signed lower right: *J. Constable*

This placid landscape with boatmen, rural buildings, tow horses, and a richly clouded sky is very much in the manner of John Constable. In fact, this painting, with a suitable signature, was acquired by the Tafts as a Constable. Charles S. Rhyne and other scholars have rightly rejected that attribution and instead claim Watts to be the artist.[1] The Taft work is very typical of Watts's Constable-like paintings. In contrast to works by Constable, here the sharply defined edges of the architecture, the slender, thinly foliated trees, the squarish figures, insistent verticals, and dashlike strokes in the foreground all indicate that this is by Watts. The exact mirror reflections in the water, the dryly repetitive shapes of the barges, and the overall tight description of form also run counter to the moist atmosphere and flowing

1931.467

movement of Constable's works. Watts's trees are not vigorously planted in animate nature but stand rootless in unresponsive ground, and Watts's sky is neither space-creating nor firmly related to the forms below.

In theme and mood, however, Watts has successfully carried on the art of Constable in his portrayal of a halcyon rustic world. As in Constable's works before the late 1820s, Watts shows diligent labor in a sunny and humane world. These images are almost nationalistic visions of a perfect agricultural society, peaceful and hardworking. Although no specific work by Constable has been imitated, Watts's painting bears generic similarity to such pictures as Constable's *Dedham Lock and Mill* (1820, London, Victoria and Albert Museum). Watts's trees, however, with their somewhat spiky leaves, are more reminiscent of those found in works by the seventeenth-century Dutch painter Hobbema.

The composition and the space of this picture as well as the subject and the atmosphere are highly Constablesque. The low horizon, monumental sky, pathway into depth at the right, general horizontality, and triangular succession of trees are all also in accord with Constable's style. The canal scenes of both artists present modern transportation and commerce in an idyllic light while retaining the communal warmth of village life and the strength of old traditions. The romantic longing for the security of an imagined past, the fresh breeze of the natural world, and the confrontation with modern ways are brought harmoniously together.

Watts's painting may be merely a charming pastiche, but it also indicates that Constable attracted some ardent followers in spite of frequent criticism from art critics and the public. Constable may never have achieved the enormous influence of his contemporary J. M. W. Turner, whose style and subjects were far more spectacular, but Constable's loving vision of commonplace rural terrain could still attract a few adherents. By the turn

of the century, his vision would come to represent the epitome of unalloyed naturalism and specifically English values.

1. Letters in the files of the Taft Museum indicate that Charles S. Rhyne, Graham Reynolds, and Mark Roskill have all questioned the attribution to Constable and favored a reattribution to F. W. Watts.

Provenance James Orrock (1888); Arthur Sanderson, Edinburgh (1897); Romer Williams, Newnham Hall, Daventry; [Agnew, London]; [Scott and Fowles, New York]; Taft collection, Mar. 18, 1914.

Exhibitions London, Grosvenor Gallery, 1888 (cat., no. 279); Paris, Galeries Georges Petit, *Exposition de cent chefs-d'oeuvre*, 1892 (cat., pp. 13–14, 44 [ill.]); Bloomfield Hills, Mich., Cranbrook Academy of Art, *Light and the Painter*, Sept. 5–28, 1952 (cat., no. 19).

Literature Cosmo Monkhouse, "A Northern Home," *Art Journal* (1897), p. 80 (ill.); Maurice W. Brockwell, *A Catalogue of Paintings in the Collection of Mr. and Mrs. Charles P. Taft*, New York, 1920, pp. xxix-xxx, no. 41; *Catalogue of the Taft Museum*, Cincinnati, 1939 and 1958, no. 88.

1931.467

Richard Parkes Bonington
Arnold, near Nottingham 1802–1828 London

Richard Parkes Bonington can be considered a French artist as well as an English one.[1] Although he was born and died in England and had gained a great reputation in Britain by the time of his early death, he was trained in France. He became a major figure in the circle of Eugène Delacroix and spent most of his adult life in France. His style is related to both the landscapes of Thomas Girtin and J. M. W. Turner and French romanticism of the 1820s.

Bonington's father, who for a time was a painter and drawing master, left Nottinghamshire in 1817 to set up a lacemaking business in Calais. There, the young Bonington met the artist Louis Francia who encouraged his talents, interested him in coastal scenery, and familiarized him with English watercolor tech-

1931.443

niques and subjects. Bonington found a patron in Dunkerque, but moved in 1818 to Paris, where he entered the Ecole des Beaux-Arts and the atelier of Antoine-Jean Gros in 1820. He studied under Gros for two years, made copies in the Louvre, and became the friend of Delacroix, Alexandre Colin, Eugène Isabey, the Fielding family of painters, Thomas Shotter Boys, and William Callow.

Bonington made the first of his sketching tours in 1821. Over the next few years he painted in watercolor (and from 1823 also in oil) small scenes of the coast of Normandy, shipping, the Seine valley, quaint villages, and Gothic architecture. Some of his drawings were published in 1825 in the second volume of Baron Taylor's immense topographical production, *Voyages pittoresques et romantiques dans l'ancienne France*. Bonington exhibited at the Salon for the first time in 1822 and gained considerable renown there in 1824, when enthusiasm for English art was especially rampant in France. Later, he also showed his work at the Royal Academy and the British Institution in London.

Bonington made sketching tours of northern France and perhaps also of Flanders in 1823. He spent much of 1824 in Dunkerque. In 1825 he visited London with Delacroix, and the two artists shared a studio in Paris on their return. He made a rapid tour of northern Italy in 1826 in the company of Baron Charles Rivet. They traveled by way of Geneva over the Simplon Pass, visiting Milan, Brescia, and Verona before reaching Venice, where they stayed for approximately one month. The return journey included visits to Padua, Ferrara, Bologna, and Florence. Bonington's Venetian scenes were eagerly sought after. He also increasingly produced small costume pieces, lively glimpses of Shakespearean and historical figures in medieval and Renaissance dress. His figure paintings have the same nuances of light and sketchlike character as his more numerous landscapes. These history paintings are intimate and genrelike rather than grand.

Bonington visited London in 1827 and returned twice to that city in 1828. The last trip was to consult a physician, but no help was possible and he died there of tuberculosis. Celebrity and high prices for his works were attained immediately after his death. Forgeries and copies infiltrated the market, and lithographic publications of Bonington's works were produced. His energetic, freely brushed watercolor style, which suggests broad spaces and complex architecture in a few strokes, was distinctive and found numerous imitators in England, where Bonington was soon adopted as a native romantic hero.

1. On Bonington, see Albert Dubuisson, *Richard Parkes Bonington: His Life and Work*, trans. C. E. Hughes, London, 1924; Marion Spencer, *R. P. Bonington*, exh. cat., Castle Museum and Art Gallery, Nottingham, 1965; Marcia Pointon, *The Bonington Circle*, Brighton, 1985; Marcia Pointon, *Bonington, Francia, and Wylde*, London, 1985; Malcolm Cormack, *Bonington*, Oxford, 1989; Patrick Noon, *Richard Parkes Bonington: "On the Pleasure of Painting,"* exh. cat., Yale Center for British Art, New Haven and London, 1991.

Richard Parkes Bonington

View near Mantes

1826

Oil on canvas, 55.6 x 84.1 cm (21⅞ x 33⅛ in.)
Signed and dated lower right: *R.P. Bonington 1826*

This oil painting displays most of the standard features of Bonington's style: soft brushstrokes, moist atmosphere, muted color, peaceful riverine subject matter, a site in northern France, Gothic architecture, a low horizon, and small figures that lead the viewer into the pictorial space. Any image so perfectly in the artist's style, however, deserves to be scrutinized for authenticity. There are numerous copies, imitations, and forgeries of Bonington's works, and imitators usually replicate the master's most distinctive traits. In the opinion of this writer, the Taft painting is indeed a genuine work by Bonington. The delicacy of light, the manner in which the dark forms flow together, and the spatial legibility all indicate that this is a work by Bonington himself. In 1924 Albert Dubuisson reproduced both the Taft painting and another version of the image and attributed both to Bonington.[1] Judging from the illustration, however, the other version is not by Bonington. The large clump of trees, for example, so subtly painted in the Taft picture, is brushed in a bold but clumsy manner in the other work so that differentiation of tree limbs and foliage is lost.

The northern French site represented in *View near Mantes*, formerly called *View near Rouen*, is almost certainly Mantes, a small city on the left bank of the Seine between Rouen and Paris.[2] Bonington's close friend and traveling companion Baron Rivet owned an estate near Mantes, and the town appears in other works by the artist (e.g., *On the Seine, near Mantes*, ca. 1823–24, London, Wallace Collection). The most prominent Gothic building in Mantes-La-Jolie (formerly called Mantes-Gassicourt) is the collegiate church of Notre Dame, begun in 1170 and completed during the fourteenth century, which appears to be similar to the distant architecture in Bonington's painting. The relative height and the detailing of the towers of the actual church, however, differ somewhat from those of the tiny building in Bonington's view. Although Bonington produced some scrupulous drawings of medieval architecture, his romantic depictions of Gothic architecture did not always include correct details or proportions, and Notre Dame remains identifiable in the Taft painting.

Bonington's painting exhibits not only nostalgic gusto for the medieval world, remembered only through weathered monuments, but also the widespread early-nineteenth-century taste for hushed rural scenery. Typically, the landscape is unspectacular and historically unimportant. The commonplace scene of nature, however, is given power and expressiveness by the glowing light that fills the large sky and blurs the edges of the forms.

1. Albert Dubuisson, *Richard Parkes Bonington: His Life and Work*, trans. C. E. Hughes, London, 1924, p. 204, describes the second version as belonging to the Metropolitan Museum of Art, New York; but, according to Katharine Baetjer of the Metropolitan's department of European paintings, no such work is or ever was part of that museum's collection. Although the church towers of the Taft picture are not visible in the Dubuisson illustration because of photographic overexposure, there is no doubt that the picture, described as formerly belonging to H. Darrell Brown, is identical with the Taft painting.

2. The painting is titled *Mantes* in Dubuisson, p. 204, and *View near Mantes* in *Loan Exhibition of Pictures and Drawings by R. P. Bonington and J. S. Cotman*, exh. cat., Paterson Gallery, London, 1913. Patrick Noon, curator of prints, drawings, and rare books at the Yale Center for British Art, in a letter to the Taft Museum, Jan. 30, 1991, has confirmed this identification of the site and noted that a closer view of Mantes appears in a Bonington in the Wallace Collection, London, and that the same architectural landmarks appear in a Bonington reproduced in Dubuisson (opp. p. 117).

Provenance Earl of Normanton, Somerby Ringwood (by 1884, in 1908); H. Darrell Brown, London (by 1910; sale, Christie's, London, May 23, 1924, no. 2 [ill.]; bt. A. Ruck); [Scott and Fowles, New York]; Taft collection, Dec. 1, 1924.

Exhibitions London, Royal Academy of Arts, 1884; London, Agnew, 1908; London, *Japan-British Exhibition*, 1910 (cat., no. 57); London, Paterson Gallery, *Loan Exhibition of Pictures and Drawings by R. P. Bonington and J. S. Cotman*, June–July 1913; New London, Conn., Lyman Allyn Museum, Dec. 2, 1942–Jan. 3, 1943; New York, Wildenstein Galleries, *From Paris to the Sea down the River Seine*, Jan. 25–Feb. 27, 1943; Boston, Museum of Fine Arts, *Paintings, Drawings, and Prints by J. M. W. Turner, John Constable, and R. P. Bonington*, Mar. 19–Apr. 28, 1946; Bloomfield Hills, Mich., Cranbrook Academy of Art, *Light and the Painter*, Sept. 5–28, 1952 (cat., no. 14 [ill.]); New Haven, Yale Center for British Art [also Paris], *Richard Parkes Bonington: "On the Pleasure of Painting,"* Nov. 13, 1991–May 17, 1992 (cat. by Patrick Noon, pp. 188–89, no. 77 [ill.]).

Literature Albert Dubuisson, *Richard Parkes Bonington: His Life and Work*, trans. C. E. Hughes, London, 1924, p. 204, ill. opp. p. 204; *Art News* (June 21, 1924); *Catalogue of the Taft Museum*, Cincinnati, 1939 and 1958, no. 199; John D. Morse, *Old Master Paintings in North America*, New York, 1979, p. 20, ill. p. 18; David Torbet Johnson, "Taft Museum," *Ventura*, vol. IV, no. 16 (June–Aug. 1991), p. 135 (ill.).

1931.443

James Abbott McNeill Whistler

Lowell, Massachusetts 1834–1903 London

Whistler was the son of an engineer, George Washington Whistler, who specialized in railroad construction.[1] The artist's mother was from North Carolina. In 1843 the family moved to Saint Petersburg, where the father was involved in building railroads for the czar. Whistler studied there until 1849, when his father died. Before returning to the United States in that year, Whistler attended school in England and lived with his half sister's family, the Hadens. In 1851 he entered West Point Military Academy but was expelled in 1854. Afterward, he worked at a locomotive factory in Baltimore and made drawings and etchings for the U.S. Coastal Survey in Washington.

In 1855 Whistler decided to devote himself to art. He first visited the Hadens in London and then settled in Paris, where he entered the studio of Charles Gleyre. While in Paris he was deeply influenced by Gustave Courbet and became friendly with Henri Fantin-Latour, Alphonse Legros, Edward John Poynter, and Georges du Maurier. Whistler settled in London in 1859, but from 1855 until 1867 he traveled back and forth across the Channel repeatedly, thus making his artistic nationality difficult to pin down. During the 1860s he became the friend of Edgar Degas and Edouard Manet, visited Courbet, and achieved notoriety at the Salon des Refusés. During the same period, he exhibited at the Royal Academy and forged strong ties with Dante Gabriel Rossetti and Albert Moore in England.

During the mid-1860s, artists in both France and England were keenly interested in Japanese art, and Whistler, after abandoning Courbet's realism, began filling his canvases with Japanese stuffs and evoking Japanese prints. His tastes were wide-ranging, however. In 1862 he planned a trip to Spain to see the works of Velázquez; he visited Amsterdam in 1863 to study seventeenth-century Dutch art, basing many of his early etchings on those of Rembrandt. In 1866 he sailed to Chile, claiming to be interested in that nation's war for independence. He may, however, have been primarily concerned with breaking ties and finding a new artistic path. During the late 1860s Whistler completed very few paintings. He voiced uncertainty about his talents, training, and direction and tried to execute some classicized Japanese compositions similar to those of Albert Moore. During the 1870s, however, he successfully finished several large, austere, and very novel portraits; created a series of moody, misty landscapes; and became a leading figure in the aesthetic movement.

Whistler proclaimed an art-for-art's-sake point of view. He collaborated on projects with the architect E. W. Godwin, including the building of Whistler's own house in Chelsea, and designed a lavish interior for his patron F. R. Leyland. At the opening exhibition of the Grosvenor Gallery in 1877, his paintings were harshly criticized by John Ruskin. Whistler sued the writer for libel, and the ensuing court case, although technically won by the painter, left Whistler bankrupt in 1879.

A commission from the Fine Art Society of London to etch views of Venice sustained Whistler and reopened his connections with the art world beyond London, where he had remained from 1867 to 1879. He returned from Venice to England in 1881 but increasingly traveled on the Continent. He exhibited at the Paris Salon, visited Holland in 1884 and Dieppe in 1885. He settled in Paris in 1892 while continuing his frequent stays in England. In 1898 he opened an art school in Paris, the Académie Carmen, but neglected teaching, and it closed in 1901. His connections with American and French artists rather than with English ones increased from the 1880s, and he became one of the most influential painters and etchers throughout Europe and America during the last two decades of the nineteenth century. His later works are primarily small-scale landscapes and portraits — soft, suggestive, and sketchlike. Delicately muted color, a simple controlled design, and homage to Velázquez mark his style of this time.

Whistler was elected a member of the Society of British Artists in 1884 and became its president in 1886. He radically revamped the doddering society's exhibition policies and practices, made the membership international, and created a stormy but stimulating institution. He was ejected from office in 1888 but in 1889 was made president of a new group, the International Society of Sculptors, Painters, and Gravers. In this post he exhibited modern Continental art in England.

In England Whistler displayed an extravagant personality. He dressed like a dandy, fought numerous private feuds in public, flung verbal barbs at friends and foes, and from the 1880s openly mocked English art and the English public. In France he became associated with Stéphane Mallarmé and the symbolist movement. Whistler's writings, often wittily vituperative, both attacked his opponents and set forth some of the major concepts of aestheticism. Among his publications are *Whistler v. Ruskin: Art and Art Critics* (1879), *The Ten o'Clock Lecture* (1888), *The Gentle Art of Making Enemies* (1890), and *The Baronet and the Butterfly* (1899).

Whistler had several mistresses, notably Joanna Heffernan during the early 1860s. He lived with his mother in London from 1863 to 1875 and in 1888 married E. W. Godwin's widow, Beatrix, who died in 1896.

1. On Whistler, see E. R. Pennell and J. Pennell, *The Life of James McNeill Whistler*, 2 vols., London and Philadelphia, 1908; Edward G. Kennedy, *The Etched Work of Whistler*, New York, 1910; T. R. Way, *Memories of James McNeill Whistler*, London and New York, 1912; Théodore Duret, *Whistler*, London, 1917; E. R. Pennell and J. Pennell, *The Whistler Journal*, Philadelphia, 1921; *James McNeill Whistler*, exh. cat., Arts Council of Great Britain, London, 1960; Denys Sutton, *Nocturne: The Art of James McNeill Whistler*, London, 1963; C. P. Barbier, ed., *Correspondance Mallarmé-Whistler*, Paris, 1964; Allen Staley, *From Realism to Symbolism: Whistler and His World*, exh. cat., Philadelphia Museum of Art, 1971; Alistair Grieve, "Whistler and the Pre-Raphaelites," *Art Quarterly*, vol. XXXIV (1971), pp. 219–28; Mervyn Levy, *Whistler Lithographs: A Catalogue Raisonné*, London, 1975; Andrew McLaren Young et al., *The Paintings of James McNeill Whistler*, 2 vols., New Haven and London, 1980; Katherine A. Lochnan, *The Etchings of James McNeill Whistler*, exh. cat., Art Gallery of Ontario, Toronto, New Haven and London, 1984.

James Abbott McNeill Whistler

At the Piano

1858–59
Oil on canvas, 67 x 91.6 cm (26⅜ x 36⅛ in.)
Signed lower left: *J. Whistler*

Whistler began this family genre scene in London in November 1858 and completed it by the spring of 1859, but it was rejected at the Paris Salon of 1859. Whistler therefore showed it privately at the studio of François Bonvin, 189 rue Saint-Jacques, alongside works by Henri Fantin-Latour, Alphonse Legros, and Théodule Ribot. Gustave Courbet admired the painting. In 1860 Whistler successfully exhibited *At the Piano* at the Royal Academy; it was his first work shown publicly in England and was bought for thirty pounds by the painter John Phillip. William Makepeace Thackeray, Dante Gabriel Rossetti, and John Everett Millais were among those who praised the painting. An art critic in *The Times* perceived the influence of Velázquez,[1] and *At the Piano* can be seen as not only the first of Whistler's numerous works in the mode of Velázquez but also the earliest example of his style to display strong silhouettes, unemotive profiles, and a lean pictorial structure. Whistler told Joseph Pennell in 1900:

> It was the second picture I painted. The first was the *Mère Gerard* [Young et al., no. 26] done in Paris, which I gave to Swinburne. In "The Piano Picture" my sister, then Mrs. Haden, is sitting at the piano, her little girl standing by it, and I gave it to Haden — in a way. Well, you know, it was hanging there but I had no particular satisfaction in that. Haden just then was playing the authority on art and he could never look at it without pointing out its faults — and telling me it would never get into the Academy — that was certain. But after it had been for a while on Haden's walls I did send it to the Academy and it was hung, and Phillip, the R.A., back from Spain with, you know, Spanish notions about things, asked who painted the picture, and they told him a youth no one knew about, who had appeared from no one knew where. Phillip looked up my address in the Catalogue and wrote to me at once to say he would like to

1962.7

buy it, and what was its price? I answered in a letter which I am sure must have been very beautiful. I said that in my youth and inexperience I did not know about these things and would leave to him the question of price. Phillip sent me thirty pounds.[2]

At the Piano is both an intimate domestic study and a portrait of the artist's family. Whistler's half sister, Deborah Delano Haden, plays the piano while her daughter, Annie Harriet Haden, listens. Deborah was the daughter of Whistler's father by his first wife. In 1847 she married Francis Seymour Haden, an English surgeon and etcher, who bought *At the Piano* after the death of John Phillip in 1867. Whistler had a falling out with Haden in later years, as illustrated by the artist's acidic view of his brother-in-law expressed in the above quotation. The Hadens' daughter, Annie, married Charles Ernest Thynne. *At the Piano* presumably depicts a room in the Haden home at 62 Sloane Street, London.

X radiographs suggest that the standing girl may not have been an initial part of the painting,[3] and one report suggests that Whistler may have had difficulty drawing the piano.[4] A sketch of Annie in a sailor suit in the Freer Gallery, Washington, D.C., may be a study for *At the Piano*.

The Taft picture, like such later planar works as *Arrangement in Grey and Black: Portrait of the Painter's Mother* (1871, Paris, Musée d'Orsay), is firmly held together by a grid of picture frames, moldings, and furniture. The shape and proportion of the pictures on the wall carefully echo those of the dado and the furnishings. The piano legs reflect the child's legs, and even the instrument case on the floor mirrors the girl's zigzag silhouette. Within this orchestrated harmony are contrasts. The black-robed mother is an enclosed form; she concentrates on her playing. In opposition, the white-clad daughter gazes outward. Her hair is unbound, and her relaxed body juts out in several directions.

The Taft painting clearly inspired Whistler's mature and influential paintings of the 1870s. However, between its completion in 1859 and Whistler's completion of the portrait of his mother more than a decade later lie very different groups of works — some in a realist manner, others indebted to classical friezes or Japanese prints. The austerity, muted color, and rectilinear design are the most precocious features of *At the Piano*. The mundane and unsentimental character of the scene is also significant, since such an undemonstrative portrayal of home life is contrary to most English genre paintings of the first three-quarters of the nineteenth century. The psychological tone is closer to that of French genre and is also present in Whistler's related etching of around the same time, *The Music Room*.[5] The strict geometric order of the Taft painting generally recalls the art of Pieter de Hooch and other seventeenth-century Dutch masters admired by Whistler. John Sandberg has suggested that

At the Piano was specifically influenced by Jan Vermeer's *Concert* (ex-coll. Isabella Stewart Gardner Museum), which Whistler may have seen in London in 1859.[6] The correspondences between the two works, however, are not exact, and as Whistler's own statement indicates, Velázquez and Spanish art in general were probably more important stimuli.

The subject matter of *At the Piano* may be borrowed from Dutch pictures, but it also looks forward to Whistler's later interest in allying art with music. Beginning in the 1870s, he gave musical titles to his paintings, likening the abstraction of the art of sound to the purported abstraction of his pictures. Yet the piano in the Taft painting functions primarily as a sign of domestic intimacy, a focal point for the family, and a psychological link between mother and daughter, player and listener.

1. *The Times* [London], May 17, 1860, as cited in Andrew McLaren Young et al., *The Paintings of James McNeill Whistler*, vol. I, New Haven and London, 1980, no. 24. Most of the factual information given in this entry can be found in this authoritative catalogue.

2. E. R. Pennell and J. Pennell, *The Whistler Journal*, Philadelphia, 1921, pp. 78–83.

3. See Young et al., no. 24; the X-ray report was made by R. D. Buck, Intermuseum Laboratory, Oberlin, Ohio, June 1965.

4. This story of drawing difficulties was published by W. L. B. Jenney in "Whistler and Old Sandy in the Fifties," *American Architect*, vol. LIX (Jan. 1, 1898), pp. 4–5. Young et al. (no. 24) point out that this tale may be without foundation and that the reference to *At the Piano* is indefinite. Still, there are numerous reports of Whistler's problems with drawing and perspective in other paintings.

5. Whistler's etchings have been catalogued by Edward G. Kennedy, *The Etched Work of Whistler*, New York, 1910: *The Music Room* (no. 33) is dated approximately 1859 and shows Mr. and Mrs. Haden and Haden's partner, Dr. Traer, relaxing in a lamplit interior. Deborah Haden also appears in *Reading by Lamplight* (no. 32) and *Portrait of a Lady* (appendix ii). Annie Haden is portrayed in a number of Whistler's etchings from around the time of *At the Piano* (nos. 8, 10, 30, 62). See also Katherine A. Lochnan, *The Etchings of James McNeill Whistler*, exh. cat., Art Gallery of Ontario, Toronto, New Haven and London, 1984, *The Music Room* (nos. 83–85), *Reading by Lamplight* (77), *Portrait of a Lady* (138), and *Annie Haden* (23, 24, 78, 137).

6. John Sandberg, "'Japonisme' and Whistler," *Burlington Magazine*, vol. CVI (1964). pp. 500–507.

Provenance John Phillip, London (1860–67); Francis Seymour Haden, Woodcote Manor, Hampshire (1867–97); [A. Reid, Glasgow, 1897]; John James Cowan, Wester Lea, Murrayfield, Edinburgh (1897; sale, Agnew, London, May 24, 1899); Sir Edmund David, London (1899; sale Christie's, London, July 7, 1939, no. 99; bt., Knoedler, London and New York); [Scott and Fowles, New York]; Mr. and Mrs. William T. Semple, Cincinnati (Jan. 1940); Louise Taft Semple bequest, 1962.

Exhibitions Paris, studio of François Bonvin, 189 rue St.-Jacques, 1859; London, Royal Academy of Arts, 1860 (cat., no. 598); London, Morgan's Gallery, Berners St., 1862; Paris, Salon of 1867 (cat., no. 1561); London, International Society of Sculptors, Painters, and Gravers, May 1898 (cat., no. 177); Edinburgh, Royal Scottish Academy, 1899 (cat., no. 143); London, New Gallery, *Memorial Exhibition of the Works of the Late James McNeill Whistler*, Feb. 22–Apr. 15, 1905 (cat., no. 75, ill. opp. p. 114); Paris, Palais de l'Ecole des Beaux-Arts, *Oeuvres de James McNeill Whistler*, May 1905 (cat., no. 2*bis*, pp. 5, 11); London, Tate Gallery, *Loan Exhibition of the Works by J. M. Whistler*, July 1912 (cat., no. 22); London, French Gallery, *Collection of Edmund Davis, Esq.*, Mar. 1915 (cat., no. 5); New York, Scott and Fowles, Jan. 1940; Baltimore Museum of Art, *From El Greco to Pollock: Early and Late Works by European and American Artists*, Oct. 22–Dec. 8, 1968 (cat., no. 89 [ill.]); Philadelphia Museum of Art [also New York], *From Realism to Symbolism: Whistler and His World*, Apr. 15–May 23, 1971 (cat., no. 4, fig. 6).

Literature *The Times* [London], May 17, 1860; W. C. Brownell, "Whistler in Painting and Etching," *Scribner's Magazine*, vol. XVIII (Aug. 1879), pp. 481–95, wood engraving p. 495; W. L. B. Jenney, "Whistler and Old Sandy in the Fifties," *American Architect*, vol. LIX (Jan. 1, 1898), pp. 4–5; G. Sauter, "The International Society of Sculptors, Painters, and Gravers," *Studio*, vol. XIV (July 1898), pp. 109–20 [ill.]; W. G. Bowdoin, *James McNeill Whistler: The Man and His Work*, New York, 1901, pp. 15, 39–40; T. R. Way and G. R. Dennis, *The Art of James McNeill Whistler*, London, 1903, pp. 7, 15, 18, 22; Arthur J. Eddy, *Recollections and Impressions of James A. McNeill Whistler*, Philadelphia and London, 1903, p. 87; George Henry Boughton, "A Few of the Various Whistlers I Have Known," *International Studio*, vol. XXI (1904), p. 211; Théodore Duret, *Histoire de J. McN. Whistler et de son oeuvre*, Paris, 1904, pp. 15–16; "The Work of J. McN. Whistler," *Edinburgh Review*, vol. CCI (Apr. 1905), pp. 445–67; Léonce Bénédite, "Artistes contemporains: Whistler," *Gazette des beaux-arts*, vol. XXXIII (1905), pp. 407–9; Bernhard Sickert, *Whistler*, London and New York, 1908, p. 102; E. R. Pennell and J. Pennell, *The Life of James McNeill Whistler*, vol. I, London and Philadelphia, 1908, pp. 74–75, 82–83, 90–91, 99, 133, 140; C. J. Holmes, "Whistler and Modern Painting," *Burlington Magazine*, vol. XIV (Jan. 1909), p. 205; Edward G. Kennedy, *The Etched Work of Whistler*, New York, 1910, no. 33; Martin T. Wood, "The Edmund Davis Collection," *Studio*, vol. LXIV (Mar. 1915), p. 83; E. R. Pennell and J. Pennell, *The Whistler Journal*, Philadelphia, 1921, pp. 78–83, 285; Luke Ionides, "Memories: Whistler in the Quartier Latin," *Transatlantic Review*, vol. I (Jan. 1924), p. 40; James Laver, *Whistler*, New York, 1930, pp. 67–69; G. D. Hobson, *Some Thoughts on the Organisation of the Arts after the War*, London, 1946, p. 37; Burns A. Stubbs, *Paintings, Pastels, Drawings, Prints . . . Attributed to American and European Artists . . .* , Washington, D.C., 1948, p. 28; Daphne du Maurier, ed., *The Young Georges du Maurier: A Selection of His Letters, 1860–67*, London, 1951, p. 4; Denys Sutton, *Nocturne: The Art of James McNeill Whistler*, London, 1963, pp. 25–27; René Gimpel, *Journal d'un collectionneur marchand de tableaux*, Paris, 1963, pp. 80–81; John Sandberg, "'Japonisme' and Whistler," *Burlington Magazine*, vol. CVI (1964), pp. 500–507; Denys Sutton, *James McNeill Whistler: Paintings, Etchings, Pastels, and Watercolors*, London, 1966, p. 8, pl. 7; Tom Prideaux, *The World of Whistler*, New York, 1970, pp. 25, 30–31, 38–39, 42; Roy McMullen, *Victorian Outsider: A Biography of J. M. Whistler*, New York, 1973, pp. 81–82, 83, 84, 87, 92, 93, 111, 145, 151; Margaret F. MacDonald, "Whistler: The Painting of the 'Mother,'" *Gazette des beaux-arts*, vol. LXXXV (Feb. 1975), pp. 73–88; Gordon Fleming, *The Young Whistler*, London, 1978, p. 164; Frances Spalding, *Whistler*, Oxford, 1979, pp. 19–20, pl. 11; Andrew McLaren Young et al., *The Paintings of James McNeill Whistler*, New Haven and London, 1980, vol. I, no. 24, vol. II, pl. 22; *La Femme: The Influence of Whistler and Japanese Print Masters on American Art, 1800–1917*, exh. cat., Grand Central Art Galleries, New York, 1983, p. 72; Kenneth Bendiner, *An Introduction to Victorian Art*, New Haven and London, 1985, pp. 85–86, fig. 44; Pierre Cabanne, *Whistler*, Paris, 1985, p. 5 (ill.); John Walker, *James McNeill Whistler*, New York, 1987, pp. 22, 24–25 (color pl.); Robin Spencer, ed., *Whistler: A Retrospective*, London, 1989, pp. 45, 59, 82, 258, 346, pl. 13; Lois Marie Fink, *American Art at the Nineteenth-Century Paris Salons*, 1990, Washington, D.C., pp. 78–79 (ill.); Kirk Savage, "'A Forcible Piece of Weird Decoration': Whistler and *The Gold Scab*," *Smithsonian Studies in American Art*, vol. IV, no. 2 (Spring 1990), pp. 48–49, fig. 9; "Whistler," *Ventura*, vol. IV, no. 15 (Mar.–May 1991), pp. 16–18 (ill.).

1962.7

Lawrence Alma-Tadema

Dronrijp, Holland 1836–1912 Wiesbaden

Laurens Tadema (who later used the name Lawrence Alma-Tadema) was born in a small village in central Friesland and grew up in nearby Leeuwarden where his father was a notary.[1] He gained admission to the Antwerp Academy in 1852, studying under Gustave Wappers and Nicaise de Keyser. Through the influence of these romantic history painters and the archaeolo-

1931.392

gist Louis de Taye, in 1856 Alma-Tadema began to paint scenes of early-medieval history. From 1859 to 1862 he furthered his training by working in the Antwerp studio of Henrik Leys, a master of Gothicized Flemish history pictures. Merovingian subjects primarily in a Leysian style continued to dominate his art until the mid-1860s. Partly inspired by the Egyptologist Georg Ebers, Alma-Tadema gradually turned to scenes of ancient Egyptian life. These soon were followed by genre paintings of ancient Rome, and from 1865 until his death the classical world preoccupied him almost exclusively.

Traveling to Rome, Naples, and Pompeii on his honeymoon in 1863 was a decisive experience for Alma-Tadema. An archaeological desire to reconstruct the past played a role in his splendid vision of ancient life. Equally important in his opulently detailed images is the atmosphere of sophisticated leisure. He imagined an idyllically indolent patrician realm where only art and pleasure were contemplated. Toil, suffering, glory, intensity, and action are nowhere present.

Alma-Tadema met Jean-Léon Gérôme in Paris in 1864 and was influenced by that Ingresque painter's polished realism. At the same time he was taken up by the international art dealer Ernest Gambart. After living in Antwerp and Paris, Alma-Tadema moved in 1865 to Brussels, where he gradually acquired a distinguished reputation throughout Europe. He was made a Knight of the Order of Leopold in 1866; in 1868 he became a Knight of the Dutch Lion, and in 1869 a Knight of Saint Michael of Bavaria. Later in life he was made a member of numerous art academies around the world.

Alma-Tadema's son died in 1865, and his wife followed in 1869, leaving the artist with two daughters. At the outbreak of the Franco-Prussian War, he moved to London, where Gambart owned the French Gallery. He had visited the city before in 1862 and 1869. Now, however, he settled there, marrying Laura Teresa Epps, one of his English pupils, in 1871. Alma-Tadema eventually became a British subject and an active participant in the London art world. He was elected associate of the Royal Academy in 1876 and full academician in 1879. He was knighted in 1899 and received the Order of Merit in 1905. He owned a lavish house in Saint John's Wood and made annual trips to the Continent, usually including Italy on the itinerary. He exhibited with several dealers as well as at the Royal Academy and was given a large retrospective at the Grosvenor Gallery in 1882.

The dark colors, planar figural arrangements, and limited space of his works of the 1860s gave way to a brighter palette

and more complex plays with space during the 1870s and 1880s. Unexpected lunges into depth, abrupt changes in scale, and fascinating juxtapositions of near and far enliven his images of Greek and Roman beauties lounging, bathing, and courting. During the 1890s and the early years of the twentieth century, close-up views of figures, trancelike expressions, rich bouquets, and strong pink and orange hues appeared in his elaborate art. Although often mocked as a dull archaeologist, Alma-Tadema created evocative Dionysian fantasies that should properly be placed within the aesthetic movement.

Alma-Tadema received numerous honors in his later years, including the award of gold medals at international expositions in Paris, Chicago, Brussels, Vienna, and Rome. A visit to Egypt in 1902 inspired some Egyptian paintings late in his career. He died in Germany, where he had gone for medical treatment.

1. On Alma-Tadema, see Edmund W. Gosse, *Lawrence Alma-Tadema,* London, 1882; Georg M. Ebers, *Lorenz Alma-Tadema,* trans. M. J. Safford, New York, 1886; Frederick Dolman, "Sir Lawrence Alma-Tadema," *Strand Magazine,* vol. XVIII (Dec. 1899); Helen Zimmern, *Sir Lawrence Alma-Tadema,* London, 1902; Percy Cross Standing, *Sir Lawrence Alma-Tadema,* London, 1905; Christopher Forbes, *Victorians in Togas,* exh. cat., The Metropolitan Museum of Art, New York, 1973; Russell Ash, *Alma-Tadema,* Aylesbury, Bucks., 1973; Vern G. Swanson, *Alma-Tadema,* New York, 1977; Russell Ash, *Sir Lawrence Alma-Tadema,* New York, 1990.

Lawrence Alma-Tadema

A World of Their Own

1905
Oil on panel, 13 x 50 cm (5⅛ x 19¾ in.)
Signed and inscribed lower left: *L Alma Tadema / Op*
CCCLXXVIII

Alma-Tadema frequently portrayed lovers in his classical Mediterranean genre scenes. The couples tease, pay court, or gently squabble, giving an amusing hint of youthful sensuality to the artist's picture of antiquity. Seemingly involved in a tête-à-tête, the young man and woman in *A World of Their Own* sprawl across a flowered plateau above the sea. In fact, the lovers do not communicate, and the title may be ironic. The youth directs his ardent attention toward the dark-haired girl who looks out at the viewer with a bored expression, seemingly oblivious to his words. If the implied narrative wittily reveals human disunity, the composition of this tiny picture at least displays elegant harmony. The lovers' undulant bodies spread laterally in tune with the painting's horizontal shape, and the landscape in turn echoes the human forms. The woods at the left mirror the youth's hunched figure while the stretch of trees at the right reflects the girl's languid body. The horizonless expanse of sea encloses the lovers, suggesting privacy, which the artist then denies by directing the girl's gaze out toward the viewer.

Alma-Tadema produced similarly harmonious scenes of lovers' disengagement in *A Difference of Opinion* (1896, England, private collection) and *The Proposal* (1892, Brighton Art Gallery). The woman in the latter work flirtatiously gazes at the viewer while her lover begs for her hand in marriage. *A World of Their Own* is slightly more subtle in its playfulness. Alma-Tadema's images of love are in the manner of *Così fan tutte* rather than *Tristan und Isolde*. Lightheartedness is a vital component of his classicism, clearly differentiating his style from the neoclassicism of the late eighteenth and early nineteenth centuries. Alma-Tadema's vision of warmth, leisure, and amorality also evokes an ideal of frivolous existence at odds with ordinary life in nineteenth-century England, while revealing much about the longings of at least a part of that society for the indulgent, perfumed world of Victorian aestheticism.

The figures in *A World of Their Own* are not based on famous antique statues or vase paintings. Generalization and idealization are also not paramount. The faces are distinctly of the nineteenth century, and the striped garments and elegantly wrought walking stick give contemporary color to the Taft painting. These features encouraged viewers of the time to see themselves in a dream of the past.

The model for the woman in the painting also appears in other works by Alma-Tadema (e.g., *A Flag of Truce*, 1900, New Orleans, collection of Mr. and Mrs. Harold H. Stream) and illustrates the artist's persistent fondness for nonclassical physiognomy. The same figure's prone posture, a pose favored by Alma-Tadema, is also seen at various angles in such works as *Pleading* (1876, London, Guildhall Art Gallery), *94 Degrees in the Shade* (1876, Cambridge, Fitzwilliam Museum), and *A Reading from Homer* (1885, Philadelphia Museum of Art). It is a pose that comprises both languor and attentiveness.

The somber glow of *A World of Their Own* displays Alma-Tadema's increased emphasis on expressive lighting in his late works, although this interest more usually took the form of brilliant colors and harsh sunlight. Hundreds of flowers turn the landscape of the Taft painting into a lush carpet. From the 1880s onward Alma-Tadema frequently depicted flowers in abundance to heighten the atmosphere of opulence. This passion is nowhere more apparent than in *The Roses of Heliogabalus* (1888, France, private collection), in which the debauched Roman emperor literally swamps his playmates in an ocean of rose petals.

Alma-Tadema, diligent and orderly, gave opus numbers to all his paintings beginning in 1851. This minuscule painting, opus CCCLXXVIII, was the only work executed in 1905. The intimate scale was not unusual, but that year was exceptionally unproductive, perhaps because of the artist's excessive labors in 1904

on one of his largest works, *The Finding of Moses* (England, private collection).

Provenance [Scott and Fowles, New York, 1905, from the artist]; Taft collection, Oct. 25, 1905.

Exhibition Williamstown, Mass., Sterling and Francine Clark Art Institute [also Baltimore, Cincinnati, and Memphis], *Empires Restored, Elysium Revisited: The Art of Sir Lawrence Alma-Tadema*, Sept. 21, 1991– Sept. 6, 1992 (cat. by Jennifer Gorden Lovett and William R. Johnston, no. 47 [ill.]).

Literature Rudolf Dircks, "The Later Works of Sir Lawrence Alma-Tadema," *Art Journal* [London] (Christmas issue, 1910); Maurice W. Brockwell, *A Catalogue of Paintings in the Collection of Mr. and Mrs. Charles P. Taft*, New York, 1920, p. xxi, no. 76; *Catalogue of the Taft Museum*, Cincinnati, 1939 and 1958, no. 10; Vern G. Swanson, *Alma-Tadema*, New York, 1977, p. 141; Russell Ash, *Sir Lawrence Alma-Tadema*, New York, 1990, pl. 36.

1931.392

Harrington Mann
Glasgow 1864–1937 London

Harrington Mann was a modestly fashionable portrait painter during the first thirty years of the twentieth century.[1] A Scot, he was associated with the Glasgow School for a time during the late 1880s and early 1890s. Like many other members of that group, he was much indebted to French art. Mann studied in Paris at the ateliers of Gustave Boulanger and Jules Lefebvre and in London at the Slade School under Alphonse Legros. He also studied in Rome.

Mann's early efforts were directed toward historical subjects, Yorkshire and Scottish scenes, and images of Italian peasants. In tune with end-of-the-century taste, he also undertook several mural projects and decorative schemes and became involved in magazine illustration. By the early 1890s, however, Mann gradually began to specialize in portraiture. The most powerful influences on this branch of his art were John Singer Sargent and James McNeill Whistler. In some of Mann's works the dashing style of the former takes precedence, while in others the softly blurred outlines and darkened style of Whistler hold sway. Mann became particularly adept at child portraiture, holding exhibitions of such works in London and New York during the 1920s.

From 1912 onward Mann spent considerable time in the United States. Not long before his death he published *The Technique of Portrait Painting* (Philadelphia, 1933), which was published again in London in 1934. In 1893 he married Florence Sabine Pasley; they had three daughters. His second wife was Yvette Adele Pfeil, whom he married in 1915. Mann was a member of the Royal Society of Portrait Painters, the International Society of Sculptors, Painters and Gravers, and the National Portrait Society. His portraits are in the public collections of Belfast, Glasgow, Sydney, Melbourne, Ghent, and Brooklyn. A minor talent with minor success, Mann kept alive nineteenth-century portrait traditions far into the twentieth century.

1. On Mann, see *The Studio*, vol. XXIX (1903), pp. 118–24; vol. XLI (1915), pp. 32, 49, 144; vol. XLIV (1918), p. 77; J. L. Caw, *Scottish Painting*, London,

1931.473

1908; *Connoisseur,* vol. xxxviii (1914), pp. 131, 135; *Who's Who,* 1916–21; *American Art News,* vol. xx, no. 16 (1922), p. 6; vol. xxii, no. 10 (1924), p. 9.

❧

Harrington Mann

Charles Frederick Fowles

1915
Oil on canvas, 76.2 x 63.8 cm (30 x 25⅛ in.)
Signed and dated lower left: *Harrington Mann / 1915*

Set against a dark background, this bust-length figure wears a black morning coat and looks down at the viewer. This posthumous portrait of Charles Frederick Fowles was painted from both a photograph and a model who resembled Fowles. Fowles was a passenger aboard the *Lusitania* when that ship was sunk by German torpedoes in 1915.

Fowles was born in Herefordshire, England, and went to the United States around 1899. He became a major art dealer in the firm of Scott and Fowles, New York, and was a key assistant in the formation of the Taft collection. So close was the association between the Tafts and their dealer that Charles Phelps Taft commissioned Mann to paint this memorial portrait.

Provenance Commissioned by Charles Phelps Taft, 1915.

Literature Maurice W. Brockwell, *A Catalogue of Paintings in the Collection of Mr. and Mrs. Charles P. Taft,* New York, 1920, no. 81; *Catalogue of the Taft Museum,* Cincinnati, 1939 and 1958, no. 557.

1931.473

Nineteenth- and Twentieth-Century Spanish Paintings

Edward J. Sullivan

Francisco de Goya
Fuendetodos 1746–1827 Bordeaux

Goya was born to a family of modest circumstances in a town situated forty kilometers southeast of the capital of the province of Zaragoza. His father, José Goya, was a master gilder of retables, and his mother, Gracia Lucientes, descended from minor Aragonese nobility. In the 1750s he attended the school of the Piarist fathers in Zaragoza, where he met Martín Zapater, who remained friendly with Goya for the rest of his life. A great deal about Goya's life is known through his lengthy correspondence with Zapater. At the age of fourteen, Goya was apprenticed to José Luzán y Martínez in whose workshop in Zaragoza he remained for four years. In 1763 Goya went to Madrid for the first time to participate in a competition at the Academy of San Fernando. He was unsuccessful then and again in a second competition in 1766. In 1770 Goya went to Italy for approximately one year. He visited Rome and possibly Naples and Lombardy. At the academy in Parma he entered a competition with a historical picture for which he won a special mention. In June 1771 he returned to Zaragoza, where he worked on the paintings in the dome of one of the chapels in the basilica of Our Lady of El Pilar. In 1774 he executed the oil-on-plaster paintings in the Charterhouse of Aula Dei near Zaragoza. On July 25, 1773, Goya married Josefa Bayeu. Little is known of their marriage, and only one of their children, Javier, survived to adulthood.

In late 1774 Goya was summoned by Anton Raphael Mengs, artistic adviser to King Charles III, to Madrid, where he began to create his many cartoons for tapestries depicting contemporary Spanish life. These were manufactured by the Royal Tapestry Factory of Santa Barbara. In July 1778 the newspaper *Gazeta de Madrid* announced the publication of nine prints by Goya after works by Diego Velázquez. From this time on, Goya would continue to produce important series of etchings and lithographs. In 1780 Goya was elected a member of the Royal Academy of Fine Arts of San Fernando. In May of that year he returned to Zaragoza to execute additional frescoes in El Pilar along with Francisco and Ramón Bayeu. In 1781 he began work on a large altarpiece for the church of San Francisco el Grande in Madrid. On June 25, 1786, he was named Painter to the King;

three years later his position was elevated to that of Painter to the Royal Bedchamber. Beginning in the 1780s Goya was commissioned to paint portraits of members of the nobility.

In Seville in the winter of 1792 Goya fell gravely ill with a malady, the exact nature of which is still uncertain. This illness left him completely deaf, and he would suffer other effects throughout his life. In September 1795 Goya was made director of the academy. During the following year he spent ten months in Andalucía with the duchess of Alba. The famous portrait of her in the Hispanic Society of America, New York, as well as numerous drawings in the Sanlúcar Albums, are testimonies to his time there. Between 1796 and 1798 he did the preparatory drawings for *Los Caprichos,* which were published in 1799. Goya's outstanding fresco project dates to 1798. In August of that year he began to decorate the interior of the Hermitage of San Antonio de la Florida in Madrid. In May 1800 the artist began a series of studies of members of the royal family in preparation for his largest group portrait, *The Family of Charles IV,* finished in June 1801.

On May 2, 1808, the Spanish War of Independence began. The country had been invaded by Napoleonic troops, and the fighting was to last for four years. The violence deeply affected the artist, and his two paintings, the *Second of May, 1808* and the *Third of May, 1808* (both 1814; Madrid, Museo del Prado), attest to his reaction to the struggle, as do the series of prints entitled *The Disasters of War* (1810–20).

Goya's wife died in June 1812. In 1816 he published his thirty-three images of the history of bullfighting, known as the *Tauromaquia.* The same year he began work on another print series, *Los Disparates.* In 1819 he bought a house on the outskirts of Madrid known as the Quinta del Sordo (Deaf Man's Villa). He decorated it with frescoes depicting witchcraft and other bizarre subjects. Known as the Black Paintings, these works were detached from the walls of the now-destroyed house and are in the Prado Museum, Madrid. They represent the height of Goya's protoromantic taste for the supernatural.

After the War of Independence, the Spanish throne was regained by Ferdinand VII, who proved to be a cruel and repressive monarch. Goya ultimately decided to leave Spain and in May 1824 asked the king for permission to travel to Plombières, France, to take the curative waters at a spa. His real intention was to settle in that country. Goya went first to Paris and then to Bordeaux. Except for visits to Madrid in 1826 and 1827, he remained in Bordeaux until his death on April 16, 1828.

Follower of Goya

Portrait of Queen María Luisa of Spain

ca. 1800
Oil on canvas, 83.5 x 67 cm (32⅞ x 26⅜ in.)

This portrait represents a half-length figure of the queen. She wears a white dress of the Empire style with black ribbons just

1931.446

below the bosom. On her bodice is a sketchily painted black-and-white decoration. The artist has paid particular attention to her jewelry. Above the necklace consisting of a single strand of blue sapphires, there is another necklace of three strands of white diamonds with a large blue diamond in the center. Her earrings are of pearls and smaller sapphires, and pearl-and-sapphire combs adorn her hair. The queen faces to the viewer's right. Her left arm is straight while the lower part of her bent right arm is hidden behind her dress. Her mouth is slightly open, and she stares at the viewer with an indeterminate expression. More detail has been lavished on the face than on any other part of the figure, although the extreme right side of the face appears unfinished, or at least painted in a summary fashion. The hair is carefully defined, with many wispy strands. The details of the queen's dress are sketchily painted with alternating thick, short and long brushstrokes. The background is executed with subtle shades of brown and green. Under close examination one can see that the picture was originally set in an oval frame.

María Luisa Teresa de Parma was born in Rome in 1751 and died there in 1819. The daughter of Philip, duke of Parma, and Princess Isabelle of France, she was married to Charles, prince of Asturias, son of King Charles III of Spain, in 1765. She and her husband ascended the throne of Spain in 1780 and reigned until the Napoleonic invasions of 1808, when the royal family was forced into exile in Italy. A woman of strong (and according to many stories, cunning) personality, she exercised a great deal of political control over her nation.

The Taft painting bears an obvious relationship to the figure of Queen María Luisa as she appears in Goya's monumental group portrait, *The Family of Charles IV* (Madrid, Museo del Prado, fig. 1), painted about 1800. In the Taft picture María Luisa wears similar clothing and stands in the same position as in the family portrait. It is known that in late May and early June of 1800 Goya procured the materials to create the large portrait and made four visits to the royal palace at Aranjuez to do a series of ten studies of the figures that would appear in the *Family*. The queen referred to the studies of herself in a letter of June 9 to her favorite, Godoy, stating that "Mañana empieza Goya otro retrato mío, todos los demás están concluidos y todos están muy propios" (Goya begins another portrait of me tomorrow; all the others are finished and they are all excellent).[1]

Several paintings have been identified as belonging to this group. The terrifyingly insightful study of the queen mother in the Prado, for instance, is undoubtedly one of the sketches executed by the master in Aranjuez. In the case of the portraits of the king and queen, however, it is uncertain if any of the works proposed as preliminary studies for *The Family of Charles IV* can in fact be connected with that painting. The *Portrait of María Luisa* in the Alte Pinakothek, Munich, for example, has been proposed as a possible candidate, but it has found little favor in the modern literature on Goya and can be judged a later work by a follower of the artist.[2]

In 1866 the catalogue of the collection of the dukes of Montpensier was published in Seville. The duchess of Montpensier was the Infanta María Fernanda, daughter of King Ferdinand VII and heir to a number of works of art that he had owned. In the collection were four portraits of members of the royal family. They were listed as numbers sixty-two to sixty-five in the catalogue and represented (respectively) Charles IV, María Luisa, Ferdinand VII as prince of Asturias, and Princess María Isabel.[3] These paintings were hung in the Palace of San Telmo in Seville and were ultimately acquired by Prince Antoine-Marie-Philippe d'Orléans, duke of Montpensier (and fifth son of King Louis Philippe), who displayed them in his residence at

Fig. 1 Francisco de Goya, *The Family of Charles IV*, ca. 1800. Oil on canvas, 280 x 336 cm (110¼ x 132¾ in.). Madrid, Museo del Prado.

Fig. 2 Workshop of Francisco de Goya, *Ferdinand VII, King of Spain, as Prince of Asturias*, ca. 1800. Oil on canvas, 83.2 x 66.7 cm (32¾ x 26¼ in.). New York, The Metropolitan Museum of Art, gift of René Fribourg, 1951 (51.70).

Sanlúcar de Barrameda. The group was later dispersed and the whereabouts of only two is known today. *Ferdinand VII, King of Spain, as Prince of Asturias* is in the Metropolitan Museum of Art, New York (fig. 2), and *María Luisa* is the picture now in the Taft Museum.

Desparmet-Fitzgerald published the Taft painting as a preliminary study for *The Family of Charles IV*.[4] Numerous other writers listed it in their catalogues of Goya's oeuvre without questioning it either as a study for the *Family* or as an autograph work by Goya.[5] In 1950 Martin S. Soria wrote to Harry Sperling of Kleinberger and Co., New York, offering his opinion of the series to which this picture belongs: "I have always felt that the studies [including the Taft portrait] . . . offer an even more incisive and biting character sketch than the finished picture, the famous *Family of Charles IV*."[6] Six years earlier, however, Xavier de Salas had written that "those sketches [for *The Family of Charles IV*] in various French, Spanish, and American collections [other than the Prado] are not by Goya's hand."[7]

In 1957 Valentín de Sambricio stated his belief that none of the four former Montpensier paintings was by Goya.[8] Although he gives no specific suggestions as to who may have painted them, he mentions Agustín Esteve (1753–1820) as the Goya colleague who would often execute officially sanctioned copies of his works, especially portraits. Other artists who are known to have made copies of Goya's paintings are Felipe Abas, Gil Arranz, and Asensio Juliá. In his catalogue of Goya's paintings, José Gudiol states that he had examined the Taft picture and decided that "it does not seem to us to be the work of Goya. . . . [I]t might have been painted by Esteve, who was commissioned, as we know, to make copies of his master's work."⁹ Based on photographs he had seen of the other ex-Montpensier pictures, he also attributes *Charles IV* and *Prince Ferdinand* to Esteve while stating his belief that the portrait study of *Princess María Isabel* is most likely by Goya himself. Gassier and Wilson, in their catalogue of Goya's work, state that "the four portraits were possibly painted by Agustín Esteve from Goya's lost original sketches for the royal family portrait."¹⁰ De Angelis reiterates the attribution to Esteve but states that the four were probably *ricordi* done after completion of *The Family of Charles IV* rather than copies of the lost preliminary paintings.¹¹

I do not believe that the attribution of this portrait to Goya can be accepted. The painting is a good replica of what was either a study done before the execution of the *Family* or a work that isolated the figure of the queen after its completion. The proud haughtiness of the monarch is well captured here, but the facture of the work does not have the strength and convincing corporeal quality of Goya's definitions of his sitters. In this regard it is appropriate to cite the words of Gudiol:

Analysis reveals how successful the efforts of the other painter were, as far as the likeness of the Queen is concerned and the exact general copying of the form and volume. But it can be seen that the interpretation of the elements is different; it is not so much a question of any very apparent difference in technique, though this does exist, as of a falling off in quality and an execution in which the brushwork is very far from having the force and infallible effect of that of Goya. What it lacks is spontaneity and richness of texture.¹²

Invoking the name of Esteve in connection with this work is as incorrect as giving the attribution to Goya himself. Although Esteve executed numerous copies of Goya's paintings (which were probably sold as authentic Goyas even in the painter's day and maybe with his knowledge),¹³ they possess certain characteristics that are quite different from those present in the Taft painting.¹⁴ A careful study of Esteve reveals him to be a master fairly close in style to Anton Raphael Mengs, who had a significant impact on Spanish art during the second half of the eighteenth century. The majority of Esteve's portraits tend to idealize and beautify their subjects, effects that are often accomplished by painting in a smooth manner with concealed brushstrokes. His figures tend to be evenly illuminated. Their eyes are usually quite large and stare out at the viewer, often in an unnaturally fixed way. These elements are, for the most part, not present in the Taft picture. The shading on the queen's face is more subtle and the brushwork more lively than is usual in Esteve's portraits. Of course, it is not impossible that Esteve may have tried to make this picture more faithful to its model than was usually the case. Nonetheless, an unquestioned acceptance of Agustín Esteve as the creator of this painting is not an acceptable alternative to an attribution to Goya. None of the other artists of Goya's time who copied his work (Arranz, Juliá, etc.) may be cited as a possible artist of the Taft picture. Their talents were minor, and they were certainly not capable of producing an image like this. The Taft painting is indeed an aesthetically

pleasing likeness of the queen, and the anonymous artist who produced it must be considered a painter of not inconsiderable talent.

1. Valentín de Sambricio, "Los Retratos de Carlo IV y María Luisa, por Goya," *Archivo español de arte*, vol. xxx, no. 118 (1957), p. 98.

2. August L. Mayer, *Francisco de Goya*, Barcelona, 1925, pp. 63, 176, no. 106b.

3. *Catálogo de los cuadros y esculturas pertenecientes a la galería de SS. AA. RR. los Serenísimos Señores Infantes de España, Duqueses de Montpensier*, Seville, 1866, p. 18.

4. X. Desparmet-Fitzgerald, *L'Oeuvre peint de Goya*, vol. ii, Paris, 1928–50, p. 118: "deuxième étude pour la *Famille de Charles IV*."

5. It is listed, for example, in the catalogues by Calvert, Lafond, Von Loga, and Mayer (see Literature).

6. This letter is in the archive of the department of European painting at the Metropolitan Museum of Art, New York. I am grateful to Walter Liedtke for allowing me access to this archive.

7. Xavier de Salas, *La Familia de Carlos IV*, Barcelona, 1944, n.p.

8. Sambricio, p. 98: "no serán de Goya los retratos ovales . . . pertenecientes a los Duques de Montpensier" (The ovoid portraits in the collection of the dukes of Montpensier are not by Goya). The Taft painting once had an ovoid frame. The three other portraits of this series also were in the form of ovals. It is not known whether Sambricio actually saw the Taft painting.

9. José Gudiol, *Goya, 1746–1828: Biography, Analytical Study, and Catalogue of His Paintings*, vol. i, New York, 1971, p. 293.

10. Pierre Gassier and Juliet Wilson, *Goya: His Life and Work*, London, 1971, p. 197.

11. Rita de Angelis, *L'Opera pittorica completa di Goya*, Milan, 1974, p. 115.

12. Gudiol, p. 293.

13. Enrique Lafuente Ferrari, prologue to Martin S. Soria, *Agustín Esteve y Goya*, Valencia, 1957, p. 22.

14. Both Lafuente Ferrari and Soria present a detailed analysis of the life, work, and artistic characteristics of Esteve.

Provenance Dukes of Montpensier, Palace of San Telmo, Seville; Infante Don Antoine-Marie-Philippe d'Orléans, duc de Montpensier, Sanlúcar de Barrameda; comtesse de Paris, Paris (sold 1911); [Durand-Ruel, Paris]; Denys Cochin, Paris; [Scott and Fowles, New York]; Taft collection, 1912.

Exhibitions The Art Institute of Chicago, *The Art of Goya: Paintings, Drawings, and Prints*, Jan. 30–Mar. 2, 1941 (cat. ed. by Daniel Catton Rich, p. 31, no. 52, ill. p. 30); Art Gallery of Toronto, *Loan Exhibition of Great Paintings in Aid of Allied Merchant Seamen*, Feb. 4–Mar. 5, 1944 (cat., p. 21, no. 26); City Art Museum of St. Louis, *Forty Masterpieces: A Loan Exhibition of Paintings from American Museums*, Oct. 6–Nov. 10, 1947 (cat., p. 50, no. 18); Minneapolis Institute of Arts, *Great Portraits by Famous Masters*, Nov. 13–Dec. 21, 1952 (cat., no. 28 [ill.]); Richmond, Virginia Museum of Fine Arts, *The Art of Francisco José de Goya y Lucientes*, Jan. 16–Mar. 1, 1953; Buffalo Fine Arts Academy-Albright Art Gallery, *Painters' Painters*, Apr. 16–May 30, 1954 (cat., p. 61, no. 17, ill. p. 29); Milwaukee Art Institute, *An Inaugural Exhibition*, Sept. 10–Oct. 20, 1957 (cat., p. 34, no. 56, ill. p. 36); Indianapolis, John Herron Museum of Art, and Providence, Museum of Art, Rhode Island School of Design, *El Greco to Goya*, Feb. 10–May 26, 1963 (cat., no. 32 [ill.]).

Literature *Catálogo de los cuadros y esculturas pertenecientes a la galería de SS. AA. RR. los Serenísimos Señores Infantes de España, Duques de Montpensier*, Seville, 1866, p. 18, no. 63; Charles Yriarte, *Goya*, Paris, 1867, p. 146; Conde de la Viñaza, *Goya, su tiempo, su vida, sus obras*, Madrid, 1887, p. 219, no. 18; Zeferino Araujo Sánchez, *Goya*, Madrid, 1896, p. 113, no. 194 (reprinted from *La España moderna*, 1895); Paul Lafond, *Goya*, Paris, n.d. [1903], p. 119, no. 29, ill. p. 15 (as an oval); Albert F. Calvert, *Goya: An Account of His Life and Works*, London, 1908, p. 122, no. 4b, pl. 155; Aureliano de Beruete y Moret, *Goya, pintor de retratos*, Madrid, 1916, p. 176, no. 33 (English ed., New York, 1922, p. 203, no. 33); Valerian von Loga, *Francisco de Goya*, Berlin, 1921, p. 184, no. 97a; August L. Mayer, *Francisco de Goya*, Munich, 1923, p. 181, no. 106 (English ed., London, 1924, p. 144, no. 106; Spanish ed., Barcelona and Buenos Aires, 1925, p. 176, no. 106); Francisco Zapater y Gómez, *Colección de cuatrocientos cuarenta y nueve reproducciones de cuadros, dibujos y aguafuertes de Don Francisco de Goya*, Madrid, 1924, pl. 20; X. Desparmet-Fitzgerald, *L'Oeuvre peint de Goya*, 4 vols., Paris, 1928–50, vol. II, p. 118, no. 400, pl. 323; Walter H. Siple, "The Taft Museum," *Bulletin of the Cincinnati Art Museum*, vol. IV, no. 1 (Jan. 1933), p. 15, ill. p. 16; *Catalogue of the Taft Museum*, Cincinnati, 1939 and 1958; no. 239; "Chicago Presents America's Best Review of Spain's Immortal Goya," *The Art Digest*, vol. XV, no. 9 (1941), p. 8 (ill.); Daniel Catton Rich, "I Always Go Straight to the Goyas," *Magazine of Art*, vol. XXXIV, no. 2 (1941), p. 64 (ill.); Valentín de Sambricio, "Los Retratos de Carlos IV y María Luisa, por Goya," *Archivo español de arte*, vol. XXX, no. 118 (1957), p. 98; Juan Antonio Gaya Nuño, *La Pintura española fuera de España*, Madrid, 1958, p. 167, no. 980; Pierre Gassier and Juliet Wilson, *Goya: His Life and Work*, London, 1971, p. 197, no. II 790; José Gudiol, *Goya, 1746–1828: Biography, Analytical Study, and Catalogue of His Paintings*, 4 vols., New York, 1971, vol. I, p. 293, no. 440, vol. II, p. 594, fig. 711; Rita de Angelis, *L'Opera pittorica completa di Goya*, Milan, 1974, p. 115, no. 385; Pierre Gassier, *Goya (Die grossen Meister des Malerei)*, vol. II, Frankfurt, 1980, p. 18, no. 380a, ill. p. 17; Eric Bruton, *Legendary Gems or Gems That Made History*, Radnor, Pa., 1986, ill. p. 62.

1931.446

Follower of Goya

Portrait of Pedro Joaquín Rodríguez (Costillares)

Mid-nineteenth century
Oil on canvas, 52.7 x 40.6 cm (20¾ x 16 in.)

This painting portrays a bust-length figure of a man, traditionally identified as the bullfighter Pedro Joaquín Rodríguez, called Costillares. He wears a blue kerchief around his head. His jacket is green and has gold and white highlights, as does his vest. He wears a white cravat and a black sash or loose collar hanging from his neck.

Goya may have known Costillares well. The artist's correspondence and contemporary biographies are full of references to Goya's intense interest in bullfighting. Throughout his career he created many images of the *corrida* in paintings, drawings, and prints. Goya did the portraits of several famous bullfighters. Pedro and José Romero, subjects of paintings in the Kimbell Art Museum (Fort Worth, Tex.) and the Philadelphia Museum of Art, respectively, were among the most popular heroes of their day. Pepe Illo, another favorite matador of the late eighteenth century, appears in a number of the plates of the *Tauromaquia*.

Costillares was as famous as Pepe Illo, the Romero brothers, and other bullfighters of his time. He was a favorite of one of Goya's most famous sitters, the duchess of Osuna, who took him under her protection possibly as a show of rivalry to the duchess of Alba, who patronized José Romero.[1] In an oft-quoted letter written by Goya on October 7, 1778, to his boyhood friend Martín Zapater, the artist discusses Costillares and Pedro

1931.393

Romero. Goya evidently was partisan to the talents of the latter bullfighter while Zapater favored the former.[2]

Pedro Joaquín Rodríguez (who was known as Costillares only after 1776) was an exact contemporary of Goya, having been born in Seville in 1746. His uncle was the famous *torero* Pedro Palomo, who gave his nephew his first lessons in this intricate art and arranged for his debut in the ring at Málaga on May 12, 1762. Costillares first appeared in Madrid in 1767 and subsequently became enormously popular both in the capital and in Spain's most famous bullring, the Real Maestranza of Seville. He is credited with innovating a number of elements that are now integral parts of the ritual of the fight, including the swift move used to kill the bull. He was known as a particularly lively and agile fighter. His costume, visible in the various portraits of Costillares ascribed to Goya, became the standard mode of dress for *toreros* and is used to this day in Spain and other countries where bullfighting is practiced. The date of his death is uncertain.[3]

The best-known version of the Costillares portrait is in the collection of the Museo Lázaro Galdiano, Madrid (fig. 1); an engraving of it was published by the firm of Hauser y Menet. The painting is somewhat larger than the Taft picture and shows the sitter in half length wearing the same clothing. Detail varies little in the two portraits, although the collar of the jacket in the Madrid portrait could also be interpreted as a black sash in the Taft picture.[4] Both Mayer and Van Loga published photographs of a third, full-length portrait of Costillares that was formerly in the collection of Ivan Stchoukine, Paris, in which the bullfighter holds a sword and cape.[5] Although the author has seen the full-length portrait in reproduction only, this poorly drawn work is clearly not by Goya's hand, an opinion also held by Camón Aznar.[6]

Several other paintings have the same subject and composition as the Taft and Lázaro Galdiano pictures. Two of them are in the collection of the Museo Taurino, Madrid (inv. nos. 23, 24). A third was sold at auction at Sotheby's, Madrid, on May 31, 1981, catalogued as a work by Eugenio Lucas Velázquez. The quality of all three is mediocre, yet they are significant as barometers of the image's popularity during the late eighteenth and nineteenth centuries.

The Lázaro Galdiano painting has been recently cleaned and is in superb condition. It displays vivid details on the jacket and vest defined by a loose brush.[7] It is difficult to attribute it to Goya, however, precisely because of the ostentatious quality of the brushwork, which is more closely related to the sensibility of artists of the mid-nineteenth century. In addition, certain awkward passages of painting separate it from Goya's oeuvre. These include details such as those of the sitter's left sleeve and right shoulder, which are especially loose. The lines of the left side of the collar create an almost meaningless abstract pattern. The face is weakly painted; the transition from the line of the chin to the neck is uncertain. The cheeks are flat and the ear poorly defined. If one compares these details to analogous passages in autograph works of Goya of the 1790s (such as the portrait of Sebastián Martínez, 1792, New York, the Metropolitan

Museum of Art), the gulf of quality between the two becomes obvious. Using this criterion, it also becomes clear that the Taft picture is another variant of a probably lost prototype. There is even greater uncertainty with regard to details here than in the Lázaro Galdiano version. The ear is awkward, as are the hairline and the upper portion of the forehead with its flat, regular brushstrokes. The brushwork is especially labored on the brow, chin, and cheek. Although the heavy embroidery of the left shoulder is convincingly evoked, the other areas of the jacket are poorly suggested, and the body seems to lose corporeality, especially at the right. The tie is also not totally coherent, lacking substance particularly in the right section and in the knot.

Several catalogues of Goya's work written in the early years of this century list both the Taft and the Lázaro Galdiano versions without commenting on their authenticity.[8] Aureliano de Beruete, however, in his book on Goya's portraiture remarks that the artist's likenesses of bullfighters were "neither numerous nor especially select."[9] Desparmet-Fitzgerald lists the Taft picture as of "doubtful authenticity."[10] This work, which must be ascribed to an anonymous artist of the mid-nineteenth century, is not listed in the catalogues of either De Angelis or Gassier and Wilson.[11]

1. Hugh Stokes, *Francisco Goya: A Study of the Work and Personality of the Eighteenth-Century Spanish Painter and Satirist*, New York and London, 1914, states: "In 1789 gossip reported that the two duchesses [Alba and Osuna] disputed the patronage of Costillares and Romero, the two most celebrated bull-fighters of Spain." He quotes as his source the *Memoires* of Manuel Godoy and the *Spanish Journal* of Lady Holland.

2. This letter is published in Mercedes Agueda and Xavier de Salas, eds., *Francisco de Goya: Cartas a Martín Zapater*, Madrid, 1984, p. 46.

3. Bullfighting was temporarily banned in Spain in 1805. After this time there are no further records indicating the whereabouts or activities of Costillares. For his biography, see the *Enciclopedia universal ilustrada europea-americana (Espasa Calpe)*, vol. LI, p. 1271.

4. It is described as a sash by Aureliano de Beruete, *Goya, pintor de retratos*, Madrid, 1919, pp. 57–58.

5. August L. Mayer, *Goya*, Barcelona and Buenos Aires, 1925, p. 188, no. 264, fig. 66; Valerian van Loga, *Francisco de Goya*, Berlin, 1921, pl. 12.

6. José Camón Aznar, *Guía abreviada del Museo Lázaro Galdiano*, Madrid, 1960, p. 145, states that the full-length painting "appears to be the work of an imitator."

7. The author is grateful to Dr. Marina Cano Cuesta, curator at the Museo Lázaro Galdiano, Madrid, for facilitating detailed study of the Madrid painting and for providing photographs.

8. Albert E. Calvert, *Goya: An Account of His Life and Works*, London, 1908, pp. 133–34; Stokes, p. 330.

9. Beruete, pp. 57–58.

10. X. Desparmet-Fitzgerald, *L'Oeuvre peint de Goya*, Paris, 1928–50, vol. II, p. 88.

11. Rita de Angelis, *L'Opera pittorica completa di Goya*, Milan, 1974; Pierre Gassier and Juliet Wilson, *The Life and Complete Work of Francisco Goya*, New York, 1971.

Provenance Conde de Asalto, Madrid; Enrique Puncet, Madrid; [Scott and Fowles, New York]; Taft collection, Feb. 16, 1916.

Exhibitions Madrid, *Exposición nacional de retratos*, 1902, no. 677; San Francisco, California Palace of the Legion of Honor, *Exhibition of Paintings, Drawings, and Prints by Francisco Goya, 1746–1828*, 1937 (cat., p. 28, no. 12 [ill.]); Columbus Gallery of Fine Arts, Ohio, *Masterpieces of Spanish Painting*, Oct. 8–Nov. 14, 1954; Grand Rapids Art Gallery, Mich.,

Fig. 1 Follower of Francisco de Goya, *Portrait of Pedro Joaquín Rodríguez (Costillares)*, mid-nineteenth century. Oil on canvas, 65 x 54 cm (25½ x 21¼ in.). Madrid, Museo Lázaro Galdiano.

Community Angels Build, Dec. 5, 1959–Jan. 3, 1960 (cat., no. 6 [ill.]); Berkeley, University of California, University Art Museum, *Art from Ingres to Pollock*, Mar. 5–Apr. 3, 1960; Dallas Museum of Fine Arts, *The Arts of Man: A Selection from Ancient to Modern Times*, Oct. 6–Dec. 31, 1962 (cat., p. 61, no. 61, ill. p. 51).

Literature Albert E. Calvert, *Goya: An Account of His Life and Works*, London, 1908, pp. 133–34; Hugh Stokes, *Francisco Goya: A Study of the Work and Personality of the Eighteenth-Century Spanish Painter and Satirist*, New York and London, 1914, p. 330, no. 79; Aureliano de Beruete, *Goya, pintor de retratos*, Madrid, 1919, pp. 57–58, 182, no. 152; August L. Mayer, *Goya*, Barcelona and Buenos Aires, 1925, pp. 31, 65, 188, no. 246, ill. p. 70, fig. 121; X. Desparmet-Fitzgerald, *L'Oeuvre peint de Goya*, Paris, 1928–50, vol. II, p. 88; Walter H. Siple, "The Taft Museum," *Bulletin of the Cincinnati Art Museum*, vol. IV, no. 1 (Jan. 1933), p. 15, ill. p. 16; *Bulletin of the Cincinnati Art Museum*, vol. V, no. 1 (Jan. 1934), cover ill.; Thomas Carr Howe, Jr., "San Francisco: Forty Goyas in the Far West," *The Art News*, vol. XXXV, no. 37 (June 12, 1937), p. 15; *Catalogue of the Taft Museum*, Cincinnati, 1939 and 1958, no. 243; José Camón Aznar, *Goya*, vol. II, Zaragoza, 1984, pp. 79, 81.

1931.393

Mariano Fortuny i Marsal
Reus 1838–1874 Rome

Fortuny was one of Spain's outstanding nineteenth-century painters. His art was appreciated internationally and was collected by some of the most significant patrons of his time. Fortuny received his earliest training in his hometown in the academies of Simeó Fort and Domingo Soberano. In 1850 his grandfather (who had taken charge of the boy's education on the death of his parents) took him to Barcelona, where he first studied with Domenèch Talarn and later enrolled for a four-year course at the School of Fine Arts. There he studied landscape painting with Lluís Rigalt, ancient art with Claudi Lorenzale, and aesthetics and composition with Pau Milà i Fontanals. Milà and Johann Friedrich Overbeck were members of the Nazarene group, and their troubadour style (a technique and subjects meant to revive the look of life and art in the Middle Ages) is reflected in many of Fortuny's early important works, such as his *Raymond Berenguer Planting the Flag of Barcelona at the Castle of Foix* (1857, Barcelona, City Council). For this painting Fortuny won the Rome Prize offered by the Diputació de Barcelona. He arrived in Rome on March 19, 1858. He regularly attended classes at the Giggi Academy and visited all the major museums and churches, making numerous studies. Throughout his life he spent much time in Italy.

In January 1860 Fortuny was commissioned by the City Council of Barcelona to depict an incident from the Spanish-Moroccan War. He accepted and left for North Africa. During this and several subsequent trips to Morocco he painted and drew many scenes of both warfare and the intimate daily lives of the Moroccans. The outstanding product of these visits was the enormous canvas *The Battle of Tetuan* (1863, Barcelona, Museu d'Art Modern). Painted after the artist had studied Horace Vernet's *Battle of Smalah* at Versailles, it documents the intervention of General Joan Prim and his troops in the Moroccan conflict.

Fortuny spent the autumn of 1866 in Paris, when he began his association with Adolph Goupil, the art dealer who would represent him in his Paris gallery for many years. Shortly thereafter he also met Jean-Léon Gérôme and Ernest Meissonier, both of whom inspired Fortuny in style and subject matter.

Throughout the 1860s and even later, Fortuny painted neo-rococo subjects, scenes of eighteenth-century life. These works are invariably small in scale and are created with shimmering, jewel-like colors and an impasto-laden brush. Works of this type, like *The Vicarage* (1868, Barcelona, Museu d'Art Modern) or *The Choice of a Model* (1873–74, Washington, D.C., Corcoran Gallery of Art), appealed, as did his orientalist subjects, to European collectors as well as to those from the United States, such as W. H. Stewart, Henry Walters, and William H. Vanderbilt.

In 1867 Fortuny married Cecilia de Madrazo, daughter of the painter Federico de Madrazo and sister of Raimundo, known for his genre pictures and society portraits. The couple had two children, María Luisa and Mariano, the latter of whom would become a well-known painter, photographer, and fabric designer.

In 1870 Fortuny spent several months in Spain. He had a particular fondness for Granada and spent the summer there in a villa on the grounds of the Alhambra. Some of the pictures painted during the last four years of his life reflect his continuing interest in the exoticism of the south of Spain and North Africa (he returned to Morocco in 1872), while others, such as *The Bull Ring* (1870–72, Madrid, Casón del Buen Retiro), reflect a greater interest in realism. In 1873 Fortuny wrote to his brother-in-law, Raimundo de Madrazo, of his disillusionment with the art of Gérôme, Léon Bonnat, Charles-François Daubigny, and others and of his enthusiasm for the young Renoir.[1] Had he lived longer, it is possible that Fortuny would have developed a style akin to that of the French impressionists. His use of sparkling color and often separated tones demonstrates a kinship with their techniques.

Fortuny spent much of the last year of his life in Italy, although he went with his biographer, Baron Charles Davillier, to London in June 1874 when he may have met Vincent van Gogh, who was employed there at Goupil & Cie.[2] In June of that year he returned to Rome and went with his family to Portici, near Naples, for the summer. There, he may have contracted the malaria from which he died in Rome on November 21.

1. Joan Ainaud de Lasarte in *Mariano Fortuny*, exh. cat., Museu d'Art Modern, Barcelona, 1974, n.p.

2. Ainaud.

Mariano Fortuny i Marsal

An Arab Guard

1863
Oil on canvas, 58.4 x 49.2 cm (23 x 19⅜ in.)
Signed and dated lower right: *Fortuny. / 1863*

1931.430

century. Although they share subject matter, some of his paintings and prints of Moroccan life (especially the more informal depictions such as this candid view of a man at his leisure) show a greater sympathy and understanding of the individuals portrayed than can be observed in the more detached or picturesque scenes by Gérôme, Horace Vernet, Ludwig Deutsch, David Roberts, or John Frederick Lewis.

1. See Francesc Fontbona, *Del neoclassicisme a la restauració, 1808–1888, Història de l'art català,* vol. vi, Barcelona, 1983, pl. 197.

Provenance D'Artez, Barcelona?; Mrs. Bloomfield Moore, London (sale, Christie's, London, May 5, 1900, no. 18, for £861 to Arthur Tooth, according to an annotated copy of the sale cat. in the library of the Sterling and Francine Clark Art Institute, Williamstown, Mass.); [Arthur Tooth and Sons, London]; Taft collection, Dec. 6, 1902.

Exhibition Barcelona and Madrid, Fundació Caixa de Pensions, *Fortuny 1838–1874,* Jan.–May, 1989 (cat., essay, "Fortuny in America: His Collectors and Disciples" by Edward J. Sullivan, pp. 108–9, fig. 6; color pl. p. 130; and p. 192, no. 8).

Literature Maurice W. Brockwell, *A Catalogue of Paintings in the Collection of Mr. and Mrs. Charles P. Taft,* New York, 1920, p. 173; *Catalogue of the Taft Museum,* Cincinnati, 1939 and 1958, no. 564; Claudie Ressort, *Mariano Fortuny et ses amis français,* exh. cat., Musée Goya, Castres [France], 1974, p. 14; Carlos González López and Montserrat Martí Ayxelà, *Maestros de arte de los siglos XIX y XX: Mariano Fortuny Marsal,* vol. i, Barcelona, 1989, p. 202, pl. 49.

1931.430

An Arab dressed in white robe and *babouches* (oriental slippers) sits on a step. In his right hand he holds a large gun pointing upward. In his left he holds a long pipe, which he smokes while resting his arm on the top of a stove on which also rest a decanter and a glazed Hispano-Moresque plate.

This painting was executed in Fortuny's studio on the via Flaminia in Rome. By 1863 he had made two trips to Morocco during which he had filled many notebooks with his impressions of life in Tangier, Tetuan, and other northern sites. From this experience he painted his massive canvas *The Battle of Tetuan,* commissioned by the City Council of Barcelona, as well as a number of intimate scenes of everyday life in Morocco, such as the Taft painting. Fortuny was a great collector of objets d'art of all varieties, and they often appear in his works. He also owned a gun such as the one held by the guard in this painting and once posed for a photograph dressed as a Moor, in which he holds the large rifle in his hands.[1]

The rich, warm colors and especially the rapid, short strokes of the brush are characteristic of Fortuny's distinctive technique, which is particularly evident in intimate pictures such as this one. In larger, more formal compositions he tended to paint in a tighter and more controlled manner.

In correspondence with the author, the art historian Carlos González López has remarked that the sitter may be a Moroccan named Ferragi, who served as guide and later became a friend of and often a model for the painter. González also notes that although the painting is signed 1863, its technique looks forward to the works of the late years of the decade.

Fortuny's images of North Africa have often been linked with those of Gérôme and other orientalist painters of the nineteenth

Raimundo de Madrazo Garreta
Rome 1841–1920 Versailles

Raimundo de Madrazo was a member of an important artistic dynasty, which included his grandfather José and his father, Federico, and which helped to shape the course of Spanish art during the nineteenth century. Raimundo was born in Rome where his father was exhibiting paintings in the Nazarene style that was popular at the time. Raimundo soon returned to Madrid where, as a young boy, he studied drawing with Federico in the latter's studio on the Paseo del Prado. Raimundo's early formal training took place at the School of Fine Arts of San Fernando with some of the most significant Spanish painters of the time, including Genaro Pérez Villamil, Juan Antonio de Ribera, and Antonio María Esquivel. In 1855 Raimundo accompanied his father to Paris, where he saw and copied works by Jean-Auguste-Dominique Ingres. The neoclassical mode espoused by Ingres would characterize Madrazo's early work, as in his first successful composition, *The Body of Saint James the Apostle Carried to Spain* (1858). Madrazo returned to Paris in 1862 and enrolled at the School of Fine Arts as a student of Léon Cogniet. He soon met a number of important artists, such as Charles Gleyre, Léon Bonnat, and Ernest Meissonier. Meissonier and Mariano Fortuny (who became Madrazo's brother-in-law in 1867) as well as Alfred Stevens would have a strong impact on his style, which changed under their influence from the classicizing correctness of his youth to the spontaneous and coloristically rich manner of his mature years.

Madrazo spent most of the decade of the 1860s in Paris, remaining there during the Franco-Prussian War when he worked for the International Red Cross. After the war he returned to Spain and married his cousin Carlota de Ochoa y de Madrazo (1847–1875). In 1874 Fortuny died in Rome, and Madrazo assumed the management of his estate and the sale of his belongings at the Hôtel Drouot in April 1875. When his wife died, the artist was left with one son, Federico.

In 1878 Madrazo showed at the Universal Exposition, Paris, where he won a first prize and was awarded the position of Knight in the Legion of Honor. In 1884 he showed in Madrid at the gallery of the well-known dealer Bosch and also exhibited in the Paris Salon. The following year he married María Hahn Echenaguncia and made his first trips to the United States and South America. From this time on he would receive many commissions for portraits from patrons in such cities as New York, Philadelphia, and Buenos Aires. In 1889 he again showed at the Universal Exposition and was accorded the rank of Officer in the Legion of Honor. Madrazo's father died in 1894. Three years after this he returned to New York for his exhibition at the Oehme Gallery. Another trip to New York in 1898 consolidated his success in that city. He was made a member of the Hispanic Society of America in 1905 by its founder, Archer M. Huntington, and in 1913 the artist donated a number of his paintings to that institution. Among Madrazo's many prominent American patrons and sitters could be counted Mrs. Harry Payne Whitney, Mrs. Cornelius Vanderbilt, Mrs. O. H. P. Belmont, and Mr. and Mrs. Charles Phelps Taft.

In about 1910 Madrazo retired from painting, spending most of the last decade of his life in France, where he died at his home in Versailles on September 15, 1920.

❧

Raimundo de Madrazo Garreta

Charles Phelps Taft

1902
Oil on canvas, 124.7 x 97.2 cm (49⅛ x 38¼ in.)
Signed and dated lower left: *R. Madrazo / 1902*

Charles Phelps Taft (1843–1929) is shown in this three-quarter-length portrait sitting in a chair. He wears gray trousers, a black jacket and vest, and a white shirt. Around his neck he wears a reddish purple ascot with a pearl tiepin. He also wears a gold watch chain. The back and the seat of the chair are green, as is the drapery background against which the sitter is posed. This painting displays the very loose brushwork that is characteristic of virtually all the portraits from Madrazo's mature period. The fluidity of handling is especially apparent in Mr. Taft's beard and hair and in the background.

Madrazo painted this image and the portrait of Mrs. Taft (see following) during one of his several long visits to the United States. The paintings were executed in the sitters' home in Cincinnati during the last weeks of 1902. Progress on the work

3.1931

is recorded in the correspondence of Mr. Taft to William Howard Taft, then serving as governor of the Philippines (Charles consistently spells the artist's name with two *z*'s).[1] In a letter of November 24 he mentions that "we are about to have [our portraits] made by a Spanish artist, Madrazzo. He is said to be a very fine artist. . . . I trust they will be moderately successful." Madrazo painted Mrs. Taft first, as we learn from another letter to William Howard dated December 8:

> Last week she spent most of her time in sitting for Madrazzo, the portrait painter. I think she is going to have a beautiful picture. I expect to go through the same operation this week. Madrazzo is an artist who has painted many portraits in New York and has a great reputation. . . . I think he has caught Annie's expression very well. Up to the present time, however, he has only tried the face, the balance of the picture he will have to fill in.

Madrazo must have enjoyed his time with the Tafts, for the letter continues: "Madrazzo has been in this country for quite a number of years and yet he cannot talk English. Annie is practising her French upon him. He thinks he is very lucky in finding somebody he can converse with." Taft grew more enthusiastic about Madrazo's work as time went on. In another letter to William Howard Taft, dated December 20, 1902, we read: "Madrazzo . . . is making a wonderful success. Annie has a splendid likeness: the expression is entirely satisfactory, and they say that my picture is all that can be desired." Both works were probably finished shortly before Christmas 1902, because on December 22 Madrazo signed a receipt in the amount of $8000 for them.

4.1931

1. All letters, William Howard Taft papers, series 1, Library of Congress, Washington, D.C.

Provenance Commissioned from the artist, Dec. 1902; lent by the estates of Louise Taft Semple and Jane Taft Ingalls.

Literature Maurice W. Brockwell, *A Catalogue of Paintings in the Collection of Mr. and Mrs. Charles P. Taft,* New York, 1920, no. 74; *Catalogue of the Taft Museum,* Cincinnati, 1939 and 1958, no. 455 (ill.); Ruth Krueger Meyer, "The Taft Collection: The First Ten Years of Its Development," *The Taft Museum: A Cincinnati Legacy,* Cincinnati, 1988, p. 1 (ill.); David Torbet Johnson, "Taft Museum," *Ventura,* vol. IV, no. 16 (June–Aug. 1991), p. 132 (ill.).

3.1931

Raimundo de Madrazo Garreta

Mrs. Charles Phelps Taft

1902
Oil on canvas, 125.1 x 97 cm (49¼ x 38⅛ in.)
Signed and dated lower left: *R. Madrazo / 1902*

Like the portrait of her husband, that of Anna Sinton Taft (1852?–1931) shows the sitter seated in three-quarter length. She is facing the viewer, and her legs are turned to the left. She wears a white dress with lace at the sleeves and neckline. Pink and yellow flowers adorn her bodice. A blue cloak is draped over the back of the chair. Around her neck she wears a black ribbon from which hangs a single large pearl. A long strand of pearls and rings on both hands complete her jewelry. She is posed

against an outdoor setting reminiscent of the backgrounds often found in English eighteenth-century portraiture. There is a blue sky, a meadow with trees, and a large tree to the extreme right of the canvas. The brushwork here is as loose as in the portrait of Mr. Taft.

In his letter of November 24, 1902, to William Howard Taft, Charles comments on the dress, which was made for Mrs. Taft in New York, stating that "O'Hara made a dress for her trimming it with old Venetian lace."¹ It is very likely that Mrs. Taft was as enthusiastic about her portrait as her husband was, for in 1903 the artist was commissioned (probably by Mrs. Taft) to paint a posthumous portrait of her mother, Jane Ellison Sinton. In 1904 Madrazo painted a likeness of Mrs. Taft's father, David Sinton. These bust-length portraits, undoubtedly painted from photographs, are now in private collections in Cincinnati (*Mrs. Sinton*) and in Shaker Heights, Ohio (*Mr. Sinton*).

1. William Howard Taft papers, series 1, Library of Congress, Washington, D.C.

Provenance Commissioned from the artist, Dec. 22, 1902; lent by the estates of Louise Taft Semple and Jane Taft Ingalls.

Literature Maurice W. Brockwell, *A Catalogue of Paintings in the Collection of Mr. and Mrs. Charles P. Taft,* New York, 1920, no. 73; *Catalogue of the Taft Museum,* Cincinnati, 1939 and 1958, no. 466 (ill.); Ruth Krueger Meyer, "The Taft Collection: The First Ten Years of Its Development," *The Taft Museum: A Cincinnati Legacy,* Cincinnati, 1988, p. 1 (ill.); David Torbet Johnson, "Taft Museum," *Ventura,* vol. IV, no. 16 (June–Aug. 1991), p. 133 (ill.).

4.1931

Joaquín Sorolla y Bastida
Valencia 1863–1923 Cercedilla (Madrid)

Joaquín Sorolla is known as a painter of light. As one of the first plein-air artists of his country, he introduced to Spanish art numerous pictorial effects that paralleled the principal notions of French impressionism while differing from them in fundamental ways. His early work can be characterized by the term "socially committed realism." Some of his paintings of the 1880s and 1890s depict scenes of poverty or crime. Historical, religious, and oriental themes were also common in his work at this time. His mature art (ca. 1900–1919) often constitutes a celebration of the types, customs, and geographic characteristics of the many regions of his native Spain. His favorite theme was the sea, and his numerous beach scenes (often depicting the shores near the towns of Valencia) convincingly capture the essence of the light of the Spanish coast. During his mature years portraiture also assumed an increasingly large position in his repertoire.

Orphaned at an early age, Sorolla and a younger sister, María Concepción, were reared by an aunt and uncle who sent the boy to study at the Superior Normal School of the Province of Valencia and later, in 1877, to the Artisans' School. At the age of eighteen Joaquín enrolled at the Academy of San Fernando in Madrid where he received traditional training in painting and drawing. At the Prado Museum he made numerous copies of works by Spanish old masters, especially Velázquez, Ribera, and El Greco. A gold medal for a composition entitled *A Praying Nun* was the first of numerous awards he received during his lifetime. In 1882 he won the National Fine Arts Competition, which allowed him to study at the Spanish Academy in Rome (1885–88). The director of the academy, Francisco Pradilla, a painter of large academic historical pictures, was highly inspirational for young Sorolla, who executed several works in his manner.

By this time Sorolla had already begun to paint outdoors, something few Spanish artists had done in the past. His interest in nature painting was evidently strengthened by his trip in 1885 to Paris, where he saw works by the impressionists. Nonetheless, he seems to have been more interested in the art of Jules Bastien-Lepage and the German Adolph von Menzel, both of whom had exhibitions in Paris at that time. Other artists who inspired him include the Swedish painter Anders Zorn and the Dane Peder Severin Krøyer. In 1888 Sorolla married Clotilde García del Castillo, daughter of the well-known photographer Antonio García. They went to Italy after their marriage. By 1890 the couple had established their residence in Madrid.

During the 1890s Sorolla's work was seen in numerous international exhibitions and competitions. One of his most significant essays in social commentary, a large canvas known as *Triste herencia (Sad Inheritance)* won the grand prize at the 1899 Universal Exposition in Paris. Sorolla's first one-person exhibition in Paris opened in June 1906. An astonishing 497 works filled the Galeries Georges Petit. He later exhibited in London and Germany. He realized a huge success in 1909 in New York where his exhibition at the Hispanic Society of America attracted record crowds. The show traveled to Buffalo and Boston, increasing his fame in America, which was further promoted by additional exhibitions in Chicago and Saint Louis.

On November 26, 1910, Sorolla received the single most important commission of his life, a series of larger-than-life-size panels (measuring 227 feet in length) portraying the provinces of Spain to decorate the library of the Hispanic Society. He worked on this project until June 1919, traveling to virtually every corner of the country and making sketches and preliminary oils of the hundreds of individual figures that would populate these canvases. During this time he also continued his career as a portraitist of high society in various countries. In 1917 King Alfonso XIII of Spain requested that Sorolla paint him in hunting garb.

The effort of the Hispanic Society panels took a great toll on the artist's health. On June 17, 1920, he suffered a stroke as he was working on the portrait of the wife of the Spanish writer Pérez de Ayala. His wife cared for him during the painful three years of his illness. He was never able to paint again and died in the town of Cercedilla, near Madrid, on August 10, 1923.

2.1931

Joaquín Sorolla y Bastida

William Howard Taft

1909
Oil on canvas, 150 x 80 cm (59 x 31½ in.)
Signed, dated, and inscribed upper right: *J. Sorolla B. / 1909 Washington / White House*

This portrait of President Taft shows him in three-quarter length. He is seated and dressed in a dark gray, vested suit, white shirt, and dark mauve tie. A gold watch chain is visible just above his waist. His body is turned partly to the right, and his head is turned slightly to the left to face the viewer. His right hand is clenched, and his left hand holds numerous papers, some of which are rolled. The seat of the chair is covered in green cloth. The chair frame that is visible below Taft's right arm is yellow. The background of the painting is dark and is composed of a blend of black and purple with blue and yellow highlights at the extreme right to indicate a window.

The artist applied the paint in a thick impasto, especially on the face and forehead. Although the predominant tones are dark, the artist's use of numerous blended colors results in an extraordinary brightness and vivacity. The skin color of the sitter's hands and smiling face is achieved through a skillful manipulation of red, pink, and yellow hues. The fingers of the right hand (the more detailed of the two) display a combination of reds, greens, and yellows along with flesh tones. The overall impression of striking immediacy and liveliness has been noted ever since the painting was completed in 1909.

By the time this painting was executed, Sorolla had become famous in his native country and very well known in other European nations. He had had successful exhibitions in France, Germany, and England.[1] Yet no nation accorded him more respect and adulation than that which he received in the United States. When Archer M. Huntington met Sorolla at the time of the artist's exhibition at the Grafton Galleries in London, in 1908, the American Hispanist became so interested in the Spaniard's work that he invited him to prepare an exhibition for the Hispanic Society of America, which Huntington had newly founded in New York. The highly successful showing came at a time when Sorolla was at the height of his talents and undoubtedly prompted the numerous portrait commissions from American patrons.

Sorolla's most prestigious commission was to paint William Howard Taft (1857–1930), the twenty-seventh president of the United States. Taft took office in January of the year that the portrait was painted. Prior to that time he was a lawyer in his native Cincinnati and in 1904 had been appointed secretary of war by President Theodore Roosevelt. He became a close adviser to Roosevelt and made a name for himself as an expert in Latin American affairs, conducting the negotiations with Cuba after the United States intervened in that country in 1906. Taft had a lively personality, and Sorolla enjoyed the days he spent with him. The president was able to converse with the painter in Spanish, which obviously pleased Sorolla, who spoke no English.[2] Something of the flavor of these sittings (which began on April 6 and ended April 12) can be gleaned from an excerpt of a letter written by Taft's military aide Archie Butt to his sister-in-law, Mrs. Lewis Butt, three days after Sorolla arrived at the White House:

> The President is having his portrait painted and we are having a great time getting him to sit still long enough to have it done. When once we get him in the chair he is a perfect study in still life, but the difficulty is to get him in the chair. The artist is a Spaniard, by name Joaquín Sorolla y Bastida, and he carries an interpreter with him, as he neither understands nor speaks English. He told me yesterday in Spanish that the President was very hard to paint for the reason that there was little expression save joviality and that it was not the expression to paint on great men. He said, too, that which I have long known to be true, that when in perfect repose his face is hard and almost sinister, and that any portrait with this expression would be disliked.[3]

This, like the other portraits executed by Sorolla in the United States at the time, was commissioned through the Hispanic Society.[4] The picture was in New York by April 15, and one month later the society paid the artist $3000 for it.[5] In the same month the portrait was sent to the home of Charles Phelps Taft (the president's half-brother) and his wife, Anna Sinton Taft. On May 18 Charles sent a letter from his residence addressed to "Will" regarding the impact the painting had on those who had seen it:

> We have had the opportunity to see the Sorolla portrait. It is a success. We have not yet found a place for it. It needs distance and a good light. Annie thinks that "all conquering smile" ought to go down to posterity. She is at my elbow now and suggests that some of your lady friends are glad to see that "dimple" immortalized. It now occupies one end of the spare bedroom, in a tolerably fair light, but not hung high enough. Again, Annie suggests that a few favored friends, almost entirely feminine, have seen the portrait and have approved of it enthusiastically. Indeed, the Sewing Circle met at the house yesterday and I think the portrait was the piece de resistance [*sic*].[6]

The painting is a highly successful likeness, a strong evocation of the sitter's personality, and a bravura tour de force of vigorous brushwork. Portraits from this phase of Sorolla's career have often been likened (for good reason) to those by John Singer Sargent. There are many points of contact between the art of the two painters, who were friends and whose styles had a reciprocal impact. This portrait of William Howard Taft could be compared, for example, with Sargent's portraits of Henry G. Marquand (1897, New York, the Metropolitan Museum of Art) and Major Henry Lee Higginson (1903, Cambridge, Mass., Harvard University Portrait Collection).

1. For the most recent critical work on Sorolla as well as a chronology and bibliography, see *The Painter Joaquín Sorolla y Bastida*, exh. cat., San Diego and Valencia, 1989.

2. Archie Butt, *Taft and Roosevelt: The Intimate Letters of Archie Butt*, vol. 1, New York, 1930, p. 47.

3. Butt, p. 47.

4. *The Painter Joaquín Sorolla y Bastida*, no. 50.

5. Copy of the receipt in Taft Museum archives.

6. Letter from Charles Phelps Taft to William Howard Taft, May 18, 1909, in the William Howard Taft papers, series 1, Library of Congress, Washington, D.C.

Provenance Commissioned by Charles Phelps Taft, 1909; lent by the estates of Louise Taft Semple and Jane Taft Ingalls.

Exhibitions Boston, Museum of Fine Arts, *Exhibition of Paintings by Joaquín Sorolla y Bastida*, 1909; Pittsburgh, *Fourteenth Annual Exhibition at the Carnegie Institute*, May 2–June 30, 1910, no. 258; San Diego, Museum of Art [also New York and Saint Louis], *Joaquín Sorolla: Painter of Light*, 1989–90 (cat. by Edmund Peel, Francisco Pons Sorolla, Carmen Gracia, and Priscilla Muller, no. 50).

Literature Archie Butt, *Taft and Roosevelt: The Intimate Letters of Archie Butt*, vol. 1, New York, 1930, p. 47; *Catalogue of the Taft Museum*, Cincinnati, 1939 and 1958, no. 277 (ill.); Bernardino de Pantorba, *La Vida y la obra de Joaquín Sorolla*, Madrid, 1970, no. 2040; Ruth Krueger Meyer, "The Taft Collection: The First Ten Years of Its Development," *The Taft Museum: A Cincinnati Legacy*, Cincinnati, 1988, p. 10 (ill.).

2.1931

Nineteenth-Century French Paintings

Lewis C. Kachur

Jean-Auguste-Dominique Ingres
Montauban 1780–1867 Paris

Ingres was the most important exponent of the neoclassical style in French painting during the years of his maturity. The son of an artist, he learned to draw at an early age. After initial training in Toulouse, he studied with the leading neoclassicist Jacques-Louis David, entering his studio in Paris in August 1797. Ingres competed for the Rome Prize in 1800, at which time he was awarded second place. He won the competition in 1801 with *The Ambassadors of Agamemnon* (Paris, Ecole des Beaux-Arts), although he did not travel to Rome until September 1806. Once in Italy, he extended his stay to eighteen years, living first in Rome, where he married Madeline Chapelle in 1813. From 1820 to 1824 he stayed in Florence, where he had gone at the suggestion of the sculptor Lorenzo Bartolini.

Ingres painted many portraits in Italy, including the imposing likeness of Count Gouriev (St. Petersburg, Hermitage) dated, like the Taft picture, to 1821. Ingres painted some of his most famous female nudes in Rome, such as the *Valpinçon Bather* (1808), followed by the *Grande Odalisque* (1814), both now in the Louvre. Also in 1814 he began his famous pencil portrait commissions. During his last decade in Italy, he created some important works in the troubadour style of historical genre painting, evoking the look of life and art in the Middle Ages. His principal friends and clients in Florence were the Gonin-Thomeguex, Pastoret, and Leblanc families. His major state commission painted during the Florence years was *The Vow of Louis XIII* (Montauban, Cathedral), and he returned to Paris in the fall of 1824 to show it in the Salon. It was well received, earning Ingres membership in the Legion of Honor and entry into the Academy of Fine Arts.

Ingres opened a studio that attracted over one hundred pupils and, in 1833, became president of the School of Fine Arts. The following year he decided to return to Rome, where he obtained the directorship of the French Academy, which he headed from 1835 to 1841. After returning to Paris in 1841 he received many official commissions, including *The Golden Age,* an allegorical painting for the château at Dampierre, southwest of Paris. He produced more masterpieces of portraiture, including the *Comtesse d'Haussonville* (1845, New York, The Frick Collection)

and *Madame Moitessier* (1856, London, National Gallery). His first wife died in 1849, and he married Delphine Ramel in 1852.

Along with Decamps and Delacroix, Ingres had a retrospective at the Universal Exposition of 1855, which included forty-three paintings and twenty-five cartoons for stained-glass windows. At this time Napoléon III made him a Grand Officer of the Legion of Honor. After his death he was accorded a memorial exhibition at the Ecole des Beaux-Arts. He left the works in his studio to his native Montauban, where they are now housed in the Musée Ingres.

ᏚᎪ

Jean-Auguste-Dominique Ingres

Mademoiselle Jeanne Gonin

1821
Oil on canvas, 76 x 60.7 cm (30 x 23⅞ in.)
Signed and dated lower left: *D. Ingres p[   ] flor. / 1821*

In this half-length portrait a young woman wears a black ribbon and comb in her dark brown hair and a blue-and-white plaid cloth at her white lace collar. She wears a demure black satin dress that buttons down the front. Her gold chain ends in a silver clasp, probably attached to a folding reading glass, which is partially tucked inside her bodice. She wears rings on the middle fingers of each of her prominent, crossed hands, "as beautiful as any in Ingres' oeuvre."[1] On her right hand is a double gold band, and on her left are three gold bands with red, silver, and white stones. This prominent display of rings, usually worn several to a finger, with the width of the bands emphasized, was typical of the romantic period. The rings are relatively simple in design, and their origin cannot easily be identified.[2]

Compared to some of Ingres's contemporary female sitters, such as *Vicountess of Senonnes* (1814, Nantes, Musée des Beaux-Arts) or *Madame Marcotte de Sainte-Marie* (1826, Paris, Musée du Louvre), this sitter is conservatively dressed. She does not wear as much jewelry or the revealing costume of most of the other women painted by Ingres. This demureness almost certainly reflects her Swiss Calvinist background.

Jeanne-Suzanne-Catherine Gonin married Pyrame Thomeguex in Fiesole, Italy, on May 4, 1822, so this picture may have been commissioned to celebrate their engagement. The same year Ingres also made a portrait drawing of Pyrame (dated December 30, 1821, in Basel, Edmond Lévy collection). The couple was originally from Geneva, and Jeanne was born in 1787, while Pyrame was two years younger. Jeanne's family had gone to live in Florence in a palazzo near San Spirito in 1815. Her brother Jean-Pierre was in the straw-hat manufacturing business, as was her future husband.

Ingres made many drawings of members of the Gonin and Thomeguex families, who were among his best friends in Florence, but the Taft portrait is the only painting. The Gonins introduced him to the Leblancs who commissioned the cele-

1931.414

brated pendant portraits of 1823 (New York, the Metropolitan Museum of Art).

Ingres remained in touch with the Gonin family for some years. Jeanne Gonin-Thomeguex apparently became friendly with Ingres's wife, who around 1829 sent her a pencil portrait of herself.[3] There is also a drawing of an unidentified sitter done in Paris in 1825, which somewhat resembles Jeanne (Geneva, Musée d'Art et d'Histoire).[4] Jeanne had a son in 1823 and a daughter in 1825. Ingres apparently visited the family again in 1841 when he made a pencil portrait of the son. Jeanne died at fifty-five in 1842, followed two years later by her husband. Her portrait stayed in the family and remained unexhibited and essentially unknown to students of Ingres until Lapauze's notice of 1923.

1. Henry Lapauze, "Sur un portrait inédit de Ingres: Mme. Gonin-Thomeguex," *La Renaissance de l'art français,* vol. VI (Aug. 1923), p. 446.

2. Letter from Diana Scarisbrick to the author, June 7, 1988. I am indebted to Mrs. Scarisbrick for her expertise regarding the rings in this painting.

3. Now Kirkland collection, Santa Barbara, Calif. See Agnes Mongan, *In Pursuit of Perfection: The Art of J.-A.-D. Ingres,* exh. cat., J. B. Speed Art Museum, Louisville, Ky., 1983, p. 146.

4. Hans Naef, *Die Bildniszeichnungen von J.-A.-D. Ingres,* vol. II, Bern, 1978, p. 400, no. 292.

Provenance Jeanne Gonin and Pyrame Thomeguex, Florence (to 1844); their son Antoine Thomeguex (to 1899); his son Albert Thomeguex, Paris (to 1918); Mme Paul Gaston Pictet (born Alice Thomeguex, Albert's sister) (to 1923); [Wildenstein (according to Georges Wildenstein, *Ingres,* Paris and London, 1954, pp. 192–93, but not so noted in the Taft Museum records)]; [Scott and Fowles, New York]; Taft collection, Feb. 1, 1924.

Exhibitions Paris, Ecole des Beaux-Arts, *J.-A.-D. Ingres,* 1867 (cat., p. 75, no. 442); The Art Institute of Chicago, *A Century of Progress: Exhibition of Painting and Sculpture,* June 1–Nov. 1, 1933 (cat., no. 217); San Francisco, California Palace of the Legion of Honor, *French Painting from the Fifteenth Century to the Present Day,* June 8–July 8, 1934 (cat., no. 112); Toronto Art Gallery, *English and French Nineteenth-Century Paintings,* Nov. 1–30, 1935 (cat., no. 112); Springfield Museum of Fine Arts, Mass. [also New York and Cincinnati], *David and Ingres,* Nov. 20–Dec. 17, 1939 (cat., no. 25); New York, Knoedler Gallery, *Centenary Exhibition,* Apr. 1–27, 1946; Detroit Institute of Arts, *French Painting from David to Courbet,* Jan. 31–Mar. 5, 1950 (cat., no. 20); Omaha, Nebr., Joslyn Art Museum, *Twentieth Anniversary Exhibition: The Beginnings of Modern Painting, France, 1800–1910,* Oct. 2–Nov. 4, 1951; Cincinnati Art Museum, *Paintings and Drawings by Ingres from the Ingres Museum at Montauban,* Feb. 4–28, 1953; New Orleans, Isaac Delgado Museum of Art, *French Masterpieces through Five Centuries,* Oct. 15–Dec. 31, 1953; The Art Institute of Chicago, *Great French Paintings,* Jan. 20–Feb. 20, 1955 (cat., no. 22); Richmond, Virginia Museum of Fine Arts, *Treasures in America,* Jan. 13–Mar. 5, 1961 (cat., no. 74); New York, Paul Rosenberg Gallery, *Ingres in American Collections,* Apr. 7–May 6, 1961 (cat., p. 37, no. 31); Indianapolis, John Herron Museum of Art, *The Romantic Era: Birth and Flowering, 1750–1850,* Feb. 21–Apr. 11, 1965 (cat., no. 28 [color ill.]); Paris, Petit Palais, *Ingres,* Oct. 27, 1967–Jan. 29, 1968 (cat., p. 176, no. 122); Minneapolis Institute of Arts, *The Past Rediscovered: French Painting, 1800–1900,* July 3–Sept. 7, 1969, (cat., no. 51); Louisville, Ky., J. B. Speed Art Museum, *In Pursuit of Perfection: The Art of J.-A.-D. Ingres,* Dec. 6, 1983–Jan. 29, 1984 (cat. by Agnes Mongan, p. 146, no. 72 [color ill.]).

Literature Ingres, Cahiers IX and X, Musée Ingres, Montauban; Edmond Saglio, "Un Nouveau Tableau de M. Ingres: Liste complète de ses oeuvres," *La Correspondance littéraire* (Feb. 5, 1857), p. 77; Charles Blanc, *Ingres,* Paris, 1870, listed p. 232; Henri Delaborde, *Ingres,* Paris, 1870, p. 250, no. 124, p. 261, no. 156; Henry Lapauze, *Les Dessins de J.-A.-D. Ingres du Musée de Montauban,* Paris, 1901, pp. 235, 248; Henry Lapauze, *Ingres,* Paris, 1911, p. 213; Henry Lapauze, "Sur un portrait inédit de Ingres: Mme. Gonin-Thomeguex," *La Renaissance de l'art français,* vol. VI (Aug. 1923), p. 446; Walter H. Siple, "Two Portraits by Ingres," *Bulletin of the Cincinnati Art Museum,* vol. 1, no. 2 (Apr. 1930), pp. 35, 37, 39, cover ill.; Louise Guerber Burroughs, "Ingres in Florence," *Creative Art,* vol. X (May 1932), p. 365; "Ingres in a Little-Known Portrait," *The Connoisseur,* vol. XCI (May 1933), pp. 347–48; *Art Digest* (June 1933), cover; "Notable Loan Exhibition of French Art Now on View," *Art News,* vol. XXXII (June 16, 1934), listed p. 11; *Catalogue of the Taft Museum,* Cincinnati, 1939 and 1958, no. 104 (ill.); Walter Pach, *Ingres,* New York and London, 1939, p. 26, ill. p. 111; *Coronet,* vol. V (Apr. 1939), cover; John Lee Clarke, Jr., "David and Ingres: The Classic Ideal," *Art News,* vol. XXXVIII (Nov. 25, 1939), listed p. 16; "David and Ingres, Classic Giants, Joined in Important New York Show," *Art Digest,* vol. XIV (Jan. 1, 1940), p. 12; "David and Ingres on View in New York," *Art News,* vol. XXXVIII (Jan. 6, 1940), listed p. 7; "David and Ingres," *Magazine of Art,* vol. XXXIII (Jan. 1940), p. 43; Ellis K. Waterhouse, "The Knoedler Centenary Exhibition," *Burlington Magazine,* vol. LXXXVIII (June 1946), p. 155, ill. p. 154; Georges Wildenstein, *Ingres,* London and Paris, 1954, no. 147, pp. 192–93, pl. 54; Martin Birnbaum, *The Last Romantic,* New York, 1960, pp. 103–5; Hans Naef, "Ingres als Porträtist seiner west-schweizerischen Freunde," *Du,* vol. XV (Aug. 1955), p. 18, fig. 6; Hans Naef and Louise Burroughs, "Ingres et les familles Gonin, Thomeguex et Guerber," *Genava,* n.s., vol. XIV (1966), pp. 124, 153–54, fig. 1; Ettore Camesasca, *Tout l'oeuvre peint d'Ingres,* Paris, 1971, no. 106; Hans Naef, *Die Bildniszeichnungen von J.-A.-D. Ingres,* vol. II, Bern, 1978, pp. 389, 391, 400 (ill.); Daniel Ternois, *Ingres,* Paris, 1980, p. 65 and p. 179, no. 158; David Torbet Johnson, "Taft Museum," *Ventura,* vol. IV, no. 16 (June–Aug. 1991), p. 137 (ill.).

1931.414

Jean-Louis-Ernest Meissonier

Lyon 1815–1891 Paris

Meissonier studied briefly with Julien Potier around 1832–33 and spent four or five months in the atelier of Léon Cogniet. During his early career he decorated fans and made illustrations for publishers. He first exhibited in the Salon of 1834. In October 1838 he married the sister of a friend, the artist L. G. A. Steinheil. Around 1840 he frequented the Club des Haschischins with Charles Baudelaire and Théophile Gautier.[1] At the Salon of 1840 he was awarded a third-class medal and the following year, a second-class medal. He earned first-class medals in 1843 and again in 1848. Meissonier's father died in 1845, leaving him enough money to live comfortably. With the inheritance, he acquired the remains of an abandoned abbey at Poissy for his home and studio.

During the 1840s Meissonier painted small, highly detailed, historical genre pictures in the vein of the seventeenth-century Dutch little masters such as Gerard Dou and Gerard ter Borch; these gained him wide acclaim. He won a grand medal of honor at the Universal Exposition of 1855, where Napoléon III purchased *Une Rixe (A Brawl)* and presented it to Queen Victoria and Prince Albert of England. In June and July 1859 he accompanied the imperial troops on the Italian campaign against the Austrians, which resulted in the first of his military pictures, *Solferino* (Château de Versailles), shown at the Salon of 1864.[2] This painting was exhibited with *1814* (Paris, Musée du Louvre), the first of his historical Napoleonic images. The artist aspired to larger scale for these military subjects, pursuing this vein of history painting throughout the rest of his career.

Meissonier made his first trip to Venice in 1860 but did not travel to Rome until 1875. He was elected a member of the Academy of Fine Arts in 1861, although he did not teach. He served in the army during the Franco-Prussian War, which inspired his *Siege of Paris.* The Galerie Georges Petit held a retrospective of his work in 1884. He was president of the international jury for the Universal Exposition of 1889 and became the first artist to receive the Grand Cross of the Legion of Honor. He also remarried in 1889, following the death of his wife the previous year. He died on January 31, 1891, at his studio on the boulevard Malesherbes and was honored with memorial retrospectives at the Galerie Georges Petit and the Ecole des Beaux-Arts.

1. Pierre-Louis Mathieu, "Victime de la célébrité," *Connaissance des arts,* no. 364 (June 1982), p. 64.

2. Constance Cain Hungerford, "Meissonier's First Military Paintings," *Arts Magazine,* vol. LIV (Jan. 1980), pp. 89–107.

Jean-Louis-Ernest Meissonier

Les Trois Amis (The Three Friends)

1847
Oil on cradled panel, 24.2 x 27 cm (9½ x 10⅝ in.)
Signed and dated lower left: *JE Meissonier 1847* (JE in monogram)

1931.399

This panel is a fine example of the highly detailed, historical genre subjects that established Meissonier's early popularity. He depicts three gentlemen (as opposed to the more frequently appearing soldiers or guardsmen) wearing Louis XV costume, smoking clay pipes, and talking in an inn. Their long coats are red, beige, and black, and they drink from two glasses and one silver tankard. A black three-cornered hat is placed on the chair at the right while another hangs on the partition behind. On the cupboard at the back left are four green bottles, a brown pitcher, pot and bowl, and another silver tankard. Two colored prints hang on the wall above the table, and a tally board is visible to the right.

Les Trois Amis is one of six works that Meissonier exhibited at the Salon of 1848, at which he was voted a member of the hanging committee. This Salon had no jury, and over five thousand works were accepted. Despite the competition, Meissonier's small-scale entries were noticed and praised by the critics. F. de la Genevais cited the fresh color and mastery of *Les Trois Amis*.[1] Another critic, DuPays, singled out this work and a park scene, *La Partie des boules*, for their "marvelous truth," suggesting a "daguerreotype of the eighteenth century." He went on to praise *Les Trois Amis* as the artist's chef-d'oeuvre at the Salon and prophetically added that it would occupy an honorable place in any museum in the world.[2] Similarly, the famous romantic writer Théophile Gautier dubbed "the painter of *Trois Amis* the equal of Metsu" and other Dutch masters. Gautier also valued the painting's scrupulously reconstructed detail, "a miracle of retrospective intuition" recalling "the habitués of the Procope café at the time of Diderot."[3]

At first the painting seemed destined for the British collections, for it was purchased from the Salon for eight thousand francs by Queen Victoria as a present for Prince Albert.[4]

A miniaturized version, *Les Trois Fumeurs*, less than half the size of the Taft panel, shows the identical figural group. But two hats hang on the partition, and no cupboard or other details are at the back left.[5] There is also a variant dated 1848 with one figure standing, which is described in the sale of Meissonier's atelier.[6]

1. F. de la Genevais, "Le Salon de 1848," *Revue des deux mondes*, vol. XXII (Apr. 15, 1848), p. 297.

2. A. J. DuPays, "Beaux Arts: Salon de 1848," *L'Illustration*, vol. XI, no. 273 (May 21, 1848), p. 188. The woodcut illustration of *Les Trois Amis* on p. 189 was executed by L. G. A. Steinheil, Meissonier's brother-in-law.

3. Théophile Gautier, "Feuilleton de la presse: Salon de 1848," *La Presse*, May 6, 1848. I am indebted to Professor Constance Cain Hungerford for her transcriptions of this and the Haussard (see Literature) reviews.

4. Léonce Bénédite, *Meissonier*, Paris, n.d., p. 27.

5. *Les Trois Fumeurs*, dated 1857, was formerly in the Ernest Secrétan collection (sale, Paris, Galerie Sedelmeyer, July 1, 1889) and later listed in Octave Gréard, *Meissonier: His Life and His Art*, New York, 1897, ill. p. 40, as in the possession of M. Thièry. It was given by Thomy-Thièry to the Louvre (R.F. 1435, 10.5 x 13.5 cm) and is on loan to the Musée de Tabac, Bergerac.

6. *Atelier Meissonier*, Galerie Georges Petit, Paris, Mar. 1893, no. 12, as *Les Fumeurs*, 1848, 16 x 21 cm.

Provenance Queen Victoria and Prince Albert, London (from 1848); Edward VII (in 1901); Princess Louise (in Feb. 1901); Arthur Nattali, Petworth, Sussex; J. Nattali, London, to Arthur Tooth and Sons, London (Apr. 1901, with half share, Leroy Gallery, Paris, May 1901); [Arthur Tooth, New York, Oct. 1902 (information from Arthur Tooth records kindly supplied by Marsha Hepworth, J. Paul Getty Provenance Index)]; Taft collection, Oct. 16, 1902.

Exhibitions Paris, Louvre, Salon of 1848, no. 3250; Detroit Institute of Arts, *The Two Sides of the Medal: French Painting from Gérôme to Gauguin*, Sept. 28–Oct. 31, 1954 (cat. by Paul L. Grigaut, no. 29, ill. p. 29).

Literature Louis Clément de Ris, "Salon de 1848," *L'Artiste*, ser. 5, vol. I, no. 5 (Apr. 9, 1848), p. 69; F. de la Genevais, "Le Salon de 1848," *Revue des deux mondes*, vol. XXII (Apr. 15, 1848), p. 297; Théophile Gautier, "Feuilleton de la presse: Salon de 1848," *La Presse*, May 6, 1848; Prosper Haussard, "Feuilleton du National: Beaux Arts: Salon de 1848," *Le National*, May 20, 1848; A. J. DuPays, "Beaux Arts: Salon de 1848," *L'Illustration*, vol. XI, no. 273 (May 21, 1848), p. 188, ill. p. 189; Maurius Chaumelin, *Portraits d'artiste: E. Meissonier*, J. Breton, Paris, 1887, p. 40, no. 24; Charles F. Fowles, *The Art Collection of Mr. and Mrs. Charles P. Taft*, New York, 1902, n.p.; Maurice W. Brockwell, *A Catalogue of the Paintings in the Collection of Mr. and Mrs.. Charles P. Taft*, New York, 1920, no. 75; *Catalogue of the Taft Museum*, Cincinnati, 1939 and 1958, no. 371; Aaron Sheon, "Monticelli and the Rococo Revival," Ph.D. diss., Princeton University, 1966, p. 63, fig. 53; Constance Cain Hungerford, "The Art of Jean-Louis-Ernest Meissonier: A Study of the Critical Years, 1834 to 1855," Ph.D. diss., University of California, Berkeley, 1977, pp. 131–32, no. 24, fig. 36; Ruth Krueger Meyer, "The Taft Collection: The First Ten Years of Its Development," *The Taft Museum: A Cincinnati Legacy*, Cincinnati, 1988, p. 15 (ill.); Constance Cain Hungerford, "Meissonier and the Founding of the Société Nationale des Beaux-Arts," *Art Journal*, vol. XLVIII (Spring 1989), p. 76.

1931.399

Alexandre-Gabriel Decamps
Paris 1803–1860 Fontainebleau

As a young man Decamps studied in the atelier of Etienne Bouhot in 1816 and in that of Abel de Pujol, a pupil of Jacques-Louis David, in 1818–19. He was, however, essentially self-taught. He copied in the Louvre in 1825, following his return from touring Italy and Switzerland the previous year. After his Salon debut in 1827, he traveled for a year in Greece and the Near East. He fought on the barricades during the July Revolution of 1830.

Decamps gained notoriety for his oriental subjects in the Salon of 1831, where he won a second-class medal. He tapped a growing taste for both exotic scenes and genre subjects. The latter included *singeries* such as *Monkey Painting*, purchased by the State from the Salon of 1833. That same year Decamps met Honoré Daumier and also executed a series of watercolors after *Don Quixote*. In 1834 he won a first-class medal at the Salon with his monumental *Defeat of the Cimbres* (Paris, Musée du Louvre). Afterward, he traveled in the south of France and in Italy, returning to the latter at the end of the decade.

During the mid-1830s, Decamps took his first students and began exhibiting works with picture dealers. In 1837 he rented a second atelier in Paris and began to paint biblical subjects. After an absence of several years, he exhibited eleven works at the Salon of 1839 and was made Knight of the Legion of Honor. In 1842 he traveled with Angelina Imbert, whom he would later marry, to Fontainebleau, spending much time there over the next two years. Following the revolution in February 1848, he

1931.432

was among the artists appointed by the Minister of Fine Arts to reform the Salon system, and from 1850 to 1853 he served as a member of the jury. In the Salon of 1850–51 he exhibited ten works, including the Taft Museum's *Albanians,* and became an Officer in the Legion of Honor. At the same time he was commissioned by the government for a picture for the Luxembourg Museum.

In need of money, Decamps auctioned some works in 1851; with the proceeds of an atelier sale in April 1853 he bought property near Barbizon. He became ill around this time and painted less. Like Ingres and Delacroix, he was accorded an extensive retrospective of forty-nine works at the Universal Exposition of 1855. This proved to be his moment of greatest renown. Soon afterward, in declining health, he retired to Fontainebleau, where he developed a friendship with Corot and was visited by the emperor. He died as a result of a riding accident.

Alexandre-Gabriel Decamps

Albanians (Albanais se reposant sur des ruines)

1849
Oil on canvas, 24 x 30.5 cm (9½ x 12 in.)
Signed and dated lower left (under stone): DECAMPS 4[ ]

This small yet important painting represents a high point of Decamps's orientalist romanticism. He depicts two soldiers wearing red-and-green robes over the white pleated skirts of the Arnauts, Greek and Albanian conscripts into the Ottoman army,

who were popular subjects for orientalist painters such as Jean-Léon Gérôme. In the sixteenth century the Turks had captured the last of the Venetian garrisons in Albania. Afterward, the Albanian conscripts were generally not paid but had to live off plunder.

The central soldier has a rifle strapped to his back and plays a lutelike, stringed instrument. The soldier to the right smokes a long pipe and wears prominent knives in his belt. In the background is a dramatic red-orange sunset.

This canvas was one of ten that Decamps exhibited in the Salon of 1850–51, where it was overshadowed by his large *Eliezer and Rebecca* (L'Abbaye de Longpont, M. de Montesquieu collection). The latter met with only mild success, and one critic termed his submissions "less original" than in the past.[1] Nonetheless, the artist was made an Officer in the Legion of Honor.

Moreau describes a small painting (unlocated, formerly Henri Didier collection), also called *Albanais,* showing three soldiers seated on rocks and two more behind them, which may be related to the present work.[2] There is also a variant of the Taft painting called *Arab Musicians.*[3]

1 A. J. DuPays, "Salon de 1850–51," *L'Illustration,* vol. XVII (1851), p. 120.

2. Adolphe Moreau, *Decamps et son oeuvre,* Paris, 1869, p. 166, a canvas, 21 x 27 cm, exhibited at the Universal Exposition of 1855. Moreau also lists a lithograph, *Albanais,* after the Taft painting (p. 123, no. 119).

3. Dewey F. Mosby, *Alexandre-Gabriel Decamps, 1803–1860,* vol. II, New York, 1977, no. 123.

Provenance M. Collet, Paris (sale, Hôtel des Ventes, Paris, May 29, 1852, no. 17, as *Armeniens au repos,* FF 1,641); Baroness Nathaniel de Rothschild, London (by 1869 until after 1886); R. Austin Robertson (estate sale, American Art Association, New York, Apr. 8, 1892, no. 107, $1,175); [Arnold and Tripp to Scott and Fowles, New York, Oct. 13, 1903]; Taft collection, Jan. 22, 1904.

Exhibition Paris, Palais National, Salon of 1850–51, no. 756, as *Albanais se reposant sur des ruines.*

Literature Adolphe Moreau, *Decamps et son oeuvre*, Paris, 1869, pp. 123, 161, no. 119; Charles Clément, *Decamps*, Paris, 1887, p. 80; Maurice W. Brockwell, *A Catalogue of Paintings in the Collection of Mr. and Mrs. Charles P. Taft*, New York, 1920, no. 47; *Catalogue of the Taft Museum*, Cincinnati, 1939 and 1958, no. 308; Dewey F. Mosby, *Alexandre-Gabriel Decamps, 1803–1860*, vol. II, New York, 1977, p. 435, no. 98, pl. 91b.

1931.432

Alexandre-Gabriel Decamps

The Slinger (Le Frondeur)

ca. 1849
Oil on canvas, 65.5 x 81 cm (25⅞ x 31⅞ in.)
Signed left center (on stone): DECAMPS

This painting contains a mixture of classicizing and romantic elements. The musculature of the dark-skinned hunter suggests that of a studio model, in the academic tradition. The setting and the Arab woman are imbued with an exotic orientalism, suggesting a romanticism that contrasts with the classicism of the man. Although there are no known academic figure drawings by Decamps (he had little formal training), the figure of the hunter seems to be an excuse to display the male anatomy.

The overpainted figure of the man seems originally to have worn a costume covering his head and bare arms.[1] Now he wears a red tunic, green sash, and white breeches and holds a stone with his left hand while he clenches his right to his chest. He is posed in tense contrapposto and focuses his attention on his prey,

a brown vulture with a white-tufted neck, which is perched on a distant architectural ruin. A young mother crouches with her child in the shadows to the left. She wears a gold earring and a red shawl over her head. The boy wears a loose blue garment and holds an orange. Above them a pair of goats forage in the underbrush.

The group at the left recalls other domestic genre pictures with a figure eating an orange, such as *Albanaise* (1843, ex-Goldschmidt collection, Paris). Decamps here utilizes the architecture to organize space, as he does in other works, including *Souvenir of Asiatic Turkey: Landscape* (1846, Amsterdam, Stedelijk Museum).

The Taft painting is a characteristic later work of Decamps. Mosby dates it to the same year as the Taft's *Albanians.*[2] Although they are quite different, both works contain similar elements such as the fallen columns and classical ruins of the Near Eastern setting.

1. This can be seen in observation under raking light.
2. Dewey F. Mosby, *Alexandre-Gabriel Decamps, 1803–1860*, vol. II, New York, 1977, p. 435.

Provenance Jules van Praët (1806–1888), Brussels (by 1880); Ernest Secrétan, Paris (sale, Charles Sedelmeyer Galleries, Paris, July 1, 1889, no. 12 [ill.]); Frederick Lothrop Ames (1835–1893), Boston; [Boussod-Valadon and Co., Paris]; H. S. Henry, New York (sale, Mendelssohn Hall, New York, Feb. 4, 1910, no. 9 [ill.], for $12,100 to Scott and Fowles, New York); Taft collection, Feb. 11, 1910.

Exhibition Paris, Galerie Georges Petit, *Exposition de peinture: Cent chefs-d'oeuvre des collections parisiennes*, opened June 12, 1883 (cat., p. 28, no. 24).

Literature Charles Tardieu, "Le Cabinet de M. Jules van Praët," *L'Art*, vol. XXIII (1880), p. 280; Maurice W. Brockwell, *A Catalogue of Paintings in the Collection of Mr. and Mrs. Charles P. Taft*, New York, 1920, no. 29;

1931.436

Catalogue of the Taft Museum, Cincinnati, 1939 and 1958, no. 561; Dewey F. Mosby, *Alexandre-Gabriel Decamps, 1803–1860,* New York, 1977, vol. I, p. 225, vol. II, pp. 435–36, no. 99, pl. 92a.

1931.436

Félix-François-Georges-Philibert Ziem

Beaune 1821–1911 Paris

After his family settled in Dijon in 1831, Ziem studied linear design and classical architecture at the school there from 1837 to 1839. In May 1842 Ziem left from Nice for his first Grand Tour across Europe, including Florence, Rome, and Venice in his itinerary. On his second visit to Venice, he wrote that he found it "a port of life"; he visited the city eighteen times throughout his career. In 1843–44 he traveled in Russia with his patrons Prince and Princess Gagarin. The following year he rented an atelier in Paris, studied English, and began writing a personal *Manual of Life.*[1] In 1844–45 Ziem lived on a houseboat in Venice.

After further travels Ziem returned to Paris in 1849 to exhibit six works at the Salon, including a painting of the Grand Canal. He was in contact with some of the Barbizon artists at this time. He exhibited at the Salon from 1849 to 1868, after which time he had attained sufficient popularity to pursue an independent career. Beginning with Thiébault-Sisson, many critics have felt that this early period was the artist's most inventive and fruitful and that it was followed by one of increasing commercialization and repetition of earlier motifs.[2]

In the Salon of 1850–51 Ziem won a third-class medal. In that same year a view of the Doge's palace was purchased by the Louvre. Another Venetian view was purchased by the State from the Salon of 1852, where Ziem won a first-class medal in the marine category and received the praise of the Goncourts and other critics.

Also in 1852 Ziem set up a studio in an old building on the rue Lepic in Montmartre. In 1854 he traveled to the Near East for the first time, reaching Egypt and, the following year, Constantinople. In 1857 he worked at Barbizon with Théodore Rousseau and was named Knight of the Legion of Honor for his Salon submissions. In 1858 the peripatetic Ziem was in Algeria. In 1861 he built a studio in Martigues in the South of France and at the Salon of that year exhibited a Venetian triptych that was widely praised.

Ziem became increasingly popular during the 1860s, although writers began to criticize the lack of "drawing" or definition in his works, a nonacademic finish for which the impressionists were also rebuked. He exhibited at the Salon for the last time in 1888. From the 1860s and 1870s he regularly sold works through Parisian dealers such as Beugniet, Détrimont, Boussod-Valadon, and Goupil.

In 1877 Ziem built a villa near Nice. His last trip to Venice was in 1897. He married his longtime companion from Provence in 1904 and attained the position of Commander of the Legion of Honor in 1908. Ziem died on November 10, 1911.

1931.419

1. Pierre Miquel, *Felix Ziem, 1821–1911: L'Ecole de la nature,* 7, 8, vol. I, Maurs-la-Jolie, 1978, p. 244.

2. Thiébault-Sisson, in *Le Temps,* Feb. 13, 1911.

Félix Ziem

The Piazza of San Marco, Venice, during a Flood

Late 1850s?
Oil on canvas, 95.5 x 69.3 cm (37⅝ x 27¼ in.)
Signed lower left: *Ziem*

Ziem was the first important French artist to adapt the tradition of painting Venetian views as pioneered by Canaletto and Guardi during the eighteenth century and furthered by Turner during the first half of the nineteenth. Later, other members of the French school would follow this path, notably Renoir and Monet.

Ziem's Venetian cityscapes approach the effects of impressionism in their emphasis on the depiction of natural light and atmosphere, boating subjects, and painterly brushstrokes. The color is high-keyed. Ziem chooses picturesque views that emphasize the scenic rather than the crumbling aspect or the political reality of the city. As a contemporary critic noted, in reviewing Ziem's pictures at the Salon of 1857, "This town completely belongs to him, because in truth he has created it; it is a Venice of the Orient, Venice of our dreams, Venice without Austrians!"[1]

The two Taft paintings by Ziem, although purchased at the same time, are not pendants but rather are complementary views of Saint Mark's Square. This tourist landmark was the focus of many of Ziem's Venetian works, which were greatly sought after by collectors during the late nineteenth century.

Pierre Miquel, Ziem's principal biographer, illustrates eleven paintings depicting Saint Mark's Square flooded by the rising waters of the Grand Canal.[2] The Taft picture is the largest of three nearly identical views looking toward the façade of Saint Mark's with the campanile to the right and various gondolas crossing the inundated square. It may be the painting exhibited at the Salon of 1857 as *Place de Saint-Marc à Venise pendant une inondation*.[3] One of the smaller variants is in the Metropolitan Museum of Art, New York. Another version, slightly larger than that in New York, was sold two weeks after the Tafts acquired theirs but has not been traced.[4]

1. Jules Verne, "Salon de 1857," *Revue des beaux-arts*, vol. VIII, no. 13 (1857), p. 251: "Cette ville lui appartient tout entière, car il l'a véritablement créée, c'est une Venise de l'Orient, la Venise de nos rêves, la Venise sans les Autrichiens!"

2. Pierre Miquel, *Félix Ziem, 1821–1911: L'Ecole de la nature, 7, 8*, vol. II, Maurs-la-Jolie, 1978, nos. 701, 868, 931, 1265, 1308, 1434, 1438, 1478, 1589, 1613, 1618 bis.

3. Salon of 1857, Paris, no. 2713. Paul de Saint-Victor described the Salon painting as "un salmigondis de tons verts, jaunes, rouges, posés et raccordés au hasard, une mascarade d'édifices, un carnaval d'architecture; la basilique est tatouée de la base au faîte; le campanile peint en bavochures, papillote et gambade comme un arlquin gigantesque" (a hodgepodge of green, yellow, and red tones, laid down and united at random, a masquerade of buildings, a carnival of architecture; the basilica is tattooed from the bottom to the top; the campanile, painted in blurs, dazzles and gambols like a gigantic harlequin; quoted in Louis Fournier, *Un Grand Peintre: Félix Ziem*, Beaune, 1897, pp. 48–49). The colors and description accord with the Taft canvas.

4. Miquel, no. 1478: 79 x 65 cm, M. J. M. Chambon of Marseille, sale, Hôtel Drouot, Paris, Mar. 28, 1906, no. 28.

Provenance James Staats Forbes (until 1904); [Scott and Fowles, New York]; Taft collection, Mar. 14, 1906.

Literature Maurice W. Brockwell, *A Catalogue of Paintings in the Collection of Mr. and Mrs. Charles P. Taft*, New York, 1920, no. 30; *Catalogue of the Taft Museum*, Cincinnati, 1939 and 1958, no. 509; Pierre Miquel, *Félix Ziem, 1821–1911: L'Ecole de la nature, 7, 8*, vol. II, Maurs-la-Jolie, 1978, no. 1589, ill. p. 218.

1931.419

Félix Ziem

Entrance to the Grand Canal, Venice

1865–70?
Oil on canvas, 72.4 x 52.7 cm (28½ x 20¾ in.)
Signed lower left: *Ziem*

1931.418

This is one of few vertical canvases in Ziem's oeuvre of the view of San Giorgio Maggiore from the *piazzetta* in front of the Doge's palace. Unlike the other picture by Ziem in the Taft collection, the artist did not paint replicas of this image.

There is a drawing of a Venetian fisherman on the Riva dei Schiavoni, dated April 25, 1868, which seems to have been a study for the figures in the foreground of this work.[1] The painting may be number 210 in Ziem's account book: *Catalogue des tableaux exécutés et sortis de l'atelier de M. Félix Ziem, 1865–70*, "Mr. Beugniet, Riva, par le travers, Saint-Georges, large, effet net vénetien, décor . . . 1500 F."[2] The previous owner, Lutz, also owned a Turkish view by Ziem.[3]

1. Pierre Miquel, *Félix Ziem, 1821–1911: L'Ecole de la nature, 7, 8*, vol. I, Maurs-la-Jolie, 1978, fig. 53.

2. Miquel, vol. II, p. 18.

3. Miquel, vol. II, no. 135.

Provenance [Possibly Beugniet, Paris]; [Détrimont, Paris]; Georges Lutz (sale, Galerie Georges Petit, Paris, May 26–27, 1902, no. 119, *Venise*, FF 18,000); [Scott and Fowles, New York]; Taft collection, Mar. 14, 1906.

Literature Maurice W. Brockwell, *A Catalogue of Paintings in the Collection of Mr. and Mrs. Charles P. Taft*, New York, 1920, no. 32; *Catalogue of the Taft Museum*, Cincinnati, 1939 and 1958, no. 4; Pierre Miquel, *Félix Ziem, 1821–1911: L'Ecole de la Nature, 7, 8*, vol. II, Maurs-la-Jolie, 1978, no. 1433, ill. p. 201.

1931.418

Adolphe-Joseph-Thomas Monticelli

Marseille 1824–1886 Marseille

Monticelli was raised on a farm outside Marseille until his parents could marry in 1835. At that time, he was brought back to Marseille, where he was tutored. Around 1839–40 he took lessons with Félix Ziem, who encouraged him to continue his studies. In 1841 he entered the Marseille drawing school, where he won first prize for life drawing in 1846. That fall he made his first trip to Paris, studying with Paul Delaroche and copying in the Louvre. In 1848 he returned to the south of France. He exhibited with the Marseille Art Society from 1852 to 1867 but never showed in the Paris Salon.

In the spring of 1855 Monticelli went north again, soon befriending the Barbizon painter Narcisse Diaz in Paris, and began his outdoor fête pictures, or *fêtes galantes,* in which ladies and gentlemen amuse themselves at outdoor parties. He returned to Marseille at the end of 1856. Around 1858 he met the young doctor Paul Gachet, who was later to become a friend of the impressionists, and the following year Monticelli painted the ceiling of the Café Eldorado in Marseille. In 1860 he proposed to his cousin Emma Ricard but was refused; he remained a bachelor. He painted outdoor landscapes in Provence with Paul Guigou during the early 1860s. Traveling via Grenoble and Lyon, he returned to Paris in late 1863 for his longest stay. He set up a studio at Roumaineville in the mid-1860s. His father died in March 1868, at which time Monticelli went back to Marseille for several months before returning to Paris. At the recommendation of Camille Corot, the museum in Lille purchased two of Monticelli's works in 1869.

Back in Marseille, the artist began the most productive period of his life. In these late works he developed thick, impasto surfaces and brighter colors that had no parallel in contemporary art, anticipating the works of Chaim Soutine. During the 1870s he began painting still lifes and landscapes without figures. Around 1883 he painted in the south with Paul Cézanne, whom he had probably known in Paris during the late 1860s. Monticelli exerted a considerable influence on Vincent van Gogh, who became acquainted with his paintings at Delarebeyrette's shop in Paris in 1886 and often wrote enthusiastically about them to his brother, Theo.

After Monticelli's death, the dealer Daniel Cottier, followed by Alexander Reid, sold his works to collectors in London, Scotland, and New York, where he was more popular than in France. Increasing interest in his work around 1900 raised prices and led to the production of forgeries. In 1904 Senator William A. Clark paid eighty thousand francs for three Monticellis from the Chave collection; he ultimately bequeathed twenty-one works to the Corcoran Gallery of Art in Washington, D.C. A retrospective of 177 works was well received at the Salon d'Automne of 1908. A unique figure, Monticelli has been termed "one of the most significant of the independent painters of France in the nineteenth century."[1]

1. Charles Sterling and Margaretta M. Salinger, *French Paintings: A Catalogue of the Collection of the Metropolitan Museum of Art,* vol. II, New York, 1966, p. 139. Biographical information is taken from this source and from Aaron Sheon, *Monticelli: His Contemporaries, His Influence,* exh. cat., Museum of Art, Carnegie Institute, Pittsburgh, 1978.

Adolphe-Joseph-Thomas Monticelli

Fête Champêtre

ca. 1860
Oil on panel, 36.5 x 74.1 cm (14⅜ x 29¼ in.)
Signed lower left: *Monticelli*

The fêtes, paintings of outdoor parties with many figures, of Monticelli's early career began around 1856 and are derived from the treatment of the same theme beginning in eighteenth-century French painting with Watteau and continuing through Diaz. As such, they are part of the larger mid-nineteenth-century rococo revival, as defined by Aaron Sheon.[1] Those by Monticelli are often painted essentially in tones of brown with touches of color.

1931.410

The Taft picture is one of the most populous of Monticelli's fêtes, depicting a large group of figures, mostly women, seated around a long table at the left center. A woman in red with a black parasol in the middle provides the coloristic accent; a dog runs by her feet. Four young women surround a table at the right; behind them is a woman on a swing, a detail that recurs in Monticelli's park scenes. Stylistically, this panel is comparable to similar subjects such as *Festival Assembly (Assemblée en Fête,* ca. 1865, Paris, Cailleux collection). Sheon has described the Taft painting as "an exceptionally good picture and one of the rare early ones in the U.S."[2]

The hazy, vague space of Monticelli's fêtes evokes an imaginary world. An old photograph of the Taft painting from Scott and Fowles (New York, Frick Art Reference Library), however, shows a greater clarity and definition in the figures, such as the turning man in the dark hat at the center. Thus, it seems that some of the pigments Monticelli used have sunk and obscured the forms. Since he painted thickly and in an improvised manner, it is not surprising that the work has altered over time.

Like Ziem, Monticelli was able to earn a living selling his works directly to Paris dealers such as Delarabeyrette. His early works were particularly popular there as well as in England and Scotland. Many of his paintings came into the market at the turn of the century: eighty-eight were in the sale of a Dr. Mireur in Paris in 1900, and another sixty-nine were in the Delas sale the following year. However, it has not been possible to trace the Taft painting to any known collection.

1. Aaron Sheon, "Monticelli and the Rococo Revival," Ph.D. diss., Princeton University, 1966, chap. 1, pp. 13–26.

2. Letter from Aaron Sheon to the Taft Museum, Aug. 31, 1984. Many early Monticelli fête paintings are in the Glasgow Art Gallery.

Provenance [Probably Scott and Fowles, New York]; Taft collection, Nov. 10, 1903.

Exhibitions Possibly London, Dowdeswell Gallery, *Adolphe Monticelli,* Jan. 1888 (cat., no. 61, as *La Fête Champêtre,* no ill., no dimensions); Boston, Robert C. Vose Gallery, *Paintings by Monticelli,* Mar. 3–22, 1947 (cat., no. 10); Houston, Museum of Fine Arts, *Corot and His Contemporaries,* May 8–June 21, 1959 (cat., n.p.).

Literature Maurice W. Brockwell, *A Catalogue of Paintings in the Collection of Mr. and Mrs. Charles P. Taft,* New York, 1920, no. 5; *Catalogue of the Taft Museum,* Cincinnati, 1939 and 1958, no. 39.

1931.410

Louis-Gabriel-Eugène Isabey

Paris 1803–1886 Lagny, near Paris

Isabey was the fourth and youngest child of the miniature painter Jean-Baptiste Isabey (1767–1855). He journeyed with his father to England and Scotland in 1820 and to Italy in 1822. In 1823–24 he collaborated with his father on a series of lithographs for a travel book on Italy. He made an auspicious debut at the Salon of 1824, winning a first-class medal for marine painting, his early specialty. He won another for his Normandy seascapes in 1827. In the summer of 1825 he traveled with Eugène Delacroix and Richard Parkes Bonington to the Cornwall coast of England.

From May to July 1830 Isabey accompanied the French expeditionary force to North Africa, but aside from views painted there, he did not produce orientalist scenes like those done by Decamps. When the count de Mornay asked Isabey to go with him to Morocco the following year, he declined, and Delacroix went instead.

In June 1832 Isabey married Laure Lebreton, the daughter of a well-known physician, and their only child, Marie, was born the following July. He became an official painter during the reign of Louis Philippe (1830–48) and recorded the visit of Queen Victoria to Tréport in September 1843 with two paintings later exhibited at the Salon. The following October he also accompanied the king on his reciprocal trip to England.

From this time on Isabey produced more historical genre pictures, such as *A Ceremony in a Church in Delft* (1847, Paris, Musée du Louvre), one of his first church interiors with numerous figures. His naturalistic coastal scenes influenced Eugène Boudin and Johan Barthold Jongkind, both of whom he met in 1845. The Dutchman came to Paris the following year to study with Isabey. Boudin and Jongkind in turn conveyed his naturalistic approach to the young impressionists, particularly Monet.

After exhibiting extensively in the Salons of the 1830s and 1840s, Isabey was elected to the hanging committee in 1848 and 1849. He rarely showed after 1851, with the exception of the Universal Expositions of 1855, 1867, and 1878. He was made an Officer in the Legion of Honor in 1852. His wife died in 1860, and he married the young widow Maria Morizot in 1864. He often visited the Normandy coast at Varengeville and traveled from there to London in the fall of 1870, like Jean-Charles Cazin, Adolphe-Joseph-Thomas Monticelli, and others fleeing the Franco-Prussian War.

Isabey returned to Varengeville via Brussels one year later. He spent the summers of 1872–74 there and after that had diminished contact with the Paris art world. In 1878 he bought a house at Lagny, moving there the following February. That year he participated in the first exhibition of the Society of French Watercolorists and in their subsequent exhibitions until his death. He was celebrated in a centenary retrospective in Paris in 1904.

Louis-Gabriel-Eugène Isabey

The Communicants

1872
Oil on canvas, 83.8 x 66 cm (33 x 26 in.)
Signed and dated lower left: *E. Isabey / 72*

At the crossing of a church five figures cluster around a white-clad priest in the middle ground. In front of the wrought-iron screen, four men and a mother with two infants are waiting at the left, and three women and a cleric are at the right. A red banner depicting the crowned Virgin is above them. The lines between the irregular blocks of the stone floor point toward a low central vanishing point.

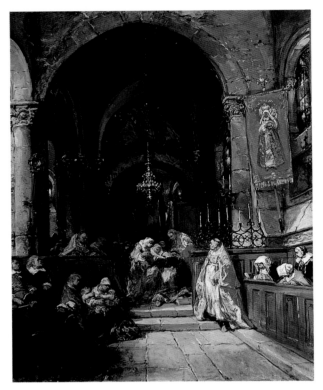

1931.417

This painting is one of Isabey's many late church interiors of somewhat lesser quality, of which Pierre Miquel catalogues some seventy-nine examples.[1] The scenes are often set in a rather theatrical space and might be considered genre subjects rather than religious paintings. Many of these interiors represent historical or generalized figure scenes. Only two are specifically linked to the theme of communion: a smaller canvas of 1869[2] now in the museum at Reims and a watercolor of the same subject shown at the Society of French Watercolorists exhibition of 1883.

1. Pierre Miquel, *Eugène Isabey, 1803–1886*, vol. II, Maurs-le-Jolie, 1980, pp. 300–301.

2. Miquel, no. 258.

Provenance The artist (not in the atelier sale of Mar. 1887); [Scott and Fowles, New York]; Taft collection, Oct. 25, 1905.

Exhibition Bloomfield Hills, Mich., Cranbrook Academy of Art, *Light and the Painter*, Sept. 5–28, 1952 (cat., no. 29).

Literature Maurice W. Brockwell, *A Catalogue of Paintings in the Collection of Mr. and Mrs. Charles P. Taft*, New York, 1920, no. 31; *Catalogue of the Taft Museum*, Cincinnati, 1939 and 1958, no. 512; Pierre Miquel, *Eugène Isabey, 1803–1886*, Maurs-la-Jolie, 1980, vol. I, ill. p. 236, vol. II, p. 220, no. 1255.

1931.417

Jean-Charles Cazin

Samer 1841–1901 Lavandou

The youngest child of a doctor, Cazin grew up in Boulogne-sur-Mer and earned his baccalaureat in Lille. In the early 1860s he moved to Paris, where he exhibited a landscape at the Salon des Refusés of 1863. He enrolled at the Free Drawing School where he studied with Horace Lecoq de Boisbaudran, who emphasized the development of one's visual memory. Through the influence of Lecoq, Cazin gained a post teaching drawing at an architecture school in Paris and then in Tours beginning in 1868. In that same year he married the painter Marie Guillet, who had studied with Rosa Bonheur.

Like a number of other French artists at the outset of the Franco-Prussian War, Cazin moved to England, where he joined his friend Alphonse Legros in an abortive effort to set up a teaching atelier. He also produced ceramics at the Fulham pottery from 1872 to 1874. In 1874 he traveled with his family to Italy and Holland before settling in his native region of Equihen.

Both Cazin and his wife submitted works to the Salon of 1876, including his *Boatyard* (Cleveland Museum of Art).[1] During the 1880s he gained acclaim for biblical subjects painted in a naturalistic style that incorporated the direct observation and loose facture used by the impressionists. Cazin won a first-class medal for *Hagar and Ishmael* in the Salon of 1880, followed by membership in the Legion of Honor in 1882 and the award of a gold medal at the Universal Exposition of 1889. He was a founder of the National Society of Fine Arts and participated in the dissident Salon of 1890, which ultimately became the annual Salon des Indépendants. He was in Italy again from 1884 to 1888. From about 1890 he eliminated figural subjects from his works and painted only pure landscapes.

Cazin was popular with American collectors during the 1890s, including Potter Palmer, Collis Huntington, and John G. Johnson. The American Art Association held a large exhibition of 112 of his works in New York, of which 68 were lent by American collectors. Many of these are now in the Corcoran Gallery of Art in Washington, D.C.

1. Gabriel P. Weisberg, "Jean Charles Cazin: Memory Painting and Observation in *The Boatyard*," *Bulletin of the Cleveland Museum of Art*, vol. LXVII, no. 1 (Jan. 1981), pp. 2–16.

Jean-Charles Cazin

Landscape

1890s
Oil on panel, 21.1 x 26 cm (8⅜ x 10¼ in.)
Signed lower left: J.C. CAZIN

This small panel is a rare subject in Cazin's oeuvre. It shows a man loading or unloading lumber from three boats in the foreground and is reminiscent of the artist's earlier, larger, and more detailed scene of boat building, *The Boatyard* (1876, Cleveland Museum of Art). The Taft picture is typical of Cazin's mature work from the 1880s onward and is difficult to date precisely. He painted many nocturnal scenes, which often included a body of water. On his excursions to Holland and in northern France, he also painted numerous windmills such as the one seen in the background here. One critic described works like this one: "Like

1931.394

all Cazin's landscapes, [it is] remarkable for the distinction of its tone, the absolute veracity of the light, the quality of atmosphere and ambience."[1]

At one time the Tafts also owned a more ambitious Cazin landscape, *A Windmill in Holland*, which they purchased in April 1902 from the dealer Arthur Tooth. It is illustrated in the 1902 catalogue of their collection but was exchanged before 1920 when *Landscape* is first listed.

1. Theodore Child, from *Some Modern French Painters*, in *Cazin*, New York, 1893, p. 7.

Provenance [Scott and Fowles, New York]; Taft collection, after 1902.

Literature Maurice W. Brockwell, *A Catalogue of the Paintings in the Collection of Mr. and Mrs. Charles P. Taft*, New York, 1920, no. 72; *Catalogue of the Taft Museum*, Cincinnati, 1939 and 1958, no. 566.

1931.394

Jehan-Georges Vibert

Paris 1840–1902 Paris

Like Cazin and many of his contemporaries, Vibert had early ambitions to be a history painter. He studied at the School of Fine Arts and, beginning at the age of sixteen or seventeen, spent six years in the ateliers of Félix Picot and Félix-Joseph Barrias. He first exhibited in the Salon of 1863 and won a medal for his *Death of Narcissus* the following year. In the Salon of 1865, Vibert showed a scene of Roman Christians being thrown to the lions and in 1870 an illustration of Swift's *Gulliver's Travels*. During the late 1860s he also painted a number of Spanish subjects. His interest in genre painting dates from this period.

Vibert fought in the Franco-Prussian War and was awarded the Legion of Honor for having been wounded at Malmaison. His *Apotheosis of M. Thiers* at the Salon of 1876 was only a partial success. During the 1870s he wrote several comedies, which were produced. In 1880 he was among the founding members of the Society of French Watercolorists. He collected Japanese art, and his Paris residence became a meeting place for a group of younger artists called the Cercle de Saint Arnaud.[1]

1. William R. Johnston, *The Nineteenth-Century Paintings in the Walters Art Gallery*, Baltimore, 1982, p. 115.

Jehan-Georges Vibert

A Cardinal

1901–2
Watercolor on paper, 247 x 180 mm (9¾ x 7⅛ in.)
Signed lower right (in red ink): *J.G.Vibert*

At the end of his life, Vibert prepared a major project that united his two principal talents, writing and painting. His two-volume autobiographical book, *Comedy in Painting (La Comédie en peinture)*, was published after his death by the dealer Arthur Tooth in two hundred deluxe copies, which sold for $250 apiece. Each set included an original watercolor.[1] The Tafts owned example number twelve of the book, which almost certainly contained this watercolor.

The work is a study for the upper illustration on page 47, entitled "La Correspondance," showing a dandified young cleric

1931.469

scrutinizing his appearance in a full-length mirror as he puts on gloves. The accompanying text describes a confidential exchange of letters between the cardinal and a duchess concerning his visit the previous day. The letters reveal that the cardinal's visit had taken place on a rainy day, thus explaining the umbrella in his left hand. The watercolor is a typical example of one of Vibert's favorite themes — mild satire of the foibles of well-to-do men of the cloth, executed in a highly realistic style with bright, clear colors. The strong hue of the cardinal's tunic illustrates what contemporaries called "Vibert's red."

1. Frederick Morton, "An Appreciation of Jehan Georges Vibert," *Brush and Pencil*, vol. x, no. 6 (Sept. 1902), p. 329. According to Tooth's records, watercolors from Vibert arrived at the gallery in unitemized groups from October 1901 through 1902.

Provenance [Arthur Tooth and Sons, London]; Taft collection, Apr. 22, 1902.

Literature Jehan-Georges Vibert, *La Comédie en peinture*, London and New York, 1902, vol. 1, p. 47; *Catalogue of the Taft Museum*, Cincinnati, 1939 and 1958, no. 548; Ruth Krueger Meyer, "The Taft Collection: The First Ten Years of Its Development," *The Taft Museum: A Cincinnati Legacy*, Cincinnati, 1988, p. 7 (ill.).

1931.469

Barbizon School Paintings

Ruth Krueger Meyer

Jean-Baptiste-Camille Corot
Paris 1796–1875 Paris

Corot was born in Paris to a family of cloth merchants.[1] When his school days ended in 1815, he was sent to work in the drapers' trade. But Corot was not suited to business and began to yearn for the life of an artist. In 1817 Corot's father bought a house at Ville-d'Avray, a Paris suburb near Versailles, which became the center for Corot's itinerant career as a landscape painter. The death of a younger sister in 1821 permitted his parents to turn over to him the money set aside for her dowry, so that he would have an income while studying art.

Achille-Etna Michallon was Corot's first teacher. Although he was four months younger than his pupil, Michallon was from a family of artists and had just returned from three years in Italy as a Rome Prize winner when Corot began his lessons. A year later Michallon died of consumption, and Corot moved to the studio of Jean-Victor Bertin, an established academic painter of the previous generation. Bertin had been Michallon's teacher too, and he endorsed the flourishing interest of young artists in plein-air painting while teaching the methods of constructing the classical French landscape. With Bertin's guidance Corot began to paint at Ville-d'Avray, around the Ile-de-France, in Normandy, and in the Forest of Fontainebleau before he made his first trip to Italy in 1825.

Three trips to Italy (1825–28, 1834, and 1843) and sojourns in Switzerland (1842), Holland (1854), and England (1862) comprised Corot's travels outside France. Within his native country he moved constantly among the painting sites named above, to Brittany and the Midi, and to Landes and the Auvergne. Corot never married and so escaped the limitations imposed on a provider. His family's estate afforded such comfort as he sought, and his income offered opportunities to indulge his generous impulses toward less fortunate fellow artists.

Corot's exhibition career in the French academy's Salons began in 1827 when two paintings were accepted. He won official recognition in 1833 and sold his first canvas to the government in 1840; six years later he was decorated with the Legion of Honor. He was rewarded with other government purchases and independent commissions. Although his works did not command high prices until the 1860s, Corot had achieved the status of an acknowledged talent, and his success also benefited other landscape painters who hailed him as their master and emulated him.

When Corot entered the Parisian art world, most artists had as their hero Eugène Delacroix. But it was another great artist of the 1820s, the English landscapist John Constable, who would demonstrate an alternative with his three paintings shown in the 1824 Salon. At that moment, cultural Paris was feverish with Anglophilia, and Constable won great critical success, influencing Corot among others. Constable's single-minded dedication to painting modest landscape details from a given vista and developing them into complex and sophisticated elegiac statements found ready acceptance among the French artists who would subsequently become known as the Men of 1830 and later as the Barbizon School.

Recent scholarship has shown that the way had been prepared in Paris for appreciation of the work of Constable and other British landscape artists. Just when it seemed that the landscape tradition of Gaspard Dughet, Claude Lorrain, and Nicolas Poussin could scarcely bear another round of reinterpretation, artists affiliated with the French academy and especially its school in Rome began to incorporate the effects of direct observation, as gathered in their sketches made outdoors, with the armature of classical landscape form developed by their seventeenth-century countrymen. The presence of an international coterie of landscape painters active in Italy during Corot's first sojourn there and his participation in this new approach has been established by Peter Galassi.[2] However, by midcentury Corot's paintings were no longer marked by the clarity of composition and brilliance of light found in his early work. Gradually he moved toward increasingly poetic and lyrical landscapes, such as those in the Taft collection.

1. On Corot, see Etienne Moreau-Nélaton, *Histoire de Corot et des ses oeuvres,* Paris, 1905; Alfred Robaut and Etienne Moreau-Nélaton, *L'Oeuvre de Corot: Catalogue raisonné et illustré,* 4 vols. and index, Paris, 1905; *Hommage à Corot,* exh. cat., Orangerie des Tuileries, Paris, 1975.

2. Peter Galassi, *Corot in Italy,* New Haven and London, 1991.

Jean-Baptiste-Camille Corot

Evening: The Festival of Pan

1855–60
Oil on canvas, 90.2 x 110.2 cm (35½ x 43⅜ in.)
Signed lower left: COROT

It is evening, and the departing sun casts its last light on a shadowed pool at the edge of a forest. Mirrored on the surface are the reflections of a rosy sunset and a classical sculpture, a herm of Pan, that stands on a sloping hillside. The sky is lightly veiled with thin clouds that carry the sunset's glow through an infinite atmosphere. As though coming forth to celebrate the close of day, two women and a child are led by dancers bearing garlands toward the herm standing enframed by saplings.

The moment Corot records in this painting is at once fleeting and timeless, an impression one receives from studying the composition's construction. For stability Corot balanced the landscape masses and the setting of the sculpture in deep shade distributed horizontally across the canvas. Having thus weighted this density of forest terrain and foliage against the atmospheric void of the sky, he intensified the pull of the diagonal recession to a vanishing point in deep space marked by the setting sun.

1931.449

Although it is optically improbable, one is led to believe that this light source illuminates the herm's reflection on the surface of the pool, which is surrounded by vegetation that catches glints of fading light while remaining nearly obscured by the twilight.

The subject of the painting is to be found in its articulation of an imagined event of modest proportions grandly described according to the principles of French classical landscape painting. Corot's vision of this festival of Pan resonates on the senses like wind chimes and soft breezes. It confides its sentiment without pretense; it enthralls the eye without force; and it gives evocative power to Corot's thesis that there have always been moments of such great earthly beauty had artists but been there to record them.

Fig. 1 Jean-Baptiste-Camille Corot, *Le Bain de Diane*, 1855–60. Oil on canvas, 168 x 257 cm (66 x 101 in.). Bordeaux, Musée des Beaux-Arts. © cliché du M.B.A. de Bordeaux.

Fig. 2 Jean-Baptiste-Camille Corot, *Bathing Nymphs and Child (Les Baigneuses à l'enfant)*, 1855–60. Oil on canvas, 82.6 x 100.3 cm (32½ x 39½ in.). The Art Institute of Chicago, Mr. and Mrs. W. W. Kimball Collection, 1922.4454. Photograph © 1991 The Art Institute of Chicago. All rights reserved.

Dated by Robaut to the period 1855–60,[1] *Evening: The Festival of Pan* is among a sizable group of classical landscape paintings with lyrical themes, which begins with *Morning: Dance of Nymphs* (1850, Paris, Musée d'Orsay), continues with *Le Bain de Diane (The Bath of Diana)* (fig. 1, 1855–60, Bordeaux, Musée des Beaux-Arts), and includes *The Shepherd's Star* (1864, Toulouse, Musée des Augustins).

The Festival of Pan is also the title given to a print made by the cliché-verre process.[2] Corot began his work in the cliché-verre medium in 1853 and produced at least seventy examples. The Taft painting also shares this composition with another painting, *Bathing Nymphs and Child* (fig. 2, 1855–60, The Art Institute of Chicago), a scene of midday ablutions.[3]

From the 1820s Corot made a series of sketches while attending the theater, and perhaps it is on one of these that he based the group of figures led by dancers. A sketchbook dated by Robaut to 1855–58, containing similar figural groups, is in the Cabinet des Dessins at the Louvre (R.F. 8728).[4] While none of these sketches corresponds directly to the grouping in the Taft painting, they are linked by their fragile gestures and idyllic mood.

1. Alfred Robaut and Etienne Moreau-Nélaton, *L'Oeuvre de Corot: Catalogue raisonné et illustré*, vol. II, Paris, 1905, no. 1111.

2. Loys Delteil, *Le Peintre-Graveur illustré (XIXe et XXe siècles)*, vol. V, *Corot*, Paris, 1910, no. 79; also catalogued by Robaut, vol. IV, no. 3199. Along with this image Delteil illustrates a drawing that is closer to the composition of the Taft Museum painting and is the reverse of the cliché-verre print. The drawing is catalogued by Robaut, vol. IV, no. 2896, and titled *La Fête du dieu terme*.

3. Robaut, vol. II, no. 1113, *Les Baigneuses à l'enfant;* oil on canvas, 82.6 x 100.3 cm, The Art Institute of Chicago, inv. no. 1922.4454.

4. *Hommage à Corot*, exh. cat., Orangerie des Tuileries, Paris, 1975, no. 160; Robaut, vol. IV, no. 3107.

Provenance Baron E. M. de Beurnonville (sale, Apr. 29, 1880, no. 1); [Goupil]; Defoer, Paris; Crabbe, Brussels (sale, June 1890, no. 2); [Arnold and Tripp]; Archibald Coates, Paisley, Scotland (1893, 1895); [Scott and Fowles, New York]; Taft collection, 1904.

Exhibitions Paris, *Exposition centennale de l'art français*, 1889 (cat., no. 184); Lawrie and Co., London, *French School of 1830*, 1893 (cat., no. 3 [ill.]); Paris, *Exposition centenaire Corot*, 1895 (cat., no. 41).

Literature *New York Herald*, Mar. 24, 1904; Alfred Robaut and Etienne Moreau-Nélaton, *L'Oeuvre de Corot: Catalogue raisonné et illustré*, vol. II, Paris, 1905, no. 1111; Maurice W. Brockwell, *A Catalogue of Paintings in the Collection of Mr. and Mrs. Charles P. Taft*, New York, 1920, no. 16; *Catalogue of the Taft Museum*, Cincinnati, 1939 and 1958, no. 281; Ruth Krueger Meyer, "The Taft Collection: The First Ten Years of Its Development," *The Taft Museum: A Cincinnati Legacy*, Cincinnati, 1988, p. 5 (ill.).

1931.449

1931.437

&

Jean-Baptiste-Camille Corot

Peasants Stopping at the Edge of a Wooded Road near a Village (formerly At Ville-d'Avray)

1860s
Oil on canvas, 54.6 x 37 cm (21½ x 14⅝ in.)
Signed lower left: COROT

Along a shaded path in a clearing of the woods, a woman and a child stand watching as a man adjusts his boot. Behind them in the distance are buildings washed with bright summer sunlight. A strong vertical accent in the composition is provided by a single, tall, nearly leafless tree that marks the center of the canvas and seems to hold apart the foliage masses that flank it. Beneath the densest trees at the right is the roof of an outbuilding that furthers the impression of a rural setting.

When this painting entered the Taft collection in 1902, it was titled *At Ville-d'Avray*. However, when Robaut's catalogue was published in 1905, no such identification of location was made, nor should it now be supported.[1] The house cannot be identified with the Corot villa in its parklike setting, nor is there any suggestion of a water element such as the pond at Ville-d'Avray,

which Corot frequently incorporated in his studies of the houses that lined its banks.[2]

1. Alfred Robaut and Etienne Moreau-Nélaton, *L'Oeuvre de Corot: Catalogue raisonné et illustré*, vol. III, Paris, 1905, no. 1977.

2. This was the opinion of Geneviève Matheron and the organizers of the exhibition *Corot à Ville-d'Avray* at the Musée Ville-d'Avray, 1987, in conversation with the author.

Provenance Albert de Saint-Albin, Paris; [Arthur Tooth and Sons]; Taft collection, Oct. 20, 1902.

Exhibitions Tokyo, Odakyu Grand Gallery, Shinjuku [also Osaka and Yokohama], *J.-B. Camille Corot*, Sept. 13, 1989–Feb. 25, 1990 (cat. by Gabriel P. Weisberg et al., pp. 150–51, no. 42, pl. 42); Manchester, N.H., The Currier Gallery of Art [also New York and Dallas], *The Rise of Landscape Painting in France: Corot to Monet*, Jan. 29, 1991–Jan. 5, 1992 (cat. by Kermit S. Champa et al., p. 126, no. 26).

Literature Charles F. Fowles, *The Art Collection of Mr. and Mrs. Charles P. Taft, Cincinnati, Ohio*, privately printed, 1902; Alfred Robaut and Etienne Moreau-Nélaton, *L'Oeuvre de Corot: Catalogue raisonné et illustré*, vol. III, Paris, 1905, no. 1977; Maurice W. Brockwell, *A Catalogue of Paintings in the Collection of Mr. and Mrs. Charles P. Taft*, New York, 1920, no. 37; *Catalogue of the Taft Museum*, Cincinnati, 1939 and 1958, no. 314.

1931.437

&

Jean-Baptiste-Camille Corot

Outside Paris: The Heights above Ville-d'Avray

1865–70
Oil on canvas, 51.4 x 100.3 cm (20¼ x 39½ in.)
Signed lower left: COROT

In a clearing on a hilltop, a man with a hoe tills the ground, observed by two women who have paused on a pathway. To the right in the composition, cows are pastured in the shelter of tall trees. The center of the canvas is held by the expanding vista that spreads beneath the palisades southwest of Paris. The spires and towers of the capital pierce the enveloping mist in the distance.

The departments of Hauts-de-Seine and Yvelines contain the suburban communes to the west of Paris. The ground is steeply elevated above the river plain, and the hillsides are densely wooded. Formerly, these were royal preserves dominated by Louis XIII's hunting lodge at Versailles, the foundation of the palatial complex built by the next Bourbon rulers.

When Corot's father acquired the family's property at Ville-d'Avray in 1817, he had little notion that his son would become its most noted resident artist, establishing the fame of the locale in hundreds of drawings, paintings, and prints. Corot worked throughout the parklike Ville-d'Avray district, which lies across the Seine just west of the Bois de Boulogne and includes in a five-kilometer radius such favorite sites as Sèvres and Saint-Cloud.

Robaut catalogued this painting among an extensive group of Ville-d'Avray canvases that he dated to the period 1865–70.[1] The composition is virtually the same as another entitled *Ville-*

1931.454

d'Avray: View from the Heights Looking toward Mount Valerian (unlocated).[2] Mount Valerian is visible north of Saint-Cloud. Comparing the two works (using a photograph of the latter), it seems that the same site was used for both and that Corot shifted his gaze slightly to the northeast, away from a direct line eastward to Paris. On these heights of Ville-d'Avray were situated an ancient monastery and the Château de Tourelles, both now demolished, but in Corot's day popular destinations as scenic overlooks.[3]

A small version of the Taft canvas, showing the group of figures at the left, is in the collection of the Musée Fabre, Montpellier (fig. 1). According to Robaut, Devillers made a copy of the Taft painting, which was signed by Corot. It was this generous practice of the artist to assist less fortunate painters that has led to the vast confusion regarding the authenticity of his later works.

1. Alfred Robaut and Etienne Moreau-Nélaton, *L'Oeuvre de Corot: Catalogue raisonné et illustré*, vol. III, Paris, 1905, no. 1499.

2. Robaut, vol. III, no. 1495.

3. The location also has similarities to two other compositions catalogued by Robaut, vol. III, nos. 1500 and 1501 (the latter now thought to be a fake), each titled *Heights above Sèvres: Pasture*. Robaut stated that this view was painted from the window of Troyon's studio at Sèvres, following that artist's death.

Provenance Luquet (sale, Hôtel Drouot, Paris, Sept. 10, 1875, to M. Chailloux); Fraissinet (sale, May 1880); George W. Burnett, London; [Scott and Fowles, New York]; Taft collection, Sept. 19, 1903.

Exhibitions Houston, Museum of Fine Arts, *Corot and His Contemporaries,* May 8–June 21, 1959; Tokyo, Odakyu Grand Gallery, Shinjuku [also Osaka and Yokohama], *J.-B. Camille Corot,* Sept. 13, 1989–Feb. 25, 1990 (cat. by Gabriel P. Weisberg et al., pp. 151–52, no. 47, pl. 47); Manchester, N.H., The Currier Gallery of Art [also New York and Dallas], *The Rise of Landscape Painting in France: Corot to Monet,* Jan. 29, 1991–Jan. 5, 1992 (cat. by Kermit S. Champa et al., p. 132, no. 34).

Literature Alfred Robaut and Etienne Moreau-Nélaton, *L'Oeuvre de Corot: Catalogue raisonné et illustré,* vol. III, Paris, 1905, no. 1499; Maurice W. Brockwell, *A Catalogue of Paintings in the Collection of Mr. and Mrs. Charles P. Taft,* New York, 1920, no. 44; *Catalogue of the Taft Museum,* Cincinnati, 1939 and 1958, no. 447; *Corot à Ville-d'Avray,* exh. cat., Musée de Ville-d'Avray, 1987, under no. 33.

1931.454

Fig. 1 Jean-Baptiste-Camille Corot, *Matinée: Effets de brouillard,* 1865–70. Oil on canvas, 25 x 35 cm (9¾ x 13¾ in.). Montpellier, Musée Fabre. Cliché Frédéric Jaulmes.

Jean-Baptiste-Camille Corot

A Brook beneath the Trees with a House in the Distance

1865–70
Oil on canvas, 56.4 x 38.7 cm (22¼ x 15¼ in.)
Signed lower right: COROT

Beside a brook beneath trees leafed in the palest greens of spring, a woman kneels on a grassy bank. Through the trees along the course of the stream can be seen distant buildings in the vernacular style of the Ile-de-France.

Although Robaut dated this painting to the decade of the 1860s without more precision, he also suggested that it was done in the vicinity of Beauvais where Corot worked most produc-

1931.438

tively in the spring of 1866.[1] His Salon entry the following year was *The Church of Marissel near Beauvais* (Paris, Musée du Louvre; Robaut, no. 1370), painted while he was staying with M. Wallet, a resident of Voisinlieu, a village just outside the city walls. Wallet's property was along the course of the Therain River, which winds sinuously through Beauvais and Marissel on its way downstream to its juncture with the river Oise.

Robaut catalogued five other paintings (nos. 1371–75) that he identified as works from Marissel or Voisinlieu. Three of these are in the Musée Saint-Denis at Reims and offer the strongest similarities to the Taft painting, which, according to Robaut, was also copied several times.

1. Alfred Robaut and Etienne Moreau-Nélaton, *L'Oeuvre de Corot: Catalogue raisonné et illustré*, vol. III, Paris, 1905, no. 1443.

Provenance Dr. Gambey (1875, 1878); Albert de Saint-Albin, Paris (1883); [Arthur Tooth]; Taft collection, 1902.

Exhibitions Paris, Ecole des Beaux-Arts, *L'Oeuvre de Corot*, May 1875 (cat., no. 82); Paris, Galerie Durand-Ruel, *Exposition rétrospective de tableaux et dessins de maîtres modernes*, 1878 (cat., no. 83); Paris, Galerie Georges Petit, *Exposition de cent chefs-d'oeuvre des collections parisiennes*, June–July 1883 (cat., no. 6); Tokyo, Odakyu Grand Gallery, Shinjuku [also Osaka and Yokohama], *J.-B. Camille Corot*, Sept. 13, 1989–Feb. 25, 1990 (cat. by Gabriel P. Weisberg et al., p. 152, no. 48, pl. 48); Manchester, N.H., The Currier Gallery of Art [also New York and Dallas], *The Rise of Landscape Painting in France: Corot to Monet*, Jan. 29, 1991–Jan. 5, 1992 (cat. by Kermit S. Champa et al., p. 131, no. 32).

Literature Charles F. Fowles, *The Art Collection of Mr. and Mrs. Charles P. Taft, Cincinnati, Ohio*, privately printed, 1902; Alfred Robaut and Etienne Moreau-Nélaton, *L'Oeuvre de Corot: Catalogue raisonné et illustré*, vol. III, Paris, 1905, no. 1443; Maurice W. Brockwell, *A Catalogue of Paintings in the Collection of Mr. and Mrs. Charles P. Taft*, New York, 1920, no. 39; *Catalogue of the Taft Museum*, Cincinnati, 1939 and 1958, no. 312.

1931.438

Jean-Baptiste-Camille Corot

Souvenir of Riva: Evening Glow

1865–70
Oil on canvas, 64.1 x 92.2 cm. (25¼ x 36⅜ in.)
Signed lower right: COROT

Early morning mists lie on the northern end of Lake Garda in the Italian Tyrol as two boatmen leave its wooded shoreline. Large trees near the water's edge darken the lakeshore and the inlet in the foreground of the canvas. On the left across the lake a distant shoreline with a low line of coastal hills makes a gentle but emphatic horizontal axis perpendicular to the vertical mass of trees on the right. The even quality of the light emphasizes the calculated balance between atmosphere and sculpted terrain Corot has achieved. Masses of foliage and reflections on the still waters punctuate the harmony of the canvas without disturbing its essential tranquility.

In 1834, during his second trip to Italy, Corot visited the village of Riva where he made a small study of a group of fishermen in a boat near the shoreline, now in the museum of Saint Gall (fig. 1).[1] From this study he made a larger canvas, which he sent to the Salon of 1835 (fig. 2).[2] According to Robaut, fifteen years later he painted two more versions of the Lake Garda vista, one of which is now in Marseille.[3] Following Robaut's chronology, the Taft canvas, painted about 1865–70, may represent the ultimate reprise of the motif,[4] although there is also a cliché-verre print identified as a *Souvenir of Lake Nemi*, dated by Delteil to 1871, which has distinctly similar landscape features although no boatmen are present.[5]

The frequency with which Corot returned to particular motifs becomes more prevalent during the last decade of his career when he could no longer travel widely but continued to paint productively. The "souvenir" quality in these works is best understood through an examination of a sequence such as has been described above, in which the original motif becomes simplified in detail but grows in poetic expression.

1. Alfred Robaut and Etienne Moreau-Nélaton, *L'Oeuvre de Corot: Catalogue raisonné et illustré*, vol. II, Paris, 1905, no. 358.

2. Robaut, vol. II, no. 357.

3. Robaut, vol. II, no. 359. *Hommage à Corot*, exh. cat., Orangerie des Tuileries, Paris, 1975, no. 74, *Vue prise à Riva (Tyrol Italien)*, oil on canvas, 73 x 123 cm, Marseille, Musée des Beaux-Arts; the variant, Robaut, no. 360, has most recently appeared at Sotheby's, New York, Feb. 17, 1993, no. 5.

1931.439

Fig. 1 Jean-Baptiste-Camille Corot, *Near Riva on Lake Garda,* 1834. Oil on canvas, 29 x 41 cm (11½ x 16 in.). Kunstmuseum St. Gallen, Sturzenegger Collection.

Fig. 2 Jean-Baptiste-Camille Corot, *Landscape near Riva on Lake Garda,* 1835. Oil on canvas, 98.6 x 141.5 cm (38¾ x 55¾ in.). Munich, Bayerische Staatsgemäldesammlungen.

4. Robaut, vol. III, no. 1805, *Boatmen Approaching under a Large Bunch of Trees at Morning (Souvenir of Riva).* André Schoeller and Jean Dieterle, *Corot: Premier Supplément à "L'Oeuvre de Corot" par Alfred Robaut et Etienne Moreau-Nélaton,* Paris, 1948, lists a replica of the Taft painting, no. 72, *Fisherman Approaching the Bank: Evening,* 33 x 55 cm, which is also thought to have been in the Alexander Young collection.

5. Loys Delteil, *Le Peintre-Graveur illustré (XIXe et XXe siècles),* vol. V, *Corot,* Paris, 1910, no. 89.

Provenance Alexander Young, London; [Scott and Fowles, New York]; Taft collection, Jan. 22, 1908.

Literature Alfred Robaut and Etienne Moreau-Nélaton, *L'Oeuvre de Corot: Catalogue raisonné et illustré,* vol. III, Paris, 1905, no. 1805; E. G. Halton, "The Collection of Alexander Young," *International Studio,* vol. XXX (1906–7), pp. 9–10; Arthur Hoeber, *The Barbizon Painters,* New York, 1915, p. 116, as *Men in Boat;* Maurice W. Brockwell, *A Catalogue of*

Paintings in the Collection of Mr. and Mrs. Charles P. Taft, New York, 1920, no. 38; *Catalogue of the Taft Museum,* Cincinnati, 1939 and 1958, no. 320.

1931.439

Narcisse Virgile Diaz de la Peña
Bordeaux 1807–1876 Menton

The childhood of Narcisse Diaz was marred by a series of unhappy events.[1] His parents were Spaniards living in France, and both had died by the time he was about ten. The orphan was left in the care of a family in Meudon, a Paris suburb, where his widowed mother had once gone to find work. Biographers were later told that Diaz had avoided schooling and passed his time exploring in the woods. One day he was stung or bitten on the leg. It had to be amputated and replaced by one of wood.

With his movement thus constrained, Diaz became an apprentice printer and later a porcelain decorator. By 1822 he was working in the ateliers of Arsène Gillet, the uncle of Jules Dupré, where he met that artist and his circle of friends. Through them he may have been introduced to François Souchon, a pupil of Jacques-Louis David, from whom he took drawing lessons. Diaz began to paint in oils and under the influence of another new friend, the painter Alexandre-Gabriel Decamps, developed a taste for the romantic themes of the Orient. Decamps traveled to Greece and the Near East in 1827 and returned with costumes and other paraphernalia that he used for a number of compositions. His example inspired Diaz to give up the porcelain trade and to paint in the increasingly popular orientalist genre.

With others of his generation Diaz gained his first public exposure in the Salon of 1831. His *Scène d'amour* (Scene of Love) was listed in the catalogue supplement, but he also submitted four landscapes. In 1834 four of six entries were accepted, including a view of Saragosa, which suggests he might have visited Spain. Critical comment on his work began with this showing and remained generally positive throughout his long career. Romantic longings for the Orient were in fashion, and Diaz was adept at depicting bazaars and harems. Over the years his critics were attracted as much by his passionate outgoing nature as by his artistic proficiency. They rarely tired of describing his gypsylike appearance, and while they astutely catalogued his appropriations from the masters — including Prud'hon, Correggio, and Leonardo — they also credited him with able use of these sources.

Diaz discovered Barbizon in 1835, the year the first of his three children was born. He was a frequent visitor to the village but never a permanent resident, as were Millet and Rousseau, with whom he maintained friendships during the following decades. On his sojourns he developed a fondness for a number of specific locales in Fontainebleau and became an acute observer of the subtle meteorological changes that made the region attractive to landscape painters.

From the mid-1830s onward Diaz met with few disappointments. In 1844 he won a third-class medal at the Salon, which allowed him to take pupils. He allied himself with the leaders of both his own and the earlier generation of artists, such as Delacroix, to whom he was often compared; and he developed his own circle of collectors, including several aristocrats who commissioned portraits from him. Awards in the 1840s culminated in his election to the Legion of Honor in 1851. After the Revolution of 1848 he experienced some financial difficulties, but his career revived, and he was able to assist artists in need, such as Jean-François Millet, Théodore Rousseau, and Constant Troyon.

The progressive critics of the 1850s and 1860s — Charles Baudelaire, Philippe Burty, and the older Théophile Gautier — were contemptuous of Diaz's outworn oriental themes but were appreciative of his landscapes. During the last decade of

1931.434

his career he won new recognition for paintings in which anecdote was suppressed and prominence was given to natural phenomena.

1. On Diaz, see Terence Mullaly, "The Barbizon School, V: Diaz," *Apollo*, vol. LXIV, no. 377 (July 1956), pp. 15–17; *Narcisse Diaz de la Peña*, exh. cat., Le Pavillon des Arts, Paris, 1968; Pierre Miquel, *Le Paysage français au XIXe siècle*, vol. II, Maurs-la-Jolie, 1975, pp. 282–319.

☙

Narcisse Virgile Diaz de la Peña

Oriental Children

1840s
Oil on canvas, 32.7 x 24.4 cm (12⅞ x 9⅝ in.)
Signed lower left: *N. Diaz*

Deep in the verdant shade of dense foliage a group of five children in vaguely oriental dress — a fez, a turban, vests, and slippers — is seated at a low table on which rests a cut melon. They are static, solemn, and impassive, lacking the gestures that might give some clue to the reason for their gathering beyond the sharing of the fruit.

Diaz was not an active traveler like other artists who were his contemporaries, such as Alexandre-Gabriel Decamps, who went to Greece and the Near East in 1827. Although Diaz probably never visited the Orient, this did not stop him from painting oriental anecdotes with costumed participants that are admired for their rich jewel-like tones and ornate brushwork. Fusing eighteenth-century French preciousness with the later orientalism of Delacroix and Decamps, Diaz, the former porcelain decorator, supplied quantities of these little gems to eager collectors before establishing himself as a landscape painter working in the Fontainebleau district.

Provenance [Scott and Fowles, New York]; Taft collection, Jan. 22, 1904.

Literature Maurice W. Brockwell, *A Catalogue of Paintings in the Collection of Mr. and Mrs. Charles P. Taft*, New York, 1920, no. 49; *Catalogue of the Taft Museum*, Cincinnati, 1939 and 1958, no. 307.

1931.434

Narcisse Virgile Diaz de la Peña

Early Autumn: Forest of Fontainebleau

1870
Oil on canvas, 84 x 111.8 cm (33⅛ x 44 in.)
Signed and dated lower left: *N. Diaz. 70*

Two great oaks flank an overgrown pathway that leads into a clearing in the Forest of Fontainebleau. Brilliant light breaking through an overcast sky illuminates two women who are gathering branches in the forest. A palette rich in green and golden tones contrasted with steel blues and grays establishes the poignant moment when oak leaves have begun their turn of color announcing the change of season.

Diaz painted such forest clearings repeatedly from the 1860s until the end of his life. Smaller studies, such as an 1862 painting in the collection of the Art Institute of Chicago[1] or another from 1863 in the Baltimore Museum of Art,[2] show a similar location peopled with the forest denizens, called *bûcherons* (or *bûcheronnes*, in this case), who gathered wood and bundled it for sale. The large number of these works has led recent authors to "wonder if all these landscapes were painted out of doors, or whether Diaz with his consummate skill thought up the variants in his studio."[3]

When this painting was made, Diaz no longer sent work to the Paris Salons but exhibited in French regional exhibitions and organized sales of his work with various dealers. This impressive late canvas, *Early Autumn: Forest of Fontainebleau*, may have entered the Coates collection in Paisley, Scotland, through one of these channels. In the fall of 1870, Diaz fled the war in France to take refuge in Brussels, where he established a studio and remained until November 1871, although it is thought that he made a trip to London during this time.

1. Oil on canvas, 68 x 89.8 cm, The Art Institute of Chicago, inv. no. 1922.4455.

2. Oil on canvas, 53.4 x 71.1 cm, Baltimore Museum of Art, the Helen and Abram Eisenberg Collection, inv. no. 1967.36.2.

3. John Sillevis and Hans Kraan, *The Barbizon School*, exh. cat., Haags Gemeentemuseum, The Hague, 1985, p. 158.

Provenance Archibald Coates, Paisley, Scotland (1893); [Scott and Fowles, New York]; Taft collection, Jan. 21, 1904.

Exhibitions London, Lawrie and Co., *French School of 1830*, 1893 (cat., no. 13); Manchester, N.H., The Currier Gallery of Art [also New York and Dallas], *The Rise of Landscape Painting in France: Corot to Monet*, Jan. 29, 1991–Jan. 5, 1992 (cat. by Kermit S. Champa et al., pp. 157, 160, no. 62).

Literature Maurice W. Brockwell, *A Catalogue of Paintings in the Collection of Mr. and Mrs. Charles P. Taft*, New York, 1920, no. 51; *Catalogue of the Taft Museum*, Cincinnati, 1939 and 1958, no. 321.

1931.464

1931.464

Constant Troyon

Sèvres 1810–1865 Paris

Troyon was born at Sèvres, where he would soon become the third generation of his family to work as decorators in the porcelain factories there.[1] After his father's death, Troyon, then aged seven, entered the ateliers under the protection of his godfather who gave him his first instruction in landscape painting. He seems to have had no other schooling. Feelings were strained between his mother and his paternal grandparents, and therefore while still a boy Troyon served as the head of the household. The bond between mother and son was the most enduring relationship of his life.

Working at Sèvres throughout his teens, Troyon also began to paint in the woods of the nearby park of Saint-Cloud, where he met older artists who had journeyed there from Paris. Camille Roqueplan is said to have given him some guidance. Although his family needed the income from his porcelain decorations, Troyon began to travel looking for landscape motifs. His meeting with Jules Dupré around 1832 gave him a friend from a similar background in the industrial arts as well as a mentor already wise in the ways of the Salon and the art marketplace in Paris. Dupré also left an imprint on Troyon's style that was visible for nearly two decades.

Troyon exhibited three scenes of the area in and around Sèvres at the 1833 Salon without drawing critical notice. A trip, possibly taken to relieve sorrow over a failed romance, caused him to miss the next Salon, but he exhibited again in 1835 with more landscapes of his native district. Finally, in 1836, his submission painted at d'Argentan in the central French region of Indre drew brief mention. Two years later the Salon of 1838 brought him his first medal, of the third class, and inaugurated his reputation as an animal painter.

According to his critics, Troyon had labored over the decade to develop his own style and moderate the influence of Dupré. They repeatedly drew attention to his robust color and thick paint laid on with touches of the brush that made the surface resemble a mosaic. Troyon may have been laboring to overcome the finicky touch of the decorator instilled in him long ago. The gradual expansion of his subject matter as he discovered new terrains in Normandy, Brittany, and Barbizon promoted a gradual alteration of his compositions. Then, as he found financial success, his income permitted him to increase the size of his canvases to meet the demands of his new clients. The larger scale of his works facilitated a more fluid style of paint application.

Following the guidance of Dupré, Troyon also sent works to provincial exhibitions. Well into the 1840s, he continued to decorate porcelains and to make pleasing sketches in the manner of Boucher and Watteau. By 1846, when he won a first-class medal at the Salon, his work had begun to sell and provided financial security for him for the remainder of his life.

A visit to Holland in 1847 wrought the final transformation in Troyon's art. There, he encountered the works of the seventeenth-century animal painters Aelbert Cuyp and Paulus Potter. From them and other Dutch artists he appropriated the use of extensive low horizons and blond tonalities. Henceforth, he

1931.421

painted animals almost exclusively and on ever-larger canvases. Rapidly gaining popular success, Troyon entered the Legion of Honor in 1859 in the company of Dupré and Camille Flers.

While making frequent trips to Barbizon throughout the 1840s, Troyon also traveled annually to Normandy where he painted in the valley of the Touques, a river that flows inland through the town of Lisieux. On the coast of Normandy in 1852, he met Eugène Boudin, who encouraged him to paint seascapes and other marine subjects. In 1859 he exhibited for the last time in Paris, thereafter sending his works abroad or to provincial exhibitions. During his last years, his popularity and income declined with the onset of mental illness. His friends, especially his neighbor Camille Corot, assisted him financially through this time. Following a brief period of insanity, he died in Paris in 1863.

1. On Troyon, see Arthur Hustin, *Constant Troyon*, Paris, 1893, and Louis Soullié, *Les Grands Peintres aux ventes publiques: Constant Troyon*, Paris, 1900.

Constant Troyon

French Coastal Scene

1841–43
Oil on panel, 45.7 x 37.5 cm (18 x 14¾ in.)
Signed lower left: *C. Troyon*

Two large double-wheeled carts are drawn by pairs of oxen alongside a boat in the shallows, so that the fishermen's catch

Fig. 1 Constant Troyon, *Beach at Trouville,* after 1841–43. Oil on cradled panel, 72 x 118.4 cm (28⅜ x 46⅝ in.). Photograph courtesy of Sotheby's, Inc., New York.

can be unloaded and conveyed to shore. On the horizon a raised sail marks the location of a distant boat. Overhead the sky is densely covered with thick clouds.

A catalogue raisonné of Troyon's paintings is being prepared by Hans-Peter Bühler of Munich. Bühler has suggested that Troyon may have painted this scene on his first trip to Normandy in 1841.[1] It may also have been painted from memory shortly thereafter in 1843 and exhibited at Rouen, the same year as *Souvenir of the Norman Coast, Storm Effect.* Bühler bases his opinions on his reading of the painting of the sky, which recalls the techniques of Jules Dupré, Troyon's teacher.

Bühler has also catalogued a second later and larger version of the scene with some alterations that he identifies with *Beach at Trouville* (fig. 1), which Troyon showed at the Universal Exposition in 1855.[2] He feels Troyon may have used the same sketches for both paintings even though there is a lapse of time and change of technique in the later painting.

1. Letter from Hans-Peter Bühler to the author, June 30, 1988.

2. This painting was sold at Sotheby's, New York, Feb. 24, 1988, no. 30.

Provenance Alexander Young, London; [Scott and Fowles, New York]; Taft collection, Jan. 17, 1907.

Literature Possibly Louis Soullié, *Constant Troyon,* Paris, 1900, p. 77, as "Bateau de pêche déchargeant du poisson. Une voiture attelée de boeufs est contre le bateau. Panneau 46 x 37 cent. Collection Creswick en 1870. Vente Mieville, à Londres. 65,000 fr."; Maurice W. Brockwell, *A Catalogue of Paintings in the Collection of Mr. and Mrs. Charles P. Taft,* New York, 1920, no. 55; *Catalogue of the Taft Museum,* Cincinnati, 1939 and 1958, no. 485.

1931.421

❧

Constant Troyon

Cattle at a Watering Place

1850–55
Oil on canvas, 78.1 x 111.4 cm (30¾ x 43⅞ in.)
Signed lower left: *C. Troyon*

A herd of cattle has reached a wide place in a stream where they pause to drink before moving into a broad plain. On the bank of the stream a short distance away, a low thatched-roof cottage is sheltered by a stand of tall windswept poplars. Farmers who labor or stand beneath the trees are dwarfed by their tremendous size. On the distant horizon a range of hills defines the limits of the plain. The sky is filled with the high, fast-moving clouds of the English Channel region.

The setting for this landscape must be the valley of the Touques River, which Troyon frequented during the 1840s and 1850s. There, he made sketches that would be composed into

1931.465

finished canvases in the studio. The influence of his 1847 visit to Holland can be discerned in the lower horizon line typical of seventeenth-century Dutch landscape artists and in the placement of farm folk in the middle distance. Following Dutch examples, Troyon has allowed the procession of cows, escorted only by a single young goat, to dominate his composition.

The paintings he saw on his visit to Holland encouraged Troyon to eliminate the heavily worked surfaces that had previously characterized his landscapes and to use thinner paints and more luminous tones. Hans-Peter Bühler offers the opinion that *Cattle at a Watering Place* is routine in execution and probably was painted in the mid-1850s when Troyon was occupied with many commissions for similar compositions.[1] Bühler suggests a correspondence with dated paintings from the 1850s in the Louvre.[2]

1. Letter from Hans-Peter Bühler to the author, June 30, 1988.

2. Letter from Bühler to the author, Sept. 2, 1991; Paris, Musée du Louvre, R.F. 1795 and 1796.

Provenance A. T. Stewart, New York (sale, Mar. 25, 1887, no. 180); [Scott and Fowles, New York]; Taft collection, Sept. 19, 1903.

Exhibition Southampton, N.Y., Parrish Art Museum [also New York], *In Support of Liberty: European Paintings at the 1883 Pedestal Fund Art Loan Exhibition*, June 29–Dec. 7, 1986 (cat. by Maureen C. O'Brien et al., p. 186, no. 86, ill. p. 187).

Literature Maurice W. Brockwell, *A Catalogue of Paintings in the Collection of Mr. and Mrs. Charles P. Taft*, New York, 1920, no. 45; *Catalogue of the Taft Museum*, Cincinnati, 1939 and 1958, no. 279.

1931.465

Jules Dupré
Nantes 1811–1889 L'Isle-Adam

Dupré was born in Nantes, his mother's home, but the family soon returned to the village of L'Isle-Adam near Paris where his father, once a landscape painter, worked decorating porcelains.[1] Because the elder Dupré later managed porcelain factories in different parts of France, young Jules was always surrounded by artists and soon became his father's apprentice. In that position he would meet artists of his own generation, and in 1825 Dupré moved to his uncle's studio in Paris where the painters Auguste Raffet, Narcisse Diaz de la Peña, and Louis Cabat were employed. When not working, Dupré found time to study with the animal painter Michel Diebolt.

Dupré's father became the director of a porcelain factory near Limoges, and Jules joined him there in 1826. For three years he made excursions in the wild countryside of the district during his leisure time, pursuing a growing interest in painting from nature. Returning to Paris in 1829, he met the artists Alexandre-Gabriel Decamps, Camille Flers, Philippe-Auguste Jeanron, and Paul Huet, who introduced him to their new attitudes concerning landscape representation. With them he rejected academic conventions and began to paint more intuitively, with visible brushwork and dramatic effects of light.

Giving up porcelain decorating to concentrate on a career as a landscape painter, Dupré joined his new colleagues in exhibiting at the Luxembourg Palace for the benefit of those injured during the Revolution of 1830. He made his Salon debut in 1831, showing three landscape studies; he sold one to the duc de Nemours and another to the director of the influential magazine *L'Artiste*. Later that year an English collector invited him to visit Britain, and he stopped in Southampton, Plymouth, Windsor, and London, making sketches for paintings.

During the 1830s and 1840s, Dupré adopted the mode of life preferred by his generation of painters. In the summer he traveled in the French provinces, and in the winter he worked in his Paris studio preparing submissions for the Salons that took place in the spring. With his friends Cabat, Théodore Rousseau, and Constant Troyon he visited the regions of Berry, Picardy, and Limoges. And they joined him at his home district of L'Isle-Adam in the nearby forests of Compiègne.

Dupré's landscapes were repeatedly accepted at the Salons, and he attracted collectors and gained recognition from critics who usually praised the freshness of his conceptions. When he won a third-class medal in 1835, he opened a studio and began to accept students. Despite this success he disagreed with the Salon system and disliked the competitiveness of the hangings. As his reputation grew Dupré emerged as a leader among the artists who would be known as the Barbizon group although he never lived in the village. He had entrepreneurial ability and promoted relationships for his friends with the independent art dealers. By the mid-1840s he was closest to Théodore Rousseau, who credited Dupré with teaching him a great deal about landscape composition. Their friendship was broken off abruptly in 1849 when Dupré was awarded the Legion of Honor and Rousseau was not.

Dupré retired to L'Isle-Adam, where he developed a liaison with his pupil Mme Quantinet. His painting style underwent a change as he abandoned direct study from nature and spent more time reworking and finishing his compositions. Although his reputation endured, his style lost the vigorous qualities of observation it previously had embodied. These changes were noted by the critics when he exhibited again in the Salon after an absence of thirteen years.

Following the death of Mme Quantinet, Dupré married in 1860. His new wife took over the management of his affairs, leaving him free to paint. He acquired a summer home at Cayeux-sur-Mer and in later life began to paint marine views. Toward the end of his long career, his landscapes became turgidly impressionistic with little of the naturalistic clarity that had earlier distinguished his art.

1. On Dupré, see Jules Claretie, *M. Jules Dupré, Les Hommes du jour*, Paris, 1879; Paul Mantz, *Atelier Jules Dupré*, sale cat., Galerie Georges Petit, Paris, Jan. 30, 1890; Marie-Madeleine Aubrun, *Jules Dupré, 1811–1889: Catalogue raisonné de l'oeuvre peint, dessiné et gravé*, Paris, 1974.

1931.427

Jules Dupré

Landscape with Cattle

1845–50
Oil on canvas, 43 x 57 cm (17 x 22½ in.)
Signed lower left: *Jules Dupré*

A summer sky is reflected on the surface of a pond to which a herdsman has led his cattle for water. On the distant side of the pond extends a prairie, where other beasts are resting. To either side in the middle distance are stands of large trees. The blue dome of the sky is dotted with clouds made golden by the sun's light.

The date of this painting is proposed in the Cronier sale catalogue, which proclaims the work a masterpiece.[1] Both the estimation and the date were sustained by Aubrun in her catalogue, although she had not located the painting at the time of her publication.[2]

Typical of the best of Dupré's mature landscapes painted during the period of his close relationship with Théodore Rousseau, *Landscape with Cattle* demonstrates their collaboration. During the decade of the 1840s they shared techniques of landscape organization that yielded a sense of fundamental order. The dense weave of the brushwork is characteristic of Dupré and betrays his early instruction in porcelain decoration.

1. Ernest Cronier sale, Galerie Georges Petit, Paris, Dec. 4, 1905, no. 64.

2. Marie-Madeleine Aubrun, *Jules Dupré, 1811–1889: Catalogue raisonné de l'oeuvre peint, dessiné et gravé*, Paris, 1974, no. 211.

Provenance Ernest Cronier (sale, Galerie Georges Petit, Paris, Dec. 4, 1905, no. 64, as *La Mare*); [Arnold and Tripp, London]; Taft collection, before 1920.

Exhibition Bloomfield Hills, Mich., Cranbrook Academy of Art, *Light and the Painter*, Sept. 5–28, 1952 (cat., no. 25).

Literature Maurice W. Brockwell, *A Catalogue of Paintings in the Collection of Mr. and Mrs. Charles P. Taft*, New York, 1920, no. 54; *Catalogue of the Taft Museum*, Cincinnati, 1939 and 1958, no. 280.

1931.427

Jules Dupré

Landscape with Cattle Drinking

1880s
Oil on canvas, 46.7 x 38.4 cm (18⅜ x 15⅛ in.)
Signed lower left: *Jules Dupré*

Two cows have waded into a stream and stand drinking beneath trees that line its shady banks. A distant point of bright reflected light may mark the site of farm buildings set back from the water's edge. Masses of white clouds rise to the azure arch of the sky, and brilliant light filters through the trees and highlights trunks and foliage.

In his later years Dupré abandoned his naturalistic depiction of landscape and became more subjective in his interpretations of the effects of light and atmosphere. This painting is an evocation of the intense contrasts of light and shadow on a summer day and is not descriptive of a particular setting. It does, however, strongly convey the artist's mood, perhaps an aging darkened temperament essaying yet again a timeworn theme.

Although Marie-Madeleine Aubrun did not catalogue this painting, when shown a photograph, she classified it among the works of the artist's last decade.

1931.435

Provenance [Scott and Fowles, New York]; Taft collection, Nov. 23, 1908.

Literature Arthur Hoeber, *The Barbizon Painters*, New York, 1915, p. 164; Maurice W. Brockwell, *A Catalogue of Paintings in the Collection of Mr. and Mrs. Charles P. Taft*, New York, 1920, no. 48; *Catalogue of the Taft Museum*, Cincinnati, 1939 and 1958, no. 306.

1931.435

Pierre-Etienne-Théodore Rousseau

Paris 1812–1867 Barbizon

Rousseau was the only child of parents who were drapers in Paris; they sent him out of the city to be raised in Lagny (Seine-et-Marne).[1] When he returned for schooling, his artistic talents were encouraged by members of his mother's family. Her cousin, the landscape painter Pau de Saint-Martin, gave him his first lessons. Copying old engravings and exploring the Bois de Boulogne, Rousseau sought motifs for his first landscape drawings.

Rousseau's interest in landscape deepened when he spent the year of 1825 as a lumberman's apprentice in the wooded, hilly terrain of the Franche-Comté near the Alps. Although he next studied for the entrance exam to the Polytechnical School, he continued to paint on holidays in the country with Saint-Martin and in Paris with J.-C.-J. Rémond. Studying the seventeenth-century Dutch landscapes and the paintings of Claude Lorrain in the Louvre fortified his landscape techniques.

Hoping to enter the Ecole des Beaux-Arts, Rousseau studied in 1828 with Guillon-Lethière, a professor of figure drawing there. Guillon-Lethière also subscribed to the more liberal ideas about landscape studies that were introduced at the school in the 1820s. Under his careful tutelage Rousseau made his first paintings in the Fontainebleau region, working in the park of Chailly and in Moret, around 1829. His paintings began to show a romantic temperament influenced by artists such as Richard Parkes Bonington, Paul Huet, and Théodore Géricault, who used strong contrasts of light and shadow in their landscapes rather than the consistent tonal patterns of their classically trained professors. Inspired by the new generation and seeking more exotic motifs, Rousseau went to the Auvergne region in the summer of 1830 to find a more challenging landscape. Volcanic mountains, rough vegetation, and lurid sunsets dominated the canvases he brought back and with which he won the admiration of the painter Ary Scheffer, who introduced him to a circle of romantic artists, writers, and their patrons. Rousseau made his Salon debut in 1831 with an Auvergnat landscape that drew critical condemnation for its tormented, slashing brushwork. For five years his work drew mixed reviews from critics who never failed to note his originality.

In 1835 Rousseau produced a large canvas, *The Descent of the Cows in the Heights of the Jura,* to summarize his experience as a landscape painter. When the ambitious work was refused by the Salon jury of 1836, Scheffer displayed it publicly in his studio, and the critic Théophile Thoré hailed it as a work for all to see. The notoriety garnered by subsequent rejections by the Salon jury made Rousseau infamous as *le grand refusé.* The agitated surfaces and brilliant colors of his canvases won him both admirers and sales outside the Salon; thus he was well known when the Revolution of 1848 created a more liberal atmosphere for his triumphant return to the Salon of 1849. But the experience of rejection had left its mark, and critics would subsequently note a hesitation in his art manifested by the reworked surfaces he presented in Salon entries.

Rousseau found his name linked frequently with that of Camille Corot, although they were merely acquaintances. His long and influential artistic association was instead with the painter Jules Dupré, who seems to have coached him to transform his spontaneous responses to nature from sketches to more marketable canvases. Dupré was the better salesman of the two and acted as agent for Rousseau. Despite their evident amity throughout the 1840s, a rupture between them occurred in 1849 when Dupré received the Legion of Honor and Rousseau did not. Rousseau turned for companionship to a new friend in the village of Barbizon, the painter Jean-François Millet. Since 1837 Rousseau had rented a painting studio there each summer, and after the Revolution of 1848 Barbizon became his permanent residence.

During his mature years Rousseau's steady concentration on the motifs of a single district enabled him to bring forth works of great confidence and understanding of the region's environment. He became a conservationist, protective of the Forest of Fontainebleau, and organized protests against the government's program to cut down the trees. His letters to Napoléon III and

1931.429

to friends were filled with a reverence for the beauty of living things and especially of the great oaks in that once royal preserve.

1. On Rousseau, see Alfred Sensier, *Souvenirs sur Th. Rousseau*, Paris, 1872; Hélène Toussaint, *Théodore Rousseau, 1812–1867*, exh. cat., Musée du Louvre, Paris, 1967; Nicholas Green, *Théodore Rousseau*, exh. cat., Sainsbury Centre for the Visual Arts, University of East Anglia, Norwich, and Hazlitt, Gooden and Fox, London, 1982.

✍

Théodore Rousseau

The Pond (formerly Evening: Fontainebleau)

1844?
Oil on canvas, 38.7 x 46.7 cm (15¼ x 18⅜ in.)
Signed lower right: *TH. Rousseau*

In the foreground a small pool ringed with grasses and aquatic plants spreads out a shallow surface that catches the last rays of the setting sun. On its banks where two figures stand with a cow, sturdy oaks are rooted, and their low, spreading branches both shade the earth and reach up to fill the evening sky. To the right on the horizon, houses and more trees mark the outskirts of a village.

In many parts of France, stream-fed pools, called *mares*, provide water and convenient forage for farm animals kept within the neighboring villages. In surveying the body of Rousseau's work, one finds many such pastoral views in which he has assembled similar elements of water and terrain, wide horizons with broad, great trees used as vertical masses, and groups of figures with animals. By varying the time of day and weather conditions, Rousseau manipulated the mood that the painting was to convey to the viewer.

The setting of this painting appears to have been misstated when it was sold to the Tafts. Published in an early sale catalogue, it was identified only as *La Mare*.[1] The major features of the landscape are identical with those of a larger painting dated 1866 and titled *Landscape with Setting Sun in the Landes* (unlocated).[2] The region of the Landes was very popular with landscape painters, and Rousseau made a trip there in 1844 with Jules Dupré. The Taft painting may date from that trip and could have served as the model for the larger 1866 canvas.

In 1844 the influence of his friend Dupré was still a guiding force in Rousseau's handling of paint. The surfaces of *The Pond* are stitched together with small strokes of monochromatic earth tones over which the artist has embroidered more vivifying hues such as the greens that signify indeterminate vegetation. In what was more typically his own manner, Rousseau has reserved the most brilliant contrasts for the sky above the oaks, where clouds have massed in shapes that echo the oaks' darkened silhouettes. A blaze of late sunlight reflected on the clouds is like the sounding of a last melodic chord on wearied senses at day's end.

1. Unidentified sale catalogue in the files of the Rijksbureau voor Kunsthistorische Documentatie, the Hague.

2. Sale catalogue of the M. I. Montaginac collection, Dec. 3–4, 1917, no. 77; formerly in the collections Sabran-Ponteves and Jules Beer and shown at the Centennial Exhibition of French Art at the Universal Exposition of 1900 in Paris, no. 594.

Provenance [Scott and Fowles, New York]; Taft collection, Sept. 21, 1903.

Literature Unidentified sale cat., no. 53 (ill.), in the files of the Rijksbureau voor Kunsthistorische Documentatie, the Hague; Maurice W.

Brockwell, *A Catalogue of Paintings in the Collection of Mr. and Mrs. Charles P. Taft,* New York, 1920, no. 62; *Catalogue of the Taft Museum,* Cincinnati, 1939 and 1958, no. 282.

1931.429

Pierre-Etienne-Théodore Rousseau

Fontainebleau

ca. 1850
Oil on panel, 28.9 x 51.6 cm (11⅜ x 20⅜ in.)
Signed lower left: *TH. Rousseau*

The broad expanse of gently rolling terrain is marked by rocky outcroppings, grassy hillocks, and stands of oaks. Pathways wind among these features and pass behind a tiny pool at the center of the composition. A darkened sky with a formation of dense, low clouds seems to announce an approaching storm.

This painting has the consistent intensity of a sketch done to preserve an immediate reaction to a climatic event. In the execution of his study, Rousseau has worked toward a statement equating the implied weight of the lowering sky with the density of the land. Even though the site is a familiar stretch in the vast Fontainebleau preserves, he has merged the ominous sky and the uninhabited panorama, which offers no place of refuge, to create an image of remote desolation.

When the painting was catalogued for sale in 1900, the site was identified as the Gorges d'Apremont, a favorite vista for Rousseau and other painters living nearby in the village of Barbizon. However, such an identification can be disputed. Although the Forest of Fontainebleau now appears much more overgrown than it did in Rousseau's day, the Gorges d'Apremont offered then (and now) a far more dramatic array of rocky precipices. A more plausible, if less picturesque, location is the Plaine de Chamfroy, which is reached from the village of Arbonne-la-Forêt. There, the terrain is sandy and the vegetation is dense and low growing. Rousseau's landscape, which is knitted together with many fine strokes of ocher-toned paints laid down on the ground of the panel, resembles more closely the wastelands of the Plaine de Chamfroy where heather and wildflowers blend into a continuous herbal tapestry.

Presently it is difficult to establish a date for this oil sketch beyond the suggestion that it must be after 1849–50, when Rousseau began to live for lengthy periods in the village of Barbizon and to go each day to the locations in the Forest of Fontainebleau frequented by the landscape painters.

Provenance Auguste Rousseau; [Galerie Georges Petit, Sept. 3, 1900, no. 38 (as *Gorges d'Apremont, après la pluie;* also misidentified as on canvas)]; Cuthbertson; [Arthur Tooth and Sons]; Taft collection, Apr. 6, 1903.

Literature Maurice W. Brockwell, *A Catalogue of Paintings in the Collection of Mr. and Mrs. Charles P. Taft,* New York, 1920, no. 57 (misidentified as on canvas); *Catalogue of the Taft Museum,* 1939 and 1958, no. 444.

1931.423

Pierre-Etienne-Théodore Rousseau

The Pond at Dagneau [Dagnan] (Forest of Fontainebleau: On the Plateau of Belle-Croix)

1858–60
Oil on canvas, 63.5 x 102.9 cm (25 x 40½ in.)
Signed lower left: *TH Rousseau;* stamped lower right: *THR.*

From the deep distance a tree-lined pathway leads to a pool where two stately oaks flank its terminus at water's edge. In the foreground a series of broad, worn rocks and low vegetation make an irregular but pervasive surface pattern. At the left in a zone between the pool and the distant plain, the faint outlines of a woodsman's thatched-roof hut are visible.

1931.423

1931.413

The pool (*mare*) reflects the light of a summery sky and the outlines of the great oaks above it. Although these pools were used as watering places for the peasants' herds, there is no sign of human or animal activity: both people and animals seem to have taken refuge from the midday heat but will find this pool and others like it at evening. Around the pool the ground has been stripped of trees except for a few misshapen trunks and thickets of brush rejected by the lumbermen who have cleared the forest. The full extent of their labors is revealed in the broad open plain in the distance where the light is most intense.

Rousseau's biographer, Alfred Sensier, may have owned a study for the Taft painting entitled *La Mare*, which was in the A. Loria collection, London.[1] Calling *The Pond at Dagneau* a masterpiece, Sensier also provided its date when the painting was sold with the artist's effects after his death.[2]

As this painting proves, it was during the late 1850s that Rousseau achieved his most successfully unified landscape transcriptions. These are works in which he has concentrated myriad observations on vegetation and terrain, climate, season, and time of day so that certain paintings, and this one in particular, seem to vibrate with hyperreality. Such works might cause one to wonder if Rousseau sensed the impending competition of the great photographers, who, like him, wanted to capture exact renditions of nature's majesty in both mundane and majestic details.

Sensier may be responsible for the misspelling of the location Rousseau painted. There is a Mare à Dagneau (but not *Dagnan*) near the Plateau of Belle-Croix, a region that Rousseau frequented to paint the small panels that he later developed into large canvases like the Taft painting. The Mare à Dagneau is clearly marked on current maps of the Forest of Fontainebleau. It is near the Mare à Piat, which today is identified by a sign posted at a crossroad in the forest. Although it is marked on maps, there are no signposts for the Mare à Dagneau, nor can one recognize which of the many forest pools Rousseau might have painted, because the lumbermen have left and the forest has reclaimed the Plateau of Belle-Croix.

Fig. 1 Pierre-Etienne-Théodore Rousseau, *La Mare*, n.d. Oil on panel, 26.7 x 41 cm (10⅝ x 16⅛ in.). Photograph courtesy of Hazlitt, Gooden and Fox gallery files, London.

1. Nicholas Green, *Théodore Rousseau, 1812–1867*, exh. cat., Sainsbury Centre for the Visual Arts, University of East Anglia, Norwich, and Hazlitt, Gooden and Fox, London, 1982, no. 54, oil on panel, 27 x 41 cm, formerly in the collection of Mrs. A. Loria from the gallery of Hazlitt, Gooden and Fox, 1958. The Hazlitt gallery files have furnished a photograph of a second *La Mare* (fig. 1), an oil study on panel, 10⅝ x 16⅛ in., thought to have been in the Loria collection although not sold by their gallery.

2. Rousseau sale, Hôtel Drouot, Paris, Apr. 27, 1868, no. 37.

Provenance The artist (sale, Hôtel Drouot, Paris, Apr. 27, 1868, no. 37); Camondo (sale, Galerie Georges Petit, Feb. 1, 1893, no. 81); [Scott and Fowles, New York]; Taft collection, Oct. 28, 1909.

Exhibitions Milwaukee Art Museum, *1888: Frederick Layton and His World*, Apr. 7–Aug. 28, 1988 (cat. by James Mundy, p. 132, ill. p. 133); Manchester, N.H., The Currier Gallery of Art [also New York, Dallas, and Atlanta], *The Rise of Landscape Painting in France: Corot to Monet*, Jan. 29, 1991–Mar. 29, 1992 (cat. by Kermit S. Champa et al., pp. 211–12, no. 106, ill. p. 215).

Literature Arthur Hoeber, *The Barbizon Painters*, New York, 1915, p. 237; Maurice W. Brockwell, *A Catalogue of Paintings in the Collection of Mr.*

Jean-François Millet
Gruchy 1814–1875 Barbizon

In the small coastal community of Gruchy not far from Cherbourg, Millet was born to a Norman peasant couple who were successful farmers.[1] The parish school of the nearby village of Greville provided him with a solid education in Latin and an appreciation of great authors from the ancients to the moderns. While a teenager his artistic talents were revealed, and in 1833 he began studies in Cherbourg with the portrait painter Dumouchel. Making good progress, Millet was released from his agricultural chores in 1835, so he could study full-time with Lucien Théophile Langlois, a pupil of the baron Gros, who advised him to copy paintings in the Cherbourg museum as preparation for entry into the Ecole des Beaux-Arts in Paris. After Millet had studied for two years, Langlois and a committee of local artists pressed the city council of Cherbourg to award Millet a stipend to study in Paris, and he was able to enter the studio of Paul Delaroche, a successful history painter.

His meager allowance and rustic manners made life in Paris difficult, but Millet found joy and inspiration in the museums. He failed in his first attempt at the Rome Prize (1838) and had his first Salon submission rejected, but he found he could supplement his stipend by selling pastels done in the still-popular style of Boucher and Watteau. Abandoning the studio of Delaroche where he had never been truly welcome, he suffered the loss of his Cherbourg scholarship. But Millet had begun to find a style of his own and had learned to pursue success outside the academic establishment.

Despite the expenses of urban life, Millet's desire to study the masters kept him in Paris. In Cherbourg on vacations he painted portraits for a living and had one of them accepted by the Salon jury in 1840. The following year he married into an extensive bourgeois family who gave him more portrait commissions. He executed these and other commissions from 1840 through 1845 in a realistic manner. At the same time he maintained an elegant pseudo-eighteenth-century style of painting in oils, his so-called *manière fleurie,* which dominated his work from about 1844 to 1847 and which he used for genre subjects that bore witness both to the multiple influences of his museum studies and to his emulation of the successful example of the painter Narcisse Diaz de la Peña with whom he became friends in 1847.

Millet and his wife, Pauline Ono, settled in Paris in 1842, but her health was fragile and she died of consumption in the spring of 1844. Millet returned to Cherbourg where he met Catherine Lemaire, a domestic servant, who became his companion and eventually bore him nine children. They were married in a civil ceremony only after the death of Millet's mother in 1853. A religious ceremony was performed in January 1875, the month of the artist's death.

Millet spent 1845 in Le Havre working as a portraitist, and until 1849 the couple lived in Paris where Millet was part of a circle that included the artists Charles Jacque, Honoré Daumier, and Théodore Rousseau along with Constant Troyon and Diaz. Alfred Sensier, a civil servant, became his patron, agent, and, ultimately, biographer. Millet won Salon acceptance in 1847 with the classical subject of Oedipus, and his first public success when a government official purchased *The Winnower,* a realistic subject, from the unjuried Salon of 1848.

Millet was admired by younger French painters and by intellectuals for his themes of agriculture and daily life among the peasants, showing deep respect for their human dignity. In 1849 Millet fulfilled a state commission with *Harvesters' Rest* (Paris, Musée d'Orsay), and in that year he settled his growing family in the village of Barbizon at the edge of the Fontainebleau forest, where he concentrated on depicting peasant life.

During the 1850s Millet made contacts with collectors and artists from Boston, eventually establishing his American reputation, which led to the American fondness for the Barbizon painters. His success was secured in 1867 when his art received a major showing at the Universal Exposition. In 1874 he was among the artists who received commissions to paint scenes from the life of Saint Geneviève, patron saint of Paris, in the Panthéon. But his preparatory studies were halted by his failing health, and he died at Barbizon in January 1875.

1. On Millet, see Alfred Sensier, *La Vie de J. F. Millet,* Paris, 1881; Julia Cartwright, *Jean François Millet: His Life and Letters,* 1st ed., 1896, London, 1902; Robert Herbert, *Jean-François Millet,* exh. cat., Arts Council of Great Britain, London, 1976; Alexandra R. Murphy, *Millet,* exh. cat., Museum of Fine Arts, Boston, 1984.

Jean-François Millet

Mother and Child

ca. 1846–48
Oil on canvas, 40.6 x 32.7 cm (16 x 12⅞ in.)
Signed lower right: *J.F. Millet*

Turning her back to the viewer as she mounts a pathway in a hilly landscape, a young mother strides forward, bearing her child slung over her right hip, so that the child's legs dangle freely behind her. Their faces are not visible. Only the crown of the child's tousled head appears above the curve of its mother's right arm, and her face is a silhouetted lost profile set against a cloudy sky. Around them the landscape seems arid and remote, creating a sense of isolation furthered by their retreating figures.

Having returned to Paris in 1845 after a year's stay in Le Havre with his new companion, Catherine Lemaire, Millet pursued the painting of landscapes and genre pictures for which he found a waiting market. As the couple's first children were born in 1846 and 1847, the artist had a growing family to support.

As a group, these works share features of draftsmanship and execution noted by Robert Herbert in 1966 when he compared *Mother and Child* (Taft) to *Woman Feeding Chickens* (fig. 1, The

1931.422

Fig. 1 Jean-François Millet, *Woman Feeding Chickens*, ca. 1846–48. Oil on canvas, 45.8 x 38.2 cm (18 x 15 in.). The Art Institute of Chicago, Henry Field Memorial Collection, 1894.1064. Photograph © 1992 The Art Institute of Chicago. All rights reserved.

Art Institute of Chicago) and gave both the same dates.[1] Discussing *Woman Feeding Chickens* and *The Bather,* also in Chicago, Herbert pointed out "the simple division of backgrounds into two or three generalized zones and the curious compression of the feet: the upper instep and ankle are attached to the sole with no substance intervening."[2] The Taft's striding young mother also has this feature.

Herbert observed that all these paintings have a thick and stuccolike paint surface. *Mother and Child* has a palette of warm reds, golden ochers, and blues like the Chicago paintings, and Millet's very tactile modeling gives their figures the same vigor and monumental stature, despite their small scale. Herbert ascribes this "more sculptural concept of the human body" to Millet's studies of Michelangelo and Poussin.

In the Taft painting the influence of Millet's appreciation for Michelangelo's figure drawings is apparent in the elongated, muscular proportions of the mother's retreating back. Her grasp on her struggling child, awkward but realistic, might have a different source in Rembrandt's *Ganymede Being Carried Off by Jupiter* (1635, Dresden, Gemäldegalerie), although Michelangelo also made well-known drawings of this subject. Millet was not unfamiliar with erotic subjects, but here he has discreetly changed the child's pose to conceal its gender and modestly draped its buttocks while continuing to assert the child's helplessness in the grip of motherly love.[3]

1. Robert Herbert, "Millet Reconsidered," *Museum Studies I* [The Art Institute of Chicago] (1966), p. 57.

2. Herbert, pp. 32–33.

3. Herbert argued for a down-to-earth reading of Millet's character rather than the nineteenth-century myth of his devout nature finding expression in his art. He was, Herbert observed, a superb painter of the female nude; and, quoting Sensier in a catalogue entry (*Jean-François Millet,* Arts Council of Great Britain, London, 1976, no. 15, *Garden of Love*), Herbert noted that erotic subjects were common during Millet's early years.

Provenance V. Claude (sale, 1853, no. 58?); [Scott and Fowles, New York]; Taft collection, Nov. 10, 1903.

Literature Arthur Hoeber, *The Barbizon Painters,* New York, 1915, ill. opp. p. 38; Maurice W. Brockwell, *A Catalogue of Paintings in the Collection of Mr. and Mrs. Charles P. Taft,* New York, 1920, no. 52; *Catalogue of the Taft Museum,* Cincinnati, 1939 and 1958, no. 305; Robert Herbert, "Millet Reconsidered," *Museum Studies I* [The Art Institute of Chicago] (1966), p. 57.

1931.422

Jean-François Millet

Maternité: A Young Mother Cradling Her Baby

1870–73
Oil on canvas, 122.2 x 90.7 cm (48⅛ x 35¾ in.)
Signed lower right: *J.F. Millet*

Seated on a wooden chair in a darkened interior space, a young mother cradles her child between her knees. The child's legs and torso have been swaddled into a solid mass giving the figure a cruciform shape. Behind the mother's shoulder on the wall a small household shrine with a crucifix is barely visible in the shadowy gloom. The child's face and body glow with light that radiates upward onto the pensive face of the mother. Her unfixed stare, both tender and sorrowful, is poignantly contrasted to the innocent face of her sleeping child.

Millet painted the subject of the mother-and-child relationship throughout his long career. Surely he was an expert observer since he was the father of nine children and several times a grandfather. In his earliest treatments of this theme he emphasized acts of nurture or instruction in the ways of daily life. Settings in cottages and farmyards predominated, and the works were modestly sized for sale by his dealers.

Apart from its domestic setting, the Taft painting is quite different from the earlier works in both scale and depth of emotion. The only close comparison is a painting of 1870–72, *Woman Sewing by Lamplight* (New York, The Frick Collection), since it is nearly the same size and its composition stresses the intimate relationship of a mother and her baby who lies sleeping in a cradle beside her.[1] The Frick's seamstress, however, conveys placid contentment and none of the lonely sorrow that the Taft's mother painfully projects.

According to Sensier, *Maternité* was begun in 1870 in Cherbourg where Millet had gone when Barbizon was occupied by the Prussians. It was completed during 1872–73 when Millet was already suffering from the illness that would lead to his death in January 1875.[2] At his home in Barbizon, surrounded by his family, including his daughter Margaret Heyman who posed for this painting,[3] Millet worked intermittently as his declining health permitted. Meditating on his own mortality, Millet reinterpreted the traditional *pietà* by placing the tightly bound body of the sleeping child to suggest the corpus of Christ lying across the madonna's lap.

Three preparatory sketches for this painting are known. The Art Institute of Chicago has a pencil drawing, *Head of a Peasant Woman,* in which Robert Herbert discerns "a nearly palpable sense of the burdens of maternity."[4] The Worcester Art Museum has a study in pencil with traces of color applied on the edge for the hands that appear in the painting (fig. 1). In the Budapest Museum of Fine Arts there is a sketch for the group (fig. 2).

1. Bernice Davidson assisted by Edgar Munhall, *Paintings in the Frick Collection: French, Italian and Spanish,* vol. II, New York, 1968, pp. 157–60.

2. Alfred Sensier, *La Vie de J.-F. Millet,* Paris, 1881, p. 349.

1931.448

3. Julia Cartwright, *Jean-François Millet: His Life and Letters,* 1st ed., 1896, London, 1902, p. 332.

4. Robert Herbert, *Jean-François Millet,* exh. cat., Arts Council of Great Britain, London, 1976, p. 166, no. 106, 21.5 x 18 cm.

Provenance The artist (studio sale, May 10, 1875, no. 46, to Charles Tillot); George W. Burnett, London; [Scott and Fowles, New York]; Taft collection, Sept. 19, 1903.

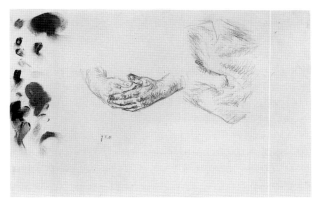

Fig. 1 Jean-François Millet, *Studies for "La Maternité,"* ca. 1870–73. Graphite and oil on paper, 20.3 x 31.8 cm (7⅞ x 12⅜ in.). Worcester Art Museum, gift of Mr. and Mrs. Daniel Catton Rich.

Fig. 2 Jean-François Millet, *Study for "La Maternité,"* ca. 1870–73. Chalk on paper, 16.5 x 12.1 cm (6½ x 4¾ in.). The Budapest Museum of Fine Arts.

Literature Alfred Sensier, *La Vie de Jean-François Millet*, Paris, 1881, p. 349; D. Croal Thomson, *The Barbizon School*, London, 1902, pp. 237–38, ill. p. 240; Julia Cartwright, *Jean-François Millet: His Life and Letters*, 1st ed., 1896, London, 1902, p. 332; Gustave Geffroy and Arsène Alexandre, *Corot and Millet*, ed. Charles Holme, New York, 1903, pl. M24; Maurice W. Brockwell, *A Catalogue of Paintings in the Collection of Mr. and Mrs. Charles P. Taft*, New York, 1920, no. 12; *Catalogue of the Taft Museum*, Cincinnati, 1939 and 1958, no. 482 (fig. 30, 1939 ed.); Robert Herbert, *Jean-François Millet*, exh. cat., Arts Council of Great Britain, London, 1976, p. 166; Ruth Krueger Meyer, "The Taft Collection: The First Ten Years of Its Development," *The Taft Museum: A Cincinnati Legacy*, Cincinnati, 1988, p. 11 (ill.).

1931.448

Charles-François Daubigny

Paris 1817–1875 Paris

Born in Paris to a family of painters, Daubigny might have been raised in a studio except that his health was poor and he was placed with a nurse in rural Valmondois until he was nine.[1] Returning to Paris, he joined his sisters in the family profession and, with little conventional schooling, began contributing to the household income. His father, Edmé, had trained with Jean-Victor Bertin, the teacher of academic landscape painting, and he gave the children lessons, as did their uncle Pierre and the family friends, artists Léopold Robert and Jacques Brascassat. Despite this background, Charles-François always thought the country childhood spent near the river Oise had been his strongest formative influence.

By the age of fifteen Daubigny was making copies of paintings in the Louvre, working in its restoration studios, and studying engraving techniques. These skills supported further academic study with Senties and permitted Daubigny's only trip to Italy in 1836. Twenty years old at the time of his return, he was then fully committed to seeking a professional career as a painter through the channels of academic recognition. He prepared his work for the landscape prize competition scheduled for 1840 and made ready his entries to the annual Salons. A view of Paris was accepted in the 1838 Salon, and two landscapes based on his Italian studies qualified in 1840. But the landscape prize that would have taken him back to Italy eluded him.

Throughout this time Daubigny expanded his career through the media of etching and engraving and showed six etchings in addition to a painting in the Salon of 1841. With a group of friends from his student days, he collaborated on a steady stream of etching commissions. He married in 1842 and took up residence on the Ile Saint-Louis in company with these other artists. During the next six years, Daubigny's illustrations supported the additions to his family of a daughter, Cécile, and a son, Charles (later called Karl). Both children continued the family artistic tradition, and Karl gained some individual fame before an early death.

In honor of political liberation and the founding of the Second Republic, the Salon of 1848 accepted all works presented. With six paintings entered, Daubigny won a second-class medal

and his first official commission for an etching after a drawing in the national museum. His success in graphic arts provided his income and sustained his reputation during the 1850s until the critics began to notice his paintings. Most found fault with his "unfinished" manner of presenting his direct observations from nature and linked Daubigny's name with that of Corot, against whom they levied similar reproaches. Thus united in the press, the two artists became friends and painting companions despite a twenty-year difference in age.

Soon, a migrating colony of artists had gathered around Corot and Daubigny as they moved from Barbizon to Burgundy, from the seacoast of Honfleur to the Oise River near Auvers. In 1857 Daubigny bought a boat and named it *Le Botin* for its boxlike appearance. It became his floating studio, and he cruised the Seine and the Oise in search of motifs. Daubigny's three paintings in the Taft collection probably derive from his seasonal navigations over a twenty-year period.

As he increased his direct contacts with nature and particularly with water, Daubigny's paintings lost whatever remained from his student years of the classical landscape tradition. Abandoning the complicated schemes of recession Corot still maintained, Daubigny explored the means of rendering atmosphere and the effects of light on relatively commonplace vistas. He perfected a single compositional format showing the near and far banks of a river flowing diagonally from one corner of the canvas to a midpoint on the opposite edge where an acute intersection with the horizon line occurs. On this structure he could work endless variations and give full play to his interest in waterside communities and their activities. Villages alternated with open fields, boatmen changed places with herdsmen watering their animals, and rows of trees or well-trodden paths were used as counterpoint to the tranquil harmony of diagonal and horizontal. The simplicity of these scenes drew increasing attention to Daubigny's sketchy handling of paint, and critics, while lamenting a lack of finished perfection, soon spoke of the "impressions" of nature that he offered.

Claude Monet was Daubigny's specific heir. They had met while painting on the seacoast near Trouville, and Monet subsequently visited the older artist at his studio on the Oise. They met again in London where both had fled the Franco-Prussian war, and Daubigny was able to recommend the young Monet to his dealer, Durand-Ruel. Back in Paris when exhibition activity was reinstated after the establishment of the Third Republic, Daubigny and Corot resumed their prewar role as champions of Monet and a group of younger artists who were then experimenting with the techniques of painting outdoors that their elders had initiated. In 1873 Daubigny was finally given the accolade of reception into the Legion of Honor, while conservative critics continued to bemoan the lack of finish in his work. But like Corot, with whom he shared this new "impressionistic" technique, Daubigny found success in his last years as the affirmation of the influence of direct observation in nature gained popularity.

1. On Daubigny, see Etienne Moreau-Nélaton, *Daubigny raconté par lui-même*, Paris, 1925; Madeleine Fidell-Beaufort and Janine Bailly-

1931.463

Herzberg, *Daubigny: La Vie et l'oeuvre*, Paris, 1975; Robert Hellebranth, *Charles-François Daubigny, 1817–1878*, Morges, 1976; *Charles-François Daubigny, 1817–1878: Dessins, gravures, peintures*, exh. cat., Hôtel de Ville d'Aulnay-sous-Bois, 1990.

Charles-François Daubigny

A River Scene: The Ferryboat at Bonnières

1861
Oil on canvas, 57.2 x 93.3 cm (22½ x 36¾ in.)
Signed and dated lower left: *C. Daubigny, 1861.*

At twilight a boatman poles a ferryboat loaded with farm animals from a wooded bank on the left to a village on the river's edge at the right. From the vantage point of his studio boat at midstream, Daubigny chose to fill the foreground of the painting with calm waters in which the houses, shorelines, and boat with its occupants are reflected. The reddish tones of a sunset alter the green landscape to earthy siennas and umbers and give the water a gold cast.

Hellebranth catalogued the Taft painting of this view on the Seine near Bonnières, a town northwest of Paris above Mantes-la-Jolie, along with four others. Two paintings he believed to precede it are small works on panel and are dated 1857 (fig. 1) and 1860.[1] The Taft painting, listed next, is a medium-size canvas and within the group is unique for its ferryboat motif.[2] *Village near Bonnières*, the fourth and largest canvas of this group, also signed and dated 1861, is said to have been shown in the Salon of 1861 along with four other paintings by Daubigny.[3] His Salon entries of that year drew hostile attacks from several critics for their lack of finish, although L. Auvray excepted the *Village near Bonnières* as "the only one of the five paintings in which we find the artist showing any traces of talent."[4]

The Taft painting bears comparison with another suite of views painted nearby in 1858–59. Four paintings catalogued by Hellebranth (nos. 81–84) are views of the village of Glouton, and three of them show a ferryboat near a riverbank bordered with a row of cottages (fig. 2). Glouton is a small village stretching along the north bank of the Seine opposite Bonnières. There

Fig. 1 Charles-François Daubigny, *The Village of Glouton.* 1857. Oil on panel, 29.8 x 53.5 cm (11¾ x 21⅛ in.). The Fine Arts Museums of San Francisco, Mildred Anna Williams Collection, 1940.4.

Fig. 2 Charles-François Daubigny, *Riverbank, Herd Drinking*, 1859. Oil on panel, 36.5 x 66 cm (14½ x 26 in.). The Brooklyn Museum, William H. Herriman Bequest.

are small islands in the river at this point, and the land mass to the right in three of the Glouton canvases may be one of them. Since Bonnières lies inland from the river Oise, it may be the village of Glouton that is shown in all these paintings. From this group of nine works dated over a period of four years, one can see Daubigny's allegiance to particular vistas where he must have moored *Le Botin* repeatedly to reconsider the motifs they provided at different times of day.

1. Robert Hellebranth, *Charles-François Daubigny, 1817–1878*, Morges, 1976, nos. 76 (see fig. 1), 77 (unlocated).

2. Hellebranth, no. 78, *Le Passage du Bac à Bonnières*.

3. Hellebranth, no. 79, *The Village of Bonnières at Twilight* (United States, private collection); no. 80, the fifth of the sequence, is known only from an old photograph.

4. L. Auvray, *Salon de 1861*, p. 50 (as cited in Pierre Miquel, *Le Paysage français au XIXe siècle*, vol. III, Maurs-la-Jolie, 1975, p. 686): "le seul des cinq tableaux dans lequel on retrouve quelques traces du talent qu'a montré cet artiste."

Provenance Alexander Young, London; [Scott and Fowles, New York]; Taft collection, 1907.

Literature Arthur Hoeber, *The Barbizon Painters*, New York, 1915, p. 251, as *On the Seine*; Maurice W. Brockwell, *A Catalogue of Paintings in the Collection of Mr. and Mrs. Charles P. Taft*, New York, 1920, no. 50; *Catalogue of the Taft Museum*, Cincinnati, 1939 and 1958, no. 443; Robert Hellebranth, *Jean-François Daubigny, 1817–1878*, Morges, 1976, no. 78.

1931.463

Charles-François Daubigny

Evening on the Oise

1863
Oil on canvas, 99.7 x 200 cm (39¼ x 78¾ in.)
Signed and dated lower left: *Daubigny 1863*

The fading light of day softens the grassy riverbanks that border a broad reach of the river Oise at a site near Bonneville. The river cuts diagonally from the lower right of the canvas into the middle distance where the intersecting planes of the bank meet in recession. One can see the tip of a small island, which is probably the one near Vaux, a hamlet downriver from Auvers-sur-Oise where Daubigny had his studio. Cattle and a plowman with his horse are on the near bank. The distant bank is shrouded by the misty, riverine atmosphere, and its blurry outlines are reflected with scant transformation by the surface of the river. The dominant horizontals of the river and its shores are gently punctuated by vertical stands of trees posed to mark recession into the distance. Above all this tranquility, the evening sky is spread with a thin layer of clouds illuminated by a pale orange and pink light.

The substantial dimensions of this canvas indicate that it was painted indoors and may have been intended to be a Salon submission.[1] Dated 1863, it was not shown there until 1866 when it was paired with a similar but contrasting composition titled

Morning on the Oise, which is slightly smaller and dated 1866 (fig. 1).[2] The elements of both works are much the same, although the handling of paint in *Morning* is slightly less forceful, suggesting the absence of an originating motif and a desire to create a contrasting vista and contrasts of light more than the feeling of discovery one might experience in a new subject. It also shows no effects of varnish and therefore has a much drier surface. The contrasts of light and shade are also more muted; perhaps the light in the morning produces more even tonalities than that of evening, as seen in the Taft painting.

Presentation of these complementary canvases devoted to nothing more than the portrayal of light effects on the same stretch of river, taken facing in opposite directions, placed Daubigny among the mid-nineteenth-century landscape painters who influenced the later development of impressionism. In 1866 Daubigny was elected for the first time to the Salon jury where he won the inclusion of a work by Camille Pissarro and defended Paul Cézanne's and Auguste Renoir's submissions, which were not admitted.

Hellebranth has catalogued a number of smaller paintings that may have served as models for the Taft work, including especially several works on the type of wooden panels Daubigny used for studies done aboard *Le Botin*. Two typical works from the Eberstadt and Altman collections are now in the Metropolitan Museum of Art, New York (fig. 2).[3]

Daubigny sent *Evening on the Oise* to an exhibition in Brussels where it won him the cross of a Knight in the Order of Leopold.[4] In 1919 the English author John Galsworthy and his wife visited Cincinnati and saw this painting in the Music Room of the Tafts' residence on Pike Street. The writer's appreciation of the painting was conveyed in his novel *Swan Song* (chap. 13) by a character who makes reference to "a very fine landscape" seen while on an American journey. Ava Galsworthy confirmed her husband's sentiment in a letter to the Taft Museum dated December 25, 1932.

1. Robert Hellebranth, *Charles-François Daubigny, 1817–1878*, Morges, 1976, no. 266.

Fig. 1 Charles-François Daubigny, *Morning on the Oise*, 1866. Oil on canvas. Rouen, Musée des Beaux-Arts.

1931.462

1976, no. 266.

2. Hellebranth, no. 279, *Effet du matin, sur l'Oise*, Rouen (Salon of 1866, no. 496). See also M. de Fontifaud, *L'Artiste*, p. 177 (as cited in Pierre Miquel, *Le Paysage français au XIXe siècle*, vol. III, Maurs-la-Jolie, 1975, p. 692).

3. Hellebranth, nos. 264 (see fig. 2), 272 (*Landscape on a River*, 21 x 38.1 cm, inv. no. 64.149.7).

4. Miquel, vol. III, p. 692.

Provenance Lady Ashburton, London; [Arthur Tooth and Sons]; Taft collection, 1902.

Exhibitions Paris, Salon of 1866, no. 497; Brussels, 1866; Manchester, N.H., The Currier Gallery of Art [also New York and Dallas], *The Rise of Landscape Painting in France: Corot to Monet*, Jan. 29, 1991–Jan. 5, 1992 (cat. by Kermit S. Champa et al., p. 151, no. 52).

Literature Charles F. Fowles, *The Art Collection of Mr. and Mrs. Charles P. Taft, Cincinnati, Ohio*, privately printed, 1902; Arthur Hoeber, *The Barbizon Painters*, New York, 1915, p. 259 (ill.); Maurice W. Brockwell, *A Catalogue of Paintings in the Collection of Mr. and Mrs. Charles P. Taft*, New York, 1920, no. 46; *Catalogue of the Taft Museum*, Cincinnati, 1939 and 1958, no. 313; Madeleine Fidell-Beaufort and Janine Bailly-Herzberg, *Daubigny: La Vie et l'oeuvre*, Paris, 1975, p. 149, no. 78; Pierre Miquel, *Le Paysage français au XIXe siècle*, vol. III, Maurs-la-Jolie, 1975, p. 692; Robert Hellebranth, *Charles-François Daubigny, 1817–1878*, Morges, 1976, no. 266; David Torbet Johnson, "Taft Museum," *Ventura*, vol. IV, no. 16 (June–Aug. 1991), p. 135 (ill.).

1931.462

Fig. 2 Charles-François Daubigny, *The Banks of the Oise*, 1863. Oil on wood, 37.5 x 67 cm (14¾ x 26⅜ in.). New York, The Metropolitan Museum of Art, bequest of Benjamin Altman, 1913 (14.40.815).

☙

Charles-François Daubigny

Evening Solitude

1867
Oil on panel, 24.8 x 40.6 cm (9¾ x 16 in.)
Signed and dated lower right: *Daubigny 1867*

The banks of a stream seem to converge as it narrows to a recessed inlet. Plunged into twilit darkness, land and water almost merge while the sky still glows with light. The dense vegetation along the stream banks, the lack of human habitation, and the tranquil passage of three ducks on the water's calm surface suggest a spot of remote seclusion.

Hellebranth catalogued this work and identified it as a scene along a river near Corbigny in the Morvan section of Burgundy.[1] Since Daubigny is not known to have visited that region after 1855, the date of 1867 on this study may refer to the date it was signed and left the artist's studio. In 1867 Daubigny made a trip in *Le Botin* up the Oise to Compiègne and also journeyed in Brittany but probably did not visit Burgundy.

1931.426

Fig. 1 Charles-François Daubigny, *A River Landscape with Storks*, 1864. Oil on wood, 24.1 x 44.8 cm (9½ x 17⅝ in.). New York, The Metropolitan Museum of Art, bequest of Benjamin Altman, 1913 (14.40.818).

Fig. 2 Charles-François Daubigny, *A Brook*. Oil on canvas, 27.3 x 34.3 cm (10¾ x 13½ in.). Philadelphia Museum of Art, The John G. Johnson Collection.

Evening Solitude is grouped by Hellebranth with other works on panel, some signed and dated, on the basis of the similarities of the site and the consistently intense observation of foliage and wildlife the artist displayed. Different from the cultivated banks of the Seine and Oise, the Morvan would have offered wild and unpopulated scenery like that also shown in *A River Landscape with Storks*, signed and dated 1864 (fig. 1);[2] *A Brook*, signed but not dated (fig. 2);[3] and *River near Corbigny*, signed but not dated.[4]

1. Robert Hellebranth, *Charles-François Daubigny, 1817–1878*, Morges, 1976, no. 475, *Riverbank with Ducks, near Corbigny*.

2. Hellebranth, no. 474.

3. Hellebranth, no. 478.

4. Hellebranth, no. 479, Seattle Art Museum.

Provenance Georges Lutz, Paris (sale, Galerie Georges Petit, 1902, no. 44); [Arthur Tooth and Sons]; Taft collection, Oct 20, 1902.

Literature Charles F. Fowles, *The Art Collection of Mr. and Mrs. Charles P. Taft, Cincinnati, Ohio*, privately printed, 1902; Maurice W. Brockwell, *A Catalogue of Paintings in the Collection of Mr. and Mrs. Charles P. Taft*, New York, 1920, no. 60; *Catalogue of the Taft Museum*, Cincinnati, 1939 and 1958, no. 278 (ill., 1958 ed.); Robert Hellebranth, *Charles-François Daubigny, 1817–1878*, Morges, 1976, no. 475.

1931.426

Hague School Paintings

Ann H. Murray

Jozef Israëls

Groningen 1824–1911 The Hague (Scheveningen)

When he died in 1911 at the age of eighty-seven, Jozef Israëls was considered to be the most famous Dutch painter of his century. He was the son of devout Jewish parents who, despite their limited financial means, encouraged his artistic inclinations. From 1835 to 1838 he attended the Academy of Minerva in Groningen where he studied drawing with Johan Joeke Gabriël van Wicheren and painting with Cornelis Bernardus Buys. In 1842 he became a pupil of Jan Adam Kruseman in Amsterdam. He also enrolled at the Amsterdam Academy where he took evening classes taught by Jan Willem Pieneman. Both Kruseman and Pieneman catered to the fashionable demand for portraits and dramatic narrative paintings.

A turning point of sorts occurred in 1845 when Israëls saw Ary Scheffer's painting *Gretchen at the Spinning Wheel* exhibited in Amsterdam. Inspired by Scheffer's example, he left for Paris where for two years he followed a grueling regimen of study. He spent long mornings making drawings after plaster casts and eventually drawing from the live model in the studio of François Picot. In the afternoons he copied paintings by Rembrandt, Raphael, and Velázquez in the Louvre, and from there he went to the School of Fine Arts where he studied with Jean-Jacques Pradier, Horace Vernet, and Paul Delaroche.

In 1847 Israëls returned to Amsterdam, where several of his paintings had been exhibited the previous year. There he relied on portraiture as a source of income while also painting genre subjects, which were to become the primary focus of his later work. For several more years, however, paintings such as *Ophelia (Day Dreaming)* (Dordrechts Museum),[1] which established his reputation in 1850, reflect the continuing influence of Scheffer. Encouraged by the success of *Ophelia,* he traveled to Düsseldorf in 1850, where he may have seen paintings by Rudolf Jordan, who had revived the peasant theme in Germany. Henry Ritter, a Canadian follower of Jordan who was training in Düsseldorf, is also credited with stimulating Israëls's interest in genre subjects at this time.[2] His return trip took him through the province of Gelderland, where he visited the village of Oosterbeek. Otherwise known as the Dutch "Barbizon," Oosterbeek was the site of an artists' colony where precursors of the Hague School, among them Johannes Bilders, whom Israëls met on his visit, were engaged in landscape painting.[3] From the late 1850s on, Oosterbeek's reputation as a center for sketching in the open air made it a favorite retreat for artists who later became part of the Hague School.

In 1853 Israëls made a second trip to Paris, where he visited Scheffer and, more importantly, went to the village of Barbizon and nearby Fontainebleau Forest, where French artists, including Théodore Rousseau, Camille Corot, Narcisse Virgile Diaz de la Peña, Charles-François Daubigny, and Constant Troyon, had painted landscapes for more than two decades. Although Israëls did not encounter the Barbizon artists on his pilgrimage, he was the first of the Hague School artists to explore this already famous region, where he sketched the simple dwellings and rustic interiors.[4] In fact, he was so impressed by the lives of the local peasants that he returned to Amsterdam having purchased several of their typical costumes for future reference.

The most crucial experience for Israëls's subsequent development occurred in Holland rather than abroad. While recuperating from an illness in 1855, he spent seven weeks in the remote fishing village of Zandvoort on the North Sea. As in Barbizon, he was immediately drawn to the local families whose humble existence was fraught with hardship and poverty. The following year this experience was reinforced by a briefer visit to Katwijk, also a fishing village, where he began to paint outdoors. After these sojourns the fashionable subjects of his earlier work declined in importance, as his already apparent inclination toward genre painting began to solidify.

In 1861 Israëls was recognized abroad by the acceptance of *Fishermen Carrying a Drowned Man* (London, National Gallery) in the annual Paris Salon. The next year he visited the International Exposition in London where the same painting received high acclaim. His reputation was now secure. In 1863 he married Aleida Schaap and, after the birth of a son and a daughter, turned with greater frequency to domestic scenes of mothers and children. His travels during this period included trips to Munich and Switzerland in 1869.

Another turning point in Israëls's career occurred in 1871 when he and his family moved from Amsterdam to the Hague. Here a number of younger artists already resided, including Jacob and Willem Maris, Jan Hendrik Weissenbruch, and Hendrik Willem Mesdag, who were soon to be joined by Johannes Bosboom and Anton Mauve. These artists, most of whom had rebelled against the kind of academic history and narrative painting that had initially won success for Israëls, were attracted to him because of his reputation. They in turn reinforced his preference for genre subjects. Israëls thus became the center of the group that, by the 1880s, was widely known as the Hague School.

Beginning in the 1870s, Israëls focused his attention on peasant folk, usually depicted in quiet moments of reflection or contemplation in their usual surroundings, which he eventually attempted to simulate by building a "peasant corner" in his garden in 1878. Although the Hague remained his primary residence, he continued to observe peasant life firsthand during summers spent amid the fishermen in nearby Scheveningen and brief trips to Katwijk and Laren as well as to parts of Brabant and Twente. It is uncertain to what extent his mood-evoking scenes were influenced by those of Jean-François Millet, the Barbizon painter whose work was certainly well known in the Hague. Israëls's Dutch contemporaries, perhaps out of nationalistic feeling, were fonder of comparing his low-key, almost monochromatic palette, sensitivity to light, and compassionate view of humanity to the work of their own countryman, Rembrandt.

From 1877 onward, Israëls regularly attended the Paris Salons with his family. In 1880 he developed a close friendship with the German painter Max Liebermann, who subsequently wrote his biography.[5] In the same year he met Edouard Manet in Paris. After the death of his wife in 1894, he extended his travels to Spain and North Africa as well as to England and Scotland.

During his lifetime, Israëls's reputation far exceeded that of any other modern Dutch painter. He belonged to the prestigious Arti et Amicitiae society in Amsterdam, and on his eightieth birthday in 1904 he received the Order of the Dutch Lion. In 1910, the year before his death, he traveled to Venice where his paintings were featured in a one-person exhibition. The mentor (and occasional teacher) of a host of younger Dutch artists, he managed to combine the lessons of the academy with the vision of Rembrandt, creating from this unlikely mix the poignant depictions of hardworking people whose way of life would soon succumb to the realities of an increasingly industrialized society.

1. A smaller version of the painting, 1859, was last known to be owned by R. Howitt, International Fine Arts Services, Cleveland, Ohio. Thanks to Dieuwertje Dekkers, Utrecht, the Netherlands, for bringing this information to our attention.

2. Ronald de Leeuw, John Sillevis, and Charles Dumas, eds., *The Hague School: Dutch Masters of the Nineteenth Century*, London, 1983, pp. 61, 189.

3. Israëls's meeting with Johannes Bilders, known as Bilders the Elder, is noted in De Leeuw et al., eds., p. 45. His son Gerard Bilders was of the same generation as the Maris brothers and Anton Mauve.

4. According to De Leeuw et al., eds., p. 45, Israëls first visited Barbizon in 1845. Generally, Israëls's first visit to the Barbizon area is dated to his second sojourn in France in 1853; see John Sillevis, *Dutch Drawings from the Age of Van Gogh from the Collection of the Haags Gemeentemuseum*, exh. cat., Taft Museum, Cinncinati, 1992, pp. 30–31.

5. Max Liebermann, "Jozef Israëls: The Man and His Work," *Pall Mall Magazine*, vol. xxv (1901), pp. 25–36. The original German text of this essay appeared in *Zeitschrift für Bildende Kunst*, vol. xii (1901), pp. 145–56, and was published separately as *Jozef Israëls*, Berlin, 1901.

Jozef Israëls

Pick-a-Back

ca. 1872
Oil on panel, 30.2 x 21.7 cm (11⅞ x 8½ in.)
Signed lower right: *Jozef Israëls*.

The theme of children wading, sailing toy boats, or playing on the beach recurs in Israëls's work. Generally called *Children of the Sea*, these scenes were inspired by his observations of fishermen and their families at Zandvoort, Katwijk, and Scheveningen. In many versions (which exist in both watercolor

1931.428

and oil) an older child, sometimes male and sometimes female, carries a toddler piggyback along the shore or in shallow water. In the present example, a boy wearing the local fisherman's cap and wooden shoes bends forward under the weight of a little girl in wooden shoes and a closely fitted bonnet.

Pick-a-Back has a close but somewhat larger and more detailed counterpart entitled *Coming Ashore* in the Toledo Museum of Art, Ohio. Also painted on panel, it has been dated about 1872 on the basis of its similarity to yet another related work of that year, which was illustrated in Jan Veth's book on the artist.[1] The broad handling suggests that *Pick-a-Back*, like *Coming Ashore*, was painted sometime during the early 1870s and in any case before Israëls's son, Isaac, began to influence his father toward more clearly articulated details, as in the Taft's *Sewing School at Katwijk*. Whether it predates the more precisely detailed *Coming Ashore* or was conceived as a study for it is impossible to determine, since the paired figures seem to have been stock types, which appear either in isolation or within larger groups in other paintings. For example, in *Children of the Sea* (Oshkosh, Wisc., Paine Art Center), Israëls has prominently incorporated the boy/girl pair among a larger group of children.

In beach scenes like *Pick-a-Back*, Israëls's sensitivity to the atmospheric effects of a seaside environment is evident. Even within the restricting vertical format, he has conveyed the open, airy quality of the shore at a moment when the sun is immediately to the left of the figures. The pair is summarily defined through broadly painted contrasts of light and dark tones, which are enlivened by warm yellow-white highlights that meld the girl and boy into a single unit at shoulder level and that brilliantly accentuate the little girl's shape against the blue sky. In the intensity of directed light, the duller tones of pants and jacket give way to accents of purer hue, notably in the boy's blue collar, the touches of yellow in his neckerchief, the girl's pink scarf, and the rosy tones of both faces. Sand and sea are less vibrant by comparison but are infiltrated nonetheless by blue and yellow. The fishing boat looms shadowlike in the distance, engulfed in an atmospheric haze and silhouetted in purple-gray against the brighter blue of the sky.

Loosely dabbed brushstrokes create an impression of splashing waves and the play of sunlight on forms — effects that Israëls began to observe and paint in the open air during his first visit to Katwijk in 1856. Unlike the French impressionists, however, he seems unconcerned with the specificity of time as indicated by light, since the shadow cast by the boat and the one that falls immediately in front of the figures are inconsistent with the light source and with the more pronounced horizontal shadow cast to the right of the boy. Israëls has suggested the typical quality of light rather than the instantaneous moment. Likewise, his figures, despite their motion, are timeless examples of the folk who inhabited these North Sea villages.

1. Jan Veth, *Josef Israëls and His Art,* Arnhem, 1904, no. 28.

Provenance [Scott and Fowles, New York]; Taft collection, Oct. 25, 1905.

Literature Maurice W. Brockwell, *A Catalogue of Paintings in the Collection of Mr. and Mrs. Charles P. Taft,* New York, 1920, no. 65; *Catalogue of the Taft Museum,* 1939 and 1958, no. 544.

1931.428

Jozef Israëls

Sewing School at Katwijk

1881
Oil on canvas, 111 x 144.7 cm (43¾ x 57 in.)
Signed lower right: *Jozef Israëls.*

Israëls returned periodically to the fishing village of Katwijk, which he first visited in 1856. Following his usual practice, he based *Sewing School at Katwijk* on numerous studies, including sketches in oil and watercolor as well as drawings in pencil and chalk.[1] One of these drawings elicited the admiration of Vincent van Gogh when he saw it exhibited at the Hague in 1881.[2] The final painting is considered to be among Israëls's finest and most ambitious works. Whereas most of his peasant interiors depict only one or two figures in a quiet, contemplative mood, the Taft painting includes eight young girls with their elderly teacher, all actively at work. Joseph de Gruyter has suggested that Israëls's interest in group activity at this time was influenced by the work of his new friend Max Liebermann, whom he had met in 1880.[3] Jan Veth has claimed that *Sewing School* was directly inspired by a multifigure composition titled *Bugle Practice* (The Hague, Rijksmuseum Hendrik Willem Mesdag), which was painted in the same year by Israëls's son, Isaac.[4] In any case, composing this many figures proved to be no easy task for the elder Israëls, as is indicated by radiographs of the painting taken during recent conservation treatment. These confirm that he changed the position of almost every head, perhaps most drastically that of the old woman whose head in the final version is located between earlier heads on either side, which were subsequently painted

1931.460

out. Other design revisions occur in the background and in the clothing.

As finally composed, the figures are carefully grouped with most of the girls clustered on the left; the teacher and a student seated opposite her are at a table on the right. The two halves of the composition are joined by a child who sits apart from the others in the center and faces directly outward. The dark interior is illuminated by bright outdoor light flooding through a window at the far right immediately next to the worktable. Each figure is sensitively modeled in relation to this single light source, and each face is individualized in its features and expression of concentration.

Within clearly drawn contours Israëls has applied the paint thickly in many layers, varying his brushstrokes to suggest a diversity of textures — fabrics with their subtle stripes and plaids, thread coiled on the lap of the girl at the table, and the nearby workbasket, in which each loosely brushed stroke provides a one-on-one equivalent for woven straw. The artist's inclusion of these and other props, such as foot warmers, potted plants, and a sleeping cat, enhance the authenticity of this humble peasant scene where the virtues of domestic work are learned at an early age.

Although Israëls's palette is most often described as monochromatic, *Sewing School at Katwijk*, which has recently benefited from cleaning, reveals his genuine sensitivity to color. A surprising array of blue, violet, dark pink, and ocher hues appears within the various fabric patterns, and flesh tones contain pinks and reds mixed with blue in the shaded areas. The view through the window suggests that Israëls was capable of approaching the pure colors of impressionism when these were appropriate to his subject.

Sewing School at Katwijk originally belonged to Scottish-born James Staats Forbes, who spent eighteen years in the Hague as a railway official. While living in the Netherlands, he became friends with Israëls and met other artists as well. Most of his collecting occurred after his return to London in 1861. Largely due to the efforts of the dealer Herman Gijsbert Tersteeg of Goupil and Co. in the Hague, Forbes amassed the largest private collection of Hague School and Barbizon paintings in Britain. His was one of several substantial collections in England, Canada, and the United States, countries where the Hague School attained its greatest popularity late in the nineteenth century.[5]

1. A nearly identical watercolor of the subject was acquired by the Rijksmuseum Vincent van Gogh in Amsterdam in 1989 (*Nineteenth-Century European and Important Hague School Pictures, Watercolours and Drawings*, Christie's, Amsterdam, Oct. 31, 1989, no. 240, *Sewing School at Katwijk*, 52 x 69.5 cm).

2. *The Complete Letters of Vincent van Gogh*, 2d ed., vol. I, Greenwich, Conn., 1959, letter 269, p. 553.

3. Joseph de Gruyter, *De Haagse School*, Rotterdam, vol. I, 1968–69, with English summaries, p. 59.

4. Ronald de Leeuw, "The Avant-Garde, 1885–1910," in *The Hague School: Dutch Masters of the Nineteenth Century*, eds., Ronald de Leeuw, John Sillevis, and Charles Dumas, London, 1983, p. 105, with reference to notes by Jan Veth now preserved in the Netherlands Institute for Art History in the Hague, quoted by E. van Schendel, *Museum Mesdag: Nederlandse Negentiende-Eeuwse Schilderijen, Tekeningen en Grafiek*, the Hague, 1975, p. 77.

5. On collecting, see Charles Dumas, "Art Dealers and Collectors," in De Leeuw et al., eds., pp. 125–36, and Marta H. Hurdalek, *The Hague School: Collecting in Canada at the Turn of the Century*, exh. cat., Art Gallery of Ontario, Toronto, 1983, pp. 9–24.

Provenance [Goupil, London, Mar. 1881]; James Staats Forbes (1823–1904), London, July 1881; [Scott and Fowles, New York (from Grafton Galleries, London?)]; Taft collection, Sept. 30, 1905.

Exhibitions Paris, Salon, 1881 (cat., no. 1190); London, McLean Gallery, 1881; Amsterdam, International Exhibition, 1883 (cat., no. 109); London, Goupil, 1886 (cat., no. 53); Munich, Jubileum Ausstellung, 1888 (cat., no. 1331); Rotterdam, Rotterdamsche Kunstkring, 1894 (cat., no. 39); London, Grafton Galleries, 1896 (cat., no. 4); London, French Gallery, 1896 (cat., no. 30); London, Guildhall Exhibition, 1903 (cat., no. 86); London, Grafton Galleries, *Collection of the Late J. Staats Forbes*, 1905 (cat., no. 191); New York, Cooper-Hewitt Museum, *Embroidered Samplers*, Feb. 21–May 27, 1984.

Literature Emilien Chesnau, "Exposition d'Amsterdam," *Annuaire illustré des beaux-arts, revue artistique universelle*, ed. F. G. Dumas, Paris, 1883, p. 285; *The Art Journal*, 1883, p. 271; *Eigen Haard* (1883), p. 427; Mrs. A. Bell, *Representative Painters of the Nineteenth Century*, 1899, p. 179; *Cyclopedia of Painters and Paintings*, ed. John Denison Champlin, Jr., New York, vol. II, 1900, p. 322; Maurice W. Brockwell, *A Catalogue of Paintings in the Collection of Mr. and Mrs. Charles P. Taft*, New York, 1920, no. 68; Thieme-Becker, vol. XIX, p. 257; *Catalogue of the Taft Museum*, Cincinnati, 1939 and 1958, no. 511; H. E. van Gelder, *Jozef Israëls*, Amsterdam, 1947, pp. 38–41, ill. opp. p. 35; Joseph de Gruyter, *De Haagse School*, Rotterdam, 1968–69, vol. I, p. 59; *The Hague School: Dutch Masters of the Nineteenth Century*, eds. Ronald de Leeuw, John Sillevis, and Charles Dumas, London, 1983, p. 105, fig. 86; David Torbet Johnson, "Taft Museum," Ventura, vol. IV, no. 16 (June–Aug. 1991), p. 138 (ill.).

1931.460

Anton Mauve
Zaandam 1838–1888 Arnhem

Shortly after Anton Mauve was born as the second son in a family of five children, his father, a Mennonite preacher, received a new assignment in Haarlem, where Anton grew up. Eventually he became a pupil of the animal painter Pieter Frederik van Os, with whom he studied from about 1854 to 1857. The following year he studied briefly with Wouterus Verschuur, whose primary subject matter was horses. The most important experience of his formative years was a visit to Oosterbeek in the summer of 1858 at the invitation of the landscape painter Paul Gabriël. From this time until 1874 Mauve spent periods of time in the Dutch "Barbizon" village of Oosterbeek, where he met Johannes and Gerard Bilders, the latter of whom was his exact contemporary. Gerard Bilders anticipated the Hague School artists in his efforts to achieve a vibrant gray-based tonality that he described in a frequently quoted passage of 1860 as "colored gray."[1] It was also in Oosterbeek that Mauve became close friends with Willem Maris in 1862. Under Maris's influence he began to paint cows in landscape settings as well as the interiors of stables, which he observed with Maris on subsequent visits to Scheveningen, near the Hague.

Between 1865 and 1871, Mauve moved frequently, residing in Amsterdam, Scheveningen, Dordrecht, and various other locations before finally settling in the Hague in 1871. With Maris's

1931.411

help he established a studio there, and in 1874 he married Ariette Sophia Jeanette Carbentus, a second cousin of Vincent van Gogh.

During the 1870s Mauve refined his earlier style in subjects that featured flocks of sheep, cows, and other animals, often accompanied by their tenders in the meadows and dunes near the Hague. A light silvery gray effectively conveys the light and sky of the damp, marshy coastal region that he painted in watercolor as frequently as in oil. To isolate and focus his motif within the vast expanse of landscape, he often framed it by looking through a rectangular hole cut in a piece of paper.[2] This device anticipates, in a less sophisticated way, the perspective frame that Van Gogh later used to establish relative distances in space.

By the mid-1870s Mauve was well established professionally. In 1876, along with Willem Maris and Hendrik Willem Mesdag, he founded the Hollandsche Teeken-Maatschappij (Dutch Drawing Society) in the Hague. Also in that year the Museum Boymans in Rotterdam purchased *Cows in the Shade,* the first of his paintings to enter a museum collection. From 1878 to 1883 he was active in the Pulchri Studio, which provided the primary meeting place for artists in the Hague. Late in 1881 Vincent van Gogh, at the outset of his own career as a painter, studied regularly with Mauve for a period of several weeks until their relationship ended abruptly in March 1882. A few months later Mauve made his first visit to Laren in the Gooi region where he returned to paint in subsequent summers, often in the company of Albert Nuyhuis, who had taken up residence there. With encouragement from Nuyhuis, Mauve and his wife moved to Laren in 1885. In this isolated area he produced some of his most important paintings and soon became a leading figure among artists who composed the Laren School.

Always in fragile health, Mauve died suddenly of a heart attack in 1888 while visiting his brother in Arnhem. When Van Gogh received this news in Arles in the south of France, he was at work on a painting of a blossoming peach tree. Despite the painful termination of their friendship, he sent this painting to Mauve's widow with the spontaneously added inscription: *Souvenir de Mauve.*[3]

1. Joseph de Gruyter, *De Haagse School,* Rotterdam, 1968–69, vol. II, p. 14 (see p. 277 for the full quotation). This tonality most typifies the landscapes of the Hague School.

2. Marta H. Hurdalek, *The Hague School: Collecting in Canada at the Turn of the Century,* exh. cat., Art Gallery of Ontario, Toronto, 1983, p. 46.

3. In letters to his sister, Wil, and his brother, Theo, Vincent van Gogh specified that he had inscribed the painting *Souvenir de Mauve. Vincent & Theo.* Theo's name, however, was ultimately left out or eliminated. See *The Complete Letters of Vincent van Gogh,* 2d ed., Greenwich, Conn., 1959, vol. III, letter W3, p. 430, and vol. II, letter 472, p. 537. The painting is now in Otterlo, Rijksmuseum Kröller-Müller.

Anton Mauve

Cattle Grazing

late 1870s
Oil on canvas, 34.3 x 70.5 cm (13½ x 27¾ in.)
Signed lower right: *A. Mauve*

Mauve's attraction to animals as subject matter was probably initiated by his two earliest teachers, Pieter van Os and Wouterus Verschuur. Later, domesticated animals harmoniously situated in landscape settings became one of his most prevalent motifs. Cattle in particular reflect the influence of Willem Maris, whom he met in Oosterbeek in 1862. However, the human element often present in Mauve's paintings is generally absent from Maris's depictions of otherwise similar motifs.

In *Cattle Grazing,* a short stocky peasant is dwarfed by the cow that eats from his hand while two other cows are grazing close behind. The group is nearly centered in the composition and is visually compartmentalized between a fence to the right and a narrow ditch leading diagonally toward the open meadow on the left. A screen of brush obscures the background and focuses attention on the interaction between the man and the animals in his care. By these simple compositional means, Mauve has made the setting emphasize the primary subject. The width of the canvas is approximately double its height, a format that suggests the vastness of the countryside without destroying the sense of intimacy with the primary subject. A gray atmosphere enhances the somber mood pervading the scene. Grass and sky are rendered in thickly built layers of paint, while lightly applied brushstrokes indicate the bare branches and brush dividing the dark green meadow from the nearly monochromatic sky.

Cattle Grazing is similar in execution to works of the late 1870s, such as *The Cowherd* of about 1879 (Montreal Museum of Fine Arts).[1] In contrast, Mauve's earlier paintings of similar subjects retain the compositional contrivances used by his teachers and by Paulus Potter, the seventeenth-century artist renowned for his paintings of cows. By the late 1870s when *Cattle Grazing* was probably painted, Mauve had learned to reject inherited formulas and to infuse his motifs with an informality and freshness resulting from direct observation of nature.

1. Marta H. Hurdalek, *The Hague School: Collecting in Canada at the Turn of the Century,* exh. cat., Art Gallery of Ontario, Toronto, 1983, no. 29 (ill.).

Provenance [Scott and Fowles, New York]; Taft collection, Jan. 21, 1904.
Literature Maurice W. Brockwell, *A Catalogue of Paintings in the Collection of Mr. and Mrs. Charles P. Taft,* New York, 1920, no. 4; *Catalogue of the Taft Museum,* Cincinnati, 1939 and 1958, no. 554.

1931.411

🙋

Anton Mauve

Changing Pasture

ca. 1887
Oil on canvas, 83.8 x 126.2 cm (33 x 49⅝ in.)
Signed lower left: *A. Mauve*

Changing Pasture, featuring a landscape of the Gooi region, was painted sometime after Mauve's first visit to Laren in 1882. In subject and composition it closely resembles several other works, notably *On the Heath in Laren* (Amsterdam, Rijksmuseum) of 1887, *Return of the Flock* (Philadelphia Museum of Art), about 1887, and *Return of the Flock, Arnhem* (Montreal Museum of Fine Arts) of 1888. In all these paintings, a centralized flock

of sheep guided by a solitary shepherd moves down a rutted roadway that recedes toward a vanishing point on the distant horizon. This kind of composition was also employed by Charles-Emile Jacque and Constant Troyon of the Barbizon School and derives ultimately from seventeenth-century Dutch masters such as Meyndert Hobbema, who used roads and waterways as recessional devices in a one-point perspective system. This compositional formula in conjunction with a horizontal format was ideal for emphasizing the vastness of the landscape as it extends both laterally and into depth.

Like other artists of the Hague School, Mauve's structuring of space is far less contrived than that of his seventeenth-century predecessors. He has accentuated the lateral expanse by presenting a wide-angle foreground view unbounded by *repoussoirs,* while recessionals are unobtrusively indicated by the right edge of the roadway and by a ditch in the grassy meadow to the left of the composition. The road itself meanders toward the horizon without ever culminating at the vanishing point. The vast, empty space thus defined easily accommodates a sizable flock of sheep moving as a single mass toward greener pastures. Only two animals at the periphery of the flock are individually articulated; the rest are suggested only by contrasts of light and dark that establish an overlapping of forms from the more sharply defined animals at the rear to the barely distinguishable ones at the front. A black sheep at the center provides a visual reference point within the surrounding white mass.

Mauve's palette consists of light but muted tones of green, brown, and blue, accented by yellow in the meadow. Paint is built up, layer upon layer, beginning with thinly applied strokes of yellow and deep gray underlying the greens and browns of the land. Brushwork becomes increasingly pronounced on the surface, where highlights as well as superimposed details of flowers and clumps of earth are loosely applied in a low impasto. The light gray-blue sky with a hint of moving clouds imparts a sense of sparkling yet diffused light, which is also suggested in

1931.457

the highlights below. The effect closely approximates one de-scribed in 1860 by the artist Gerard Bilders, whose ideas Mauve encountered on his early visits to Oosterbeek:

> I'm looking for a tone we call "coloured grey," that is, all colours, however strong, so united as to give the impression of a fragrant, warm grey. . . . My aim is not to paint a cow for its own sake, or a tree for its own sake, but to create a whole impression of the kind nature sometimes makes — a magnificent, beautiful impression — and to do so by the simplest possible means.[1]

Through composition, brushwork, and a palette consisting of gray-based tonalities, Mauve has successfully captured the char-acter of the heath in an image that conveys the freshness of na-ture he observed while sketching on the spot.

1. As quoted in Joseph de Gruyter, *De Haagse School,* Rotterdam, 1968–69, vol. II, p. 14.

Provenance Judge Bronson, New Haven, Conn.; [Scott and Fowles, New York]; Taft collection, Feb. 6, 1905.

Exhibition The Hague, Haags Geementemuseum, *Painters of the Hague School,* June 18–Sept. 12, 1965.

Literature F. Hopkinson Smith, *Outdoor Sketching,* New York, 1915, pp. 42–43; *Ladies' Home Journal,* Mar. 1917, p. 45 and ill.; Maurice W. Brockwell, *A Catalogue of Paintings in the Collection of Mr. and Mrs. Charles P. Taft,* New York, 1920, no. 70; *Catalogue of the Taft Museum,* Cincinnati, 1939 and 1958, no. 483; Peter C. Sutton, *Northern European Paintings in the Philadelphia Museum of Art: From the Sixteenth through the Nineteenth Century,* Philadelphia, 1990, p. 203, fig. 71-1.

1931.457

Jan Hendrik Weissenbruch

The Hague 1824–1903 The Hague

A lifelong resident of the Hague, Jan Hendrik Weissenbruch (originally named Hendrik Johannes) was recognized only at the end of his life as being one of the greatest artists of the Hague School. He came from a bourgeois family with an avid interest in art. His father was a collector who dabbled in painting when not otherwise occupied with his business as a restaurant owner and cook. A brother, an uncle, and a nephew were all engravers, and a cousin, Jan Weissenbruch, who was two years his elder, was an established painter of town views and river scenes. Jan Hendrik's son, Willem Johannes, became a painter as well.

At an early age Weissenbruch established the practice of walk-ing about the Hague and recording his impressions of nature's fleeting moments in quickly executed charcoal sketches. Even then he was especially attracted by instantaneous effects such as the sun breaking through storm clouds. His desire to convey the effects of nature in paint also led him to the Mauritshuis where, during his student days, he copied works by Dutch old masters, especially those of Jacob van Ruisdael, Johannes Vermeer, and Paulus Potter.

Weissenbruch's first drawing master was J. J. Löw, with whom he studied from 1840 to 1843. He then enrolled in evening classes at the Hague Academy where he worked with Bart van Hove, who was known primarily for his street scenes. It is uncertain whether he ever studied formally with Andreas Schelfhout, who also taught at the Hague Academy. Schelfhout's experimental landscapes, which anticipate those done by members of the Hague School in their compositional simplicity and emphasis on atmosphere and light, appear to have influenced Weissen-bruch's early work. Weissenbruch first exhibited at the Hague in 1847 at the Exhibition of Living Masters and in the same year became a founding member of the Pulchri Studio, established for the purpose of discussing the work of its members and sketching from the clothed model. In 1849 the Teyler Museum in Haarlem purchased a landscape titled *Dekkersduin,* of a rural area on the outskirts of the Hague where Weissenbruch fre-quently sketched in those years.

Weissenbruch's early works show the continuing influence of Ruisdael. Like his mentor from the seventeenth century, he was fascinated by the dunes, the expansive sky with its variously configured clouds, and the patterns of light and shadow on the land. During his early maturity he also painted interiors and city views, making watercolors on the spot, which he sometimes used as studies for more calculated and highly finished oil paintings executed in the studio. In 1863 he married Susanna Petronella Geertruida Schouw; their son, Willem Johannes, was born the following year. During the next decade Weissenbruch worked primarily in and around the Hague. Only in 1868, at the age of forty-four, did he attract the notice of critics. In that year he was also invited to join the Belgian Society of Watercolorists in Brussels, attesting to the continuing importance of watercolor in his oeuvre.

In 1875 Weissenbruch became interested in the towns of Nieuwkoop and Noorden, locales that also attracted Paul Gabriël, Willem Roelofs, and other artists with Hague School connections. From that point on he spent springs and autumns in Nieuwkoop, painting scenes that reflect his preoccupation with changes in season and weather. At other times he gravitated north of the Hague to Haarlem and to the seaside village of Scheveningen rather than to the dunes and polders (reclaimed land) that had provided motifs for his earlier paintings.

Gradually Weissenbruch began to enjoy some degree of pro-fessional success, as is indicated by an exhibition of drawings and sketches at Arti et Amicitiae in Amsterdam in 1877, the regu-lar sale of paintings after 1880, and a gold medal at the Inter-national Exhibition in Amsterdam in 1883. By this time his generalized forms, loosely applied brushstrokes, and harmony of light and atmosphere had begun to show stylistic affinities with impressionism. His greatest oils and watercolors, dating from 1890 onward, combine these features with a timeless qual-ity that transcends the transience of the moment.

In 1899, on the occasion of his seventy-fifth birthday, Weissenbruch was honored by the Pulchri Studio. In that year he was also given a retrospective exhibition at the firm of Frans Buffa and Sons in Amsterdam, the proceeds of which enabled him to visit the French village of Barbizon where he made studies *en plein air.* This was his first and only trip outside his homeland.

1931.452

Jan Hendrik Weissenbruch

A Gray Day in Holland

1899
Oil on canvas, 72.4 x 103.5 cm (28½ x 40¾ in.)
Signed and dated lower left: *J.H. Weissenbruch 99*

Painted in 1899, *A Gray Day in Holland* exemplifies the compositional simplicity, atmospheric unity, and breadth of execution through which Weissenbruch successfully distilled the enduring characteristics of his subjects while remaining sensitive to the specific conditions of weather and season dictated by the damp northern climate of Holland. From a vantage point overlooking a canal, the scene encompasses houses grouped to the left and right of a bridge spanning the water directly in the middle ground. Beyond the bridge, the scene opens to reveal the generalized shapes of distant buildings that block the view of anything farther back except for the faint silhouette of a church tower. Such scenes, often glimpsed from a bridge crossing one of the many canals that cut through Dutch towns and cities, are as typical of Holland as are the flat meadowlands, low horizons, towpaths, and projecting windmills of the countryside. Weissenbruch's success in capturing these characteristic views won praise from Vincent van Gogh, who wrote in 1889 that "Weissenbruch knows and does the muddy towpaths, the stunted willows, and the foreshortening, the strange and subtle perspective of the canals as Daumier does lawyers."[1]

In its compositional structure *A Gray Day in Holland* resembles an undated watercolor titled *View of the Spaarne at Haarlem* (private collection) and, to a lesser degree, *At Noorden near Nieuwkoop* (Dordrecht, Rijksmuseum Van Bilderbeek–Lamaison), an oil painting of 1901.[2] In all three works Weissenbruch has used the device of the bridge parallel to the picture plane and one or two openings that provide access to a lighter area beyond.

In the Taft painting the artist has forged an overall harmony by imposing a pervasive gray tonality on the local colors of buildings and landscape. A bleak mood is set by the sky in which underlying blue is overpainted with whites and grays to produce an overcast effect. The reds, browns, and whites of the houses are modulated by gray, resulting in a rich variety of muted tones that deepen almost to black when reflected in the murky water. The presence of a boat is difficult to discern even at relatively close range, since its shape is suggested only through occasional highlights and by the silhouetting of one side against the area of reflected light flooding through an open passageway beneath the bridge. A group of figures barely takes shape against the buildings on the left bank.

Within the houses and water, the paint is applied in varying consistencies with boldly dragged or swirling strokes that assume a life of their own apart from the objects or textures they define. This fluidity of technique, which is typical of Weissenbruch's later oil paintings, was undoubtedly influenced by his watercolors, in which paint applied to wet paper creates a generalized massing of forms rather than articulating specific detail. In the patch of light reflected in the water, oil paint is sometimes applied so sparingly that traces of blue merely accent the weave of the canvas, creating a transparency akin to that of a watercolor wash that reveals the white of the paper beneath. In other areas highlights are more thickly brushed on to establish the edges of rooftops, windows, and bridge railing.

Weissenbruch's directness and spontaneity of execution is like that generally associated with impressionism, but his blended and muted tonalities create a timeless effect rather than the record of a momentary visual impression.

1. *The Complete Letters of Vincent van Gogh*, 2d ed., vol. III, Greenwich, Conn., 1959, letter 605, p. 207.

2. Both works are illustrated in Ronald de Leeuw, John Sillevis, and Charles Dumas, eds., *The Hague School: Dutch Masters of the Nineteenth Century*, London, 1983, nos. 143, 145.

Provenance [Scott and Fowles, New York]; Taft collection, Oct. 25, 1905.
Literature Maurice W. Brockwell, *A Catalogue of Paintings in the Collection of Mr. and Mrs. Charles P. Taft*, New York, 1920, no. 71; *Catalogue of the Taft Collection*, Cincinnati, 1939 and 1958, no. 552.

1931.452

Jacob Maris

The Hague 1837–1899 Carlsbad, Bohemia

Jacob Maris was the eldest of the three Maris brothers, all of whom became artists. According to their early biographer, D. Croal Thompson, their grandfather had been a Bohemian conscript under Napoléon early in the nineteenth century.[1] He eventually settled in the Hague, changed the spelling of his name from Maresch to Morris (or Maris), and married a Dutch woman. Their son, the father of the Maris brothers and of two daughters, struggled to support his family. Determined that his sons be spared the hardships he experienced in his own work as a printer, the elder Maris encouraged them to begin drawing at an early age in preparation for careers as artists.

When he was about twelve, Jacob enrolled at the Hague Academy where he studied with Johannes Strobel and Jacobus van den Berg. After three years he was accepted as a pupil of Huib van Hove, whom he accompanied to Antwerp in 1854. He remained there for almost three years, during which time he enrolled at the academy in an evening class taught by Nicaise de Keyser. Eventually, he shared living quarters with his brother Matthijs, who joined him in Antwerp in 1855, and with Lawrence Alma-Tadema, who was a fellow student at the Antwerp Academy. His work was first exhibited in 1854 at the Exhibition of Living Masters in the Hague.

In 1857 Jacob returned to the Hague, where he continued to study at the academy under its director, J. P. Koelman. In 1858 Matthijs also returned to the Hague, and in that year the two brothers received a commission from Princess Marianne (Willem I's youngest daughter) to copy eight portraits of the family of William of Orange for her country house. This grant enabled them to visit the villages of Oosterbeek and Wolfheze, located in a forested area near Arnhem, in 1859 and 1860. These villages were known as the Dutch "Barbizon" because, like the areas of Barbizon and the Fontainebleau Forest in France, they provided a retreat for artists seeking intimate contact with nature. In Oosterbeek Jacob painted his earliest known landscapes. In 1861 he and Matthijs extended their travels to Germany, Switzerland, and France, where they visited both Paris and Fontainebleau.

From 1865 to 1871 Jacob resided in Paris, beginning his stay with six months of study with Ernest Hébert, an established academic painter. For Hébert he produced a series of *Italiennes* (Italian peasant girls), which were highly fashionable at the time and in steady demand by the art dealer Adolphe Goupil. After leaving Hébert, Maris continued catering to the vogue for *Italiennes* and also painted occasional pictures in the equally marketable orientalist mode. At the same time he was assimi-

lating other influences and solidifying his interest in landscape painting. An excursion to Fontainebleau Forest took him to the village of Marlotte and its environs, which had begun to attract a young group of French artists drawn to Fontainebleau by the example of the Barbizon School. In the summer of 1865 Auguste Renoir, Alfred Sisley, and Claude Monet all worked in or around Marlotte, painting *en plein air*. Whether Maris encountered the emerging impressionists is unknown. As his priorities shifted increasingly toward landscape, he responded most noticeably to the influence of Camille Corot, Charles-François Daubigny, and his own countryman Johan Barthold Jongkind. Their example gradually led him to abandon the technical precision of academic painting in favor of a looser, broader, more spontaneous technique suited to the immediacy of his new subject matter.

In 1867 Jacob Maris married C. H. Horn, and in 1869 they were joined in Paris by Matthijs Maris, who remained there after the Franco-Prussian War and ensuing Commune prompted the return of Jacob and his family to the Hague in 1871. The same year, Jozef Israëls, who had already established himself as a successful academic history painter and portraitist in Amsterdam, moved to the Hague, where he became a magnet for lesser-known artists like Jacob and Willem Maris, Anton Mauve, Jan Hendrik Weissenbruch, Johannes Bosboom, and Hendrik Willem Mesdag. This group of artists subsequently constituted the Hague School.

As one of the primary members of this group, Jacob Maris excelled at both oil painting and watercolor and also worked in etching and lithography. His expansive land- and cityscapes with low horizons and diagonal recessions recall the seventeenth-century vistas of Jacob van Ruisdael and Meyndert Hobbema. He was especially sensitive to the subtle atmospheric variations produced by the damp climate of his homeland. His muted palette and active brushwork, together with compositional devices derived from Dutch landscapes of the seventeenth century, enabled him to convey the sense of air, light, and space of his native Holland.

After a long and successful career at the Hague, Jacob Maris died at the age of sixty-two in Carlsbad, Bohemia.

1. D. Croal Thompson, *The Brothers Maris,* ed. Charles Holme, London and Paris, 1907, p. xi.

Jacob Maris

The Quay: A Dutch Town

1880s?
Oil on canvas, 83.8 x 127.6 cm (33 x 50¼ in.)
Signed lower left: *J. Maris*

This broadly painted view of an unspecified town is typical of Jacob Maris's cityscapes of the 1880s, although the free execution, the horizontal format, and the subject of a town at water's edge are also found in his work of the 1870s and 1890s, making

1931.456

it difficult to establish a precise date. Like other artists of the Hague School, Maris has drawn heavily on devices used by the seventeenth-century masters who typified Holland's Golden Age. Vermeer's *View of Delft*, which had been on view in the Mauritshuis (The Hague) since 1822, has been claimed as a model for all Maris's cityscapes.[1] More obvious are compositional features borrowed from Jacob van Ruisdael's panoramic landscapes that also influenced Barbizon artists such as Charles-François Daubigny in France. An example of such features is seen in *The Quay: A Dutch Town*, where a diagonal slope of land enters the picture at the left and interlocks with slivers of water at the right; beyond, a landscape vista with a markedly low horizon is punctuated by masts and windmills, which provide visual reference points within the expansive space.

Like his predecessors of the seventeenth century, Maris has attempted to capture the spatial and atmospheric effects of Holland, but the result is far less contrived than theirs. Instead of being guided visually into the scene by a road or waterway, the viewer confronts a pair of workhorses, one of which faces inward, leading directly into the working activities of the quay. Where Ruisdael used alternating bands of light and dark to define spatial levels, Maris has harmonized a range of red-brown tonalities that operate throughout the land mass, gradually lightening in value to enhance a feeling of distance and space. These tonalities, infiltrated by muted contrasts of blue, blue-green, and occasional dashes of pure color, are echoed in the blues, grays, and whites of the cloudy sky, which dominates at least two-thirds of the composition. Descriptive details are only sketchily indicated but, as in the waving flags atop projecting masts, help to suggest the ambience of the place under typical weather conditions.

1. Joseph J. Rishel, "The Hague School: Some Forgotten Pictures in the Collection," *Philadelphia Museum Bulletin,* vol. LXVI (July, 1971), p. 19.

Provenance [Scott and Fowles, New York]; Taft collection, Oct. 25, 1905.

Literature Maurice W. Brockwell, *A Catalogue of Paintings in the Collection of Mr. and Mrs. Charles P. Taft,* New York, 1920, no. 66; *Catalogue of the Taft Museum,* Cincinnati, 1939 and 1958, no. 503.

1931.456

Jacob Maris

Rotterdam

1880s?
Oil on canvas, 97.5 x 111.8 cm (36⅜ x 44 in.)
Signed lower right: *J. Maris*

Unlike *The Quay: A Dutch Town* (see 1931.456), this city view is depicted from a vantage point overlooking the water. Tall-masted boats dominate the right half of the composition but diminish in scale to indicate depth according to a one-point perspective system with an off-center vanishing point that coincides with the arched opening of a bridge to the far left. Silhouetted against the sky, the verticals of nearby masts are echoed by a massive church tower projecting above the horizon. Its sketchy rendering in lighter tones helps to establish spatial relationships between foreground and background, while its location to the right of center balances the composition by providing a visual focus that competes with the established vanishing point. This compositional structure originated in Dutch landscapes of the seventeenth century and was later adopted by Vincent van Gogh, a great admirer of the artists of the Hague School.[1]

Although the painting is titled *Rotterdam,* the church tower appears to be that of the Grote Kerk in Dordrecht, which figures prominently in other specifically identified cityscapes by Jacob Maris (*Ships in the Harbor of Dordrecht* and *Dordrecht by Night,* both Amsterdam, Rijksmuseum; *Dordrecht: The Grote Kerk,*

1931.458

Montreal, Museum of Fine Arts; and *Souvenir of Dordrecht,* The Burrell Collection, Glasgow Art Gallery and Museum). This familiar landmark might suggest that the Taft painting should be retitled. But, since Maris frequently combined components of several cities into a single view, a specific identification must remain tentative.[2]

The scene is broadly painted in muted tonalities accented by a patch of blue and rich yellow-white in the clouds and by spontaneously applied streaks of white that highlight and define the configuration of water and boats. These features again suggest a tentative date in the 1880s, the highlights resembling those in *Souvenir of Dordrecht,* which was painted prior to 1886.[3] The total effect combines the enduring characteristics of a Dutch town with an immediacy suggested through summary brushstrokes and details such as waving flags, soaring birds, and a lone oarsman rowing his boat past the larger stationary vessels.

1. Ann H. Murray, " 'Strange and Subtle Perspective . . . ': Van Gogh, the Hague School, and the Dutch Landscape Tradition," *Art History,* vol. III, no. 4 (Dec. 1980), pp. 410–24.

2. Marta H. Hurdalek, *The Hague School: Collecting in Canada at the Turn of the Century,* exh. cat., Art Gallery of Ontario, Toronto, 1983, p. 37.

3. Illustrated in Ronald de Leeuw, John Sillevis, and Charles Dumas, eds., *The Hague School: Dutch Masters of the Nineteenth Century,* London, 1983, no. 65; the catalogue entry notes that this picture, formerly dated to 1890, was in a private collection in Edinburgh by 1886.

Provenance [Scott and Fowles, New York]; Taft collection, Nov. 10, 1903.

Literature Maurice W. Brockwell, *A Catalogue of Paintings in the Collection of Mr. and Mrs. Charles P. Taft,* New York, 1920, no. 82; *Catalogue of the Taft Museum,* Cincinnati, 1939 and 1958, no. 510.

1931.458

Jacob Maris

A View of a Dutch Town

ca. 1890s
Oil on canvas, 40.3 x 60.6 cm (15⅞ x 23⅞ in.)
Signed lower right: *J. Maris*

This view again shows a town from a vantage point overlooking a river or canal. The composition here is more symmetrically balanced than in the Taft's *Rotterdam,* with a gabled roof and foliage on the left and a row of gabled buildings on the right receding toward a low horizon located just to the left of center. This painting is more broadly executed than the other two works in the Taft Museum by Jacob Maris, perhaps indicating a date in the 1890s.[1]

Paint is thickly built up and worked over with loosely applied brushstrokes that create a mere impression of the scene. Buildings, water, and boats are summarily defined by highlights and accents in impasto that provide only the barest suggestion of surfaces and contours within the dark tonalities dominating the lower half of the canvas. Masts and riggings are sketchily rendered with ample use of a dry brush. Silhouetted against the cloud-laden sky, they help to establish relative distances within an otherwise nearly indecipherable space. Boldly applied ocher highlights draw attention to a distant church tower, which immediately stands out as the most prominent feature on the horizon. The blocky structure of this monument again suggests the Grote Kerk in Dordrecht.

1931.433

1. It is again impossible to establish a specific date, since some of Maris's oils from the 1870s and 1880s are as broadly painted as those assigned to the 1890s. The treatment of water and houses is similar to that in *Amsterdam* (Toronto, Art Gallery of Ontario), assigned by Hurdalek to pre-1899 (Marta H. Hurdalek, *The Hague School: Collecting in Canada at the Turn of the Century,* exh. cat., Art Gallery of Ontario, Toronto, 1983, no. 23).

Provenance Taft collection, before 1920.

Literature Maurice W. Brockwell, *A Catalogue of Paintings in the Collection of Mr. and Mrs. Charles P. Taft,* New York, 1920, no. 69; *Catalogue of the Taft Museum,* Cincinnati, 1939 and 1958, no. 570.

1931.433

Matthijs Maris

The Hague 1839–1917 London

Like his elder brother, Jacob, Matthijs Maris was encouraged as a child toward a career in art. In 1851 at the age of twelve, he became a pupil of Isaac Cornelis Elink Sterk, who specialized in portraiture. He attended the Hague Academy from 1852 to 1855 and in 1854 began working with the marine painter Johan Hendrik Louis Meijer. Meijer was instrumental in securing Matthijs a stipend of forty guilders a month from Queen Sophia, which enabled him to join Jacob in Antwerp in 1855. There, he studied under Nicaise de Keyser and shared living quarters with his brother and another student, Lawrence Alma-Tadema. In Antwerp he also became friends with the German artist George Laves who stimulated his interest in German romantic painting. In 1858 Matthijs returned to the Hague where he shared a studio with Jacob and began instructing his younger brother, Willem. Meijer again facilitated a royal commission, this time from Princess Marianne (see biography of Jacob Maris for details). Thanks to this stipend, he and Jacob were able to visit the villages of Wolfheze and Oosterbeek (the Dutch "Barbizon") in

1859–60 and to travel extensively the following year in Germany, Switzerland, and France. Matthijs's earlier interests were reinforced on this trip by firsthand exposure to work by German romantics and to the cathedral, castle, and wood-constructed houses of Lausanne, which figure prominently in his later paintings. His watercolor titled *View of Lausanne: L'Escalier du Vieux Marché* (The Hague, Haags Gemeentemuseum) gained him honorary membership in the Belgian Society of Watercolorists in Brussels in 1863.

In 1868 Matthijs joined Jacob and his wife in Paris where he was a member of the Municipal Guard during the Franco-Prussian War. He remained in Paris until at least 1875, long after Jacob and his family had returned to the Hague. Although living in poverty, he gained financial support from a young dealer, Elbert J. van Wisselingh, who had been assigned to the Paris branch of the Dutch firm Goupil and Co. and who began to purchase occasional works. He was also encouraged by the Scottish dealer Daniel Cottier, who was based in London and who persuaded Wisselingh to move there to work for him in 1875. Sometime thereafter, Matthijs also moved to London, allegedly to design stained-glass windows for Cottier.[1] At this time he became interested in the English Pre-Raphaelites. After living briefly with Wisselingh, he resided with Cottier until 1887, traveling with him to Norway, Brittany, and Paris until increasingly bitter disagreements resulted in a severing of relations.

From that time Matthijs remained in London, living in poverty and disillusionment. Despite continued support from Wisselingh, he completed few paintings, and these reflect a sensibility far removed from that of other Hague School artists. Matthijs's primary subjects were brides and christenings, fairy-tale or fantasy themes, visionary landscapes, and otherworldly figures that threaten to dissolve into an ethereal haze. A move to better quarters in 1908 did not result in greater productivity, and he failed to complete any further paintings after this time.

Without ever having returned to his native Holland, Matthijs Maris died in London in 1917.

1. D. Croal Thompson, *The Brothers Maris,* ed. Charles Holme, London and Paris, 1907, p. xvi. Most sources cite 1877 as the year of Matthijs's move to London. However, young Vincent van Gogh, who was employed at the London branch of Goupil and Co. from June 1873 through May 1875, had occasional talks with Matthijs during that time: see *The Complete Letters of Vincent van Gogh,* 2d ed., vol. ii, Greenwich, Conn., 1959, letter 332, p. 163.

Matthijs Maris

The Boy with a Hoop

1863
Oil on canvas, 47.3 x 31.6 cm (18⅝ x 12½ in.)
Signed and dated center right: M.M. 63.

The Boy with a Hoop provides a securely dated example of Matthijs Maris's early work, painted after the completion of his studies at the Hague and Antwerp academies and following his travels with his brother Jacob. Initialed and dated 1863, it already reveals a distinctly personal artistic vision. Although he, like his brothers, sometimes painted landscapes and city views, his more typical works are figural images. These exude an in-

creasingly mystical, dreamlike, and evocative quality, which reflects his early fascination with German romanticism and his later interest in the English Pre-Raphaelites, ultimately allying him with the symbolists of the fin-de-siècle.

This early example already points in the direction of his later, mist-enshrouded figures. The boy, standing quietly with stick and hoop in hand, seems more like an apparition than an active child interrupted in play. Contributing to the sense of ethereality are softly blurred contours, indistinct facial features, and, to the right, an enveloping Rembrandtesque shadow that seems both to bind the boy to the radiant yellow wall and to create a shallow yet unspecified spatial ambience. The all-pervasive golden tones also dominate the figure, which is sensitively modeled in warm red-browns and accented by touches of pure blue and red in the hoop, stick, and shoes. Through color, Maris has evoked a quiet harmony and a sense of mystical unity between the boy and his setting.

The Boy with a Hoop was originally in the collection of Edward B. Greenshields of Montreal, a prominent collector of Hague School paintings and the author of *The Subjective View of Landscape with Special Reference to J. H. Weissenbruch from Works of His in Canada* (1904) and *Landscape Painting and Modern Dutch Artists* (1906).

Provenance Edward B. Greenshields, Montreal; [Scott and Fowles, New York]; Taft collection, Oct. 20, 1909.

Exhibition London, French Galleries, 1909 (cat., no. 4 [ill.]).

Literature Edward B. Greenshields, *Landscape Painting and Modern Dutch Artists,* 1906, ill. opp. p. 164; *The Connoisseur,* vol. XLIX (1917), pp. 108–9; D. Croal Thompson, *The Brothers Maris,* London and Paris, 1917, pl. 34; Maurice W. Brockwell, *A Catalogue of Paintings in the Collection of Mr. and Mrs. Charles P. Taft,* New York, 1920, no. 64; *Catalogue of the Taft Museum,* Cincinnati, 1939 and 1958, no. 565.

1931.431

1931.431

Willem (Wentzel) Maris
The Hague 1844–1910 The Hague

Of the three Maris brothers, Wentzel, better known as Willem, had the least amount of formal training. Like his older brothers, Jacob and Matthijs, who were his first teachers, his first serious efforts at drawing began at about the age of twelve when, according to the biography by Thompson, he was encouraged to sketch cows in the fields before and after his day at school.[1] Like his brothers, he attended evening classes at the Hague Academy, but apparently for only a brief period of time. There he met Bernard Blommers. During his formative years he also made copies after old masters in the Mauritshuis at the Hague and consulted Pieter Stortenbeker, who specialized in animal painting.

About 1862 Willem visited the village of Oosterbeek (the Dutch "Barbizon"), where he began a lifelong friendship with Anton Mauve. In the same year his painting *Cows on the Heath* was accepted for exhibition at the Exhibition of Living Masters in Rotterdam, thus reinforcing his inclination toward landscape painting with an emphasis on animals in their natural settings. In 1863 he also began to exhibit at the Hague, where he shared a studio with his two brothers.

Willem Maris traveled far less extensively than either Jacob or Matthijs. In 1865 he and Bernard Blommers went to Germany where they explored the Rhineland on foot and by boat. In 1868 they spent a year in Amsterdam and by 1870 were back in the Hague sharing a studio. Except for a short sketching trip to Norway with Frederick van Seggeren and Alexander Wust in 1871, Willem's artistic activity remained centered in his native city, where in 1872 he married Maria Jacoba Visser. His primary subjects are those that had intrigued him from the first — cows, ducks, and the flat marshy meadowlands immediately accessible from the Hague.

In 1876 Willem Maris, along with Mauve and Hendrik Willem Mesdag, founded the Hollandsche Teeken-Maatschappij (Dutch Drawing Society). His pupils included George Hendrik Breitner, who studied with him in 1880. Carrying on the Maris tradition, the elder of his two sons also became a painter.

1. D. Croal Thompson, *The Brothers Maris,* ed. Charles Holme, London and Paris, 1907, pp. xx–xxi.

❧

Willem Maris

Ducks

before 1907
Oil on panel, 21.9 x 42 cm (8⅝ x 16⅝ in.)
Signed lower right: *W. Maris*

Ducks and ducklings were among Willem Maris's favorite subjects and are so prevalent in his work that it is impossible to suggest a specific date for this especially beautiful example. As is generally the case, the ducks are centered within a long narrow format and viewed from a close vantage point that creates a

sense of immediacy as we approach them in their natural habitat. Eschewing the expansive landscape vistas of many Hague School painters, Maris has zeroed in on a small segment of the larger whole, a fragment of lush greenery at water's edge, artfully snatched from its broader context of meadows and sky. As if through the lens of a camera, we glimpse the ducks in their typical actions and poses. The mother followed by her offspring is caught in the instant of transition from land to water. One duckling is about to imitate her example while another quacks nervously lest it be left behind. A dark-colored variant looks protectively on the group while two others assume the characteristic pose of sleeping with their heads turned upon their backs.

Maris has conveyed a genuine sense of movement through loosely brushed strokes that also suggest the wispiness of feathers and fuzz. Here, as in the setting, the texture of brushwork creates a visual impression akin to what one would observe on the spot. The artist has even adjusted his strokes to indicate degrees of focus, ranging from sharp to blurred within this intimately observed scene.

Maris's directness of vision approaches that of the French impressionists, yet his palette remains based on the gray-green tonalities that aptly convey the climate and atmosphere of Holland. Instead of utilizing unblended strokes of color, he has applied the paint layer on layer with accents of pure hues that suggest the play of light without creating a chromatic equivalent for its brilliance. The difference between Maris and the impressionists is perhaps best observed in his treatment of water. Where the impressionists boldly juxtaposed dabs of color to indicate movement and reflections, Maris blended his strokes to create a glassy surface that remains undisturbed by momentary outside intrusions.

Provenance [Agnew and Sons, and Wallis and Son, London (in 1907, according to Thompson; see Literature)]; Taft collection, before 1920.

Exhibition The Hague, Haags Gemeentemuseum, *Painters of the Hague School,* June 18–Sept. 12, 1965.

Literature D. Croal Thompson, *The Brothers Maris,* ed. Charles Holme, London and Paris, 1907, pl. W. 5; Maurice W. Brockwell, *A Catalogue of*

1931.408

1931.453

Paintings in the Collection of Mr. and Mrs. Charles P. Taft, New York, 1920, no. 2; *Catalogue of the Taft Museum,* Cincinnati, 1939 and 1958, no. 560.

1931.408

&

Willem Maris

Cattle in the Meadows

before 1905
Oil on canvas, 86.7 x 127 cm (34⅛ x 50 in.)
Signed lower right: *Willem Maris*

Cows, either singly or in groups, are the most frequent, if rarely dated, subjects of Willem Maris's oeuvre. *Cattle in the Meadows* is a typical example, depicting three animals in a deceptively simple arrangement within the vast empty space of the field. The nearest is shown in strict profile and stands apart from the other two, which are represented in contrasting foreshortened views, one facing diagonally inward, the other directly out. Despite their different spatial orientations, the cattle are compositionally unified by a deliberate echoing of characteristic bovine shapes — for example, the sloping back of the cow in profile corresponds to the back of the cow facing inward, whose head in turn overlaps without obscuring the most distant member of the trio. The connection between this more distant pair is further emphasized by their immediately juxtaposed heads. All three animals are fused with the land that sustains them. Their contours barely project above the horizon line and harmonize with the gentle curves given to the flat terrain by the windswept grass.

Despite the quietude of this simple scene, Maris's broad, loose brushstrokes applied in many layers impart a sense of sponta-

neity, which is enhanced by dashes of pure color within the darker tonalities. The impasto is sometimes so heavy that it seems the color was squeezed directly from the tube. Even the darkest areas are composed of deep blues and reds that reveal Maris's sensitivity to color. In contrast to the physical solidity of the cows, the meadow attains an abstract quality that suggests rather than describes the natural habitat. The light blue sky with wispy white clouds and flying birds completes the impression of a typical breezy day in the meadows.

Provenance [Scott and Fowles, New York]; Taft collection, Oct. 25, 1905.

Literature Maurice W. Brockwell, *A Catalogue of Paintings in the Collection of Mr. and Mrs. Charles P. Taft,* New York, 1920, no. 67; *Catalogue of the Taft Museum,* Cincinnati, 1939 and 1958, no. 484.

1931.453

Head of a Girl

Leslie Griffin Hennessey

❧

Unknown Artist

Head of a Girl

Europe, nineteenth century
Oil on canvas, 41 x 32.4 cm (16⅛ x 12¾ in.)

1931.475

The *Head of a Girl* is a pleasing nineteenth-century copy of a mildly erotic, bust-length image from the mid-eighteenth century, which may have originated in Paris with François Boucher and which was often painted by his contemporary Pietro Rotari during his final years at the Russian imperial court.[1]

The picture is smoothly painted in a subdued palette. Set against a slate gray background, the figure leans back slightly, resting her head on an ample green velvet pillow. With her blue eyes half closed and her rosy lips half open to reveal a row of even, pearly teeth, she appears to be midway between sleep and wakefulness as she dreamily acknowledges the viewer. She wears a teal blue shawl, and in the eighteenth-century fashion, her bodice, edged with softly twisted fabric, reveals a generous expanse of bosom.

The artist has enhanced the picture's languid eroticism by evoking all the senses: the woman's open mouth, the shimmering pendant earrings of gold, ruby, and pearl, the gathered folds of her black lace choker, and the soft pink petals of the rose corsage at her breast evoke sensations of taste, sight, sound, smell, and touch. Sensuality, and not any particular sitter, is the true subject of the painting.

There are well over a dozen versions and copies of this "portrait" of a young woman with light brown hair and delicate features. The subject — executed in pastel, in oil on canvas, and in etching with engraving — has been variously titled *La Voluptueuse, Le Reveil, Verträumt blickendes Mädchen, Reclining Woman,* and *La Belle Morphy,* a late, perhaps fanciful, identification of the subject as a portrait of the brunette mistress of Louis XV.[2]

An etching with engraving similar to the Taft *Head of a Girl* was made by J. F. Poletnich in Paris between 1750 and 1780 for Huquier *fils,* who published a number of works after Boucher. The print, *La Voluptueuse,* one impression of which is now in the Edmond de Rothschild collection of engravings at the Louvre (fig. 1), reverses the woman's pose while retaining the rose at the right. The inscription at the lower left reads *F. Boucher pinxit.*[3]

There are, in fact, at least a half-dozen pastel versions of this reclining woman that have been associated with Boucher's stu-

dio.[4] One of them, which appeared in the Kraemer sale in Paris on June 2, 1913, was considered by Georges Wildenstein to be a copy of an original pastel by Boucher described in a 1785 sale catalogue for the collection of Jacques-Onésyme Bergeret as "une jeune fille, à mi-corps, la tête sur un oreiller vert" (a girl, bust-length, her head on a green pillow [fig. 2]).[5] The Taft *Head of a Girl* is strikingly similar to the Kraemer pastel. It is closer, in fact, to it than to the Poletnich print, and the pastel may be the very work that the Taft painter copied.

However, a discussion of the original pictorial source for the Taft picture does not end with an attribution to Boucher. To be sure, coquettes are a characteristic theme of the French artist and his engravers, beginning with Gilles Petit's *Times of Day* series printed in 1734 and concluding with Louis Bonnet's color engravings from 1767, which most closely capture the elegance and gaiety of Boucher's treatment of the genre.[6] Nevertheless, the Kraemer image per se is not stylistically convincing as Boucher's design. It differs from known works by the artist in its quiet pose and mood, which are quite unlike the playful spirit of the French rococo. It seems fair to say that the genre of the alluring young girl goes back at least to Boucher, but the source for this specific image may not.[7] As Ananoff has written in his monograph on Boucher, no artist has been more plagiarized and copied or more popularized in prints than Boucher.[8]

If the original design for Poletnich's engraving, *La Voluptueuse,* is not by Boucher, it could well be by Pietro Rotari, some

Fig. 1 J. F. Poletnich, after Boucher, *La Voluptueuse*, 1750–80. Etching-engraving. Paris, Musée du Louvre, Edmond de Rothschild Collection. Paris, courtesy of the Musées Nationaux.

Fig. 2 Atelier of François Boucher, *Le Reveil*, ca. 1785. Pastel on paper, 41 x 32 cm (16½ x 12¾ in.). London, Witt Library, Courtauld Institute of Art.

Fig. 3 Pietro Rotari, *Portrait of a Young Woman*, ca. 1760. Oil on canvas, 46.4 x 38.8 cm (18½ x 15½ in.). Museum of Art and Archaeology, University of Missouri–Columbia, gift of the Samuel H. Kress Foundation.

Fig. 4 Jean-Richard Michel, after Boucher, *La Dormeuse*, 1750–80. Etching-engraving. Paris, Musée du Louvre, Edmond de Rothschild Collection. Paris, courtesy of the Musées Nationaux.

of whose works entered Paris under the name "Jeaurat" during the years 1756–62 when he worked as court painter for Empress Elizabeth in Russia.[9] Rotari, who spent much of his career as a history painter in his native Verona, left Italy in 1750 to paint portraits at the courts of Vienna, Dresden, and, at the end of his life, Saint Petersburg. Influenced by Rosalba Carriera's bust-length portraits, by the French pastelists, and by the works of Jean-Etienne Liotard, Rotari created literally hundreds of female portraits, both real and imaginary. Rotari's distinctive fancy pictures, virtually all on canvas, often incorporate exotic Russian facial types and record picturesque variations of local dress as well as the French-inspired fashions of the upper classes.[10]

The image of a young woman posed against a pillow appears in at least six variations firmly attributed to Rotari, in which the sitter's features range from ethnic Russian to a more idealized type. Rotari's *Portrait of a Young Woman* (fig. 3) in the Kress collection at the University of Missouri, for example, is very similar to the Taft *Head of a Girl*.[11] Compared to the livelier spirit and brighter palette of the French school, the more restrained mood and the cool gray-green pigments that characterize Rotari's portraits are a step closer to the Taft painting.

But there are important differences in style and conception as well: Rotari's numerous portraits for Empress Elizabeth possess a combination of volumetric solidity and provocative psychological realism, the result of his academic training and northern Italian background.[12] The Taft *Head* displays none of the plasticity of classical Italian *settecento* painting. Surfaces are suavely, somewhat moistly painted, and the forms are enervated. Eighteenth-century piquancy and immediacy have been transformed into something vaguely hallucinatory. Any sign of personality has been erased from the girl's doll-like features; she is no longer active in any sense of the word. What is presented here instead is a passively erotic condition, tinged with melancholy. For the artist who appropriated this image, direct observation has given way to nostalgic reinvention. The eighteenth century has become a remote, somewhat licentious world. This conception of the ancien régime as a romantic fantasy marks the Taft copy as a product of nineteenth-century taste. In America, this taste for the rococo revival in art collecting and interior design carried over into the early twentieth century when the Tafts formed their collection.[13]

The nationality of the artist can only be conjectured. The picture's wan sentimentality combined with the slightly moist-looking paint surface suggests English, even Victorian, pictures of the last century.[14] Given Rotari's importance for the history of the image, however, a Continental or even a Russian origin cannot be ruled out.

The bust-length fancy portrait on which the Taft picture is based served essentially domestic and decorative purposes. Boucher's single-figure pastels, Rotari's Russian canvases, and the countless engravings in the genre were all part of a widespread artistic response to the new demand for smaller art works to adorn collector's cabinets or to cover the walls of the modestly scaled rooms of middle-class residences. (The dimensions of the various versions of the Taft picture are strikingly standardized, many of them in the range of 43 x 33 cm, or 17 x 13 in.)

As luck would have it, a version of the Taft picture turns up in an engraving published in Berlin in 1771–72. The tiny print by the Polish artist Daniel Chodowiecki depicts his own studio and includes Rotari's *Portrait of a Young Woman* among the many art works displayed on the back wall of the interior. Chodowiecki's print is only one of many such eighteenth-century interior views documenting the fashion of displaying small-scale pictures stacked from floor to ceiling.[15] Finally, this portrait type, acquired singly by the Tafts in the twentieth century, must be imagined in yet another more incongruous setting: as one of 367 female heads, all by Rotari, that were hung row upon row by Empress Elizabeth's successor, Catherine II, in the Cabinet des Muses et des Grâces at the Peterhof Palace.[16]

Like their male counterparts, the *teste di carattere*, the single-figure fancy portraits could also be hung in pairs, quartets, or larger configurations. These individual images designed for decorative flexibility were often conceptually linked by such well-known conceits as the Four Seasons, the Elements, the Times of Day, the Continents, the Liberal Arts, or the Ages of Man, all themes that could also be discerned in rococo vignettes and mythological *galantes* of the period. From Bergeret's time to the present, versions of the Taft *Head of a Girl* have often appeared in sale catalogues as a single aspect of paired and contrasting conditions such as waking and sleeping, or indoor and outdoor pleasures (fig. 4).[17] These "portraits" were placed over doors, above mantelpieces, along corridors, flanking furniture, and so on. Finally, such modestly scaled works could be incorporated directly into the furniture itself: yet another version was set as the centerpiece in a late-eighteenth-century French upright secretary, now in the Metropolitan Museum of Art.[18]

1. For Boucher (1703–1770), see *François Boucher*, exh. cat., Metropolitan Museum of Art, New York, 1986; see also Alexandre Ananoff and Daniel Wildenstein, *François Boucher*, 2 vols., Lausanne and Paris, 1976. For Rotari (1707–1762), see Carola Fiocco Drei, "Pietro Rotari," *Antichità viva*, vol. XIX (1980), pp. 23–32; Lada Nikolenko, "Pietro Rotari in America," *Connoisseur*, vol. CLXXV (July 1969), pp. 191–96; Emilio Barbarani, *Pietro Rotari*, Verona, 1941; and R. Brenzoni, "Pietro Rotari," in Thieme-Becker, vol. XXIX, pp. 82–83.

2. The photographic files of the Witt Library, London, contain numerous examples of this image and document the tendency of dealers and collectors to attribute the pastel versions to Boucher's studio and the oil-on-canvas versions to Pietro Rotari. The title *La Belle Morphy* was first added to a pastel version once belonging to baron de Rocquemaurel in the catalogue to the Cels sale at Giroux in Brussels on Apr. 8, 1933, no. 174.

3. Pierrette Jean-Richard, *Musée du Louvre, cabinet des dessins . . . Ecole française, Vol. 1: L'Oeuvre gravé de François Boucher dans la collection Edmond de Rothschild*, Paris, 1978, pp. 355–56, nos. 1476–77. One version of the print is inscribed: "La Voluptueuse, F. Boucher Pinxit . . . Policnith Sculp . . . A Paris chez Huquier fils graveur, rue St. Jacques, au dessus de cels des Mathurins au gd. St. Remy." The other version gives the publisher as "Jac. Francois Chereau, rue St. Jacques aux 2 Piliers d'or." *La Voluptueuse* is a pendant to *La Dormeuse*, engraved by Jean-Baptiste Michel after Boucher and published by Huquier and by Chereau. See Jean-Richard, nos. 1419–20.

4. The Witt photographic files include the following examples, which are in some instances paired with the image of the sleeping girl: Hôtel Drouot, Paris, Dec. 21, 1908; Kraemer sale, Paris, June 2–5, 1913, no. 112; Lepke, Berlin, Nov. 6–7, 1929, no. 359; Cels sale, Brussels, Apr. 8, 1933, no. 174. See also Carl C. Dauterman, James Parker, and Edith Standen, *Decorative Art from the Samuel H. Kress Collection at the Metropolitan*

Museum of Art, London, 1964, pp. 96–99, no. 16, which lists a pastel formerly in the collection of D. I. Stchoukine, Moscow, now in the Pushkin Museum, and another pastel in the Art Gallery of Western Australia, Perth. This information was generously provided by the late David Cohen, associate curator of decorative arts at the J. Paul Getty Museum, Malibu, Calif.

A letter from Gabriel Rouchès, assistant curator of paintings, Musée du Louvre, to the Taft Museum, June 13, 1936, states that the Lepke sale pastel came from a Russian imperial collection and mentions two pastel versions attributed to Pietro Rotari at Wertheim, Berlin, Mar. 25, 1930.

Finally, for a version in government collections in Berlin before World War II, see Elfried Bock, *Die Reichsdrucke: Eine Sammlung von Kupferstichen, Radierungen . . . und Pastellen,* Berlin, 1928, p. 375, no. 669.

5. Georges Wildenstein, "Un Amateur de Boucher et de Fragonard: Jacques-Onésyme Bergeret, 1715–1785," *Gazette des beaux-arts,* ser. 6, vol. LVIII (1961), p. 67, fig. 25.

6. For Boucher's Times of Day (*Le Matin: La Dame à sa toilette, Le Midi: La Dame reglant sa montre, Le Soir: La Dame allant au bal,* and the lost *L'Après dîner*), see Ananoff and Wildenstein, vol. I, pp. 240–41, figs. 430–32. For Bonnet's color prints, see figs. 154 and 156.

7. The Witt Library files contain photographs of a pair of pastel-and-chalk drawings in a private collection in Paris, which depict one girl lying awake and another asleep on a cushion. These pictures, which bear only a distant relationship to the prints by Poletnich and Michel, possess all the vitality and freedom of execution one associates with Boucher's style. They would make more convincing candidates for the works described in no. 41 of the Bergeret collection catalogue than those discussed by Georges Wildenstein (see note 5 above).

8. Ananoff and Wildenstein, vol. I, p. vii.

9. The Taft *Head of a Girl* was first attributed to Pietro Rotari by Paul Drey in 1935 and by George Isarlov in 1936; see Taft files. A letter from Gabriel Rouchès to the Taft Museum, June 13, 1936, points out the link between Rotari and the little-known Jeaurat.

In the present writer's view, there are at least two other possible scenarios involving Poletnich, Rotari, and the image of the reclining woman. For a decade beginning in 1770, Poletnich worked in Russia where he could have copied Rotari's picture and sent it back to Paris as a Boucher. Alternatively, Rotari may have seen Poletnich's print and have begun around 1756 to incorporate the pose into his own female portraits.

Whoever the originator of the design may have been, the image reappears as a picture within a print by Daniel Chodowiecki. The bust-length image of a reclining woman appears at the left in Chodowiecki's *Cabinet d'un peintre,* published in Berlin in 1771–72. According to records in the British Museum Print Room, Chodowiecki may have engraved six of Rotari's works. An impression of Chodowiecki's print is in the Metropolitan Museum of Art and is illustrated in Bock 1928, p. 157, no. 52; and also in Elfried Bock, *Geschichte der graphischen Kunst,* Berlin, 1930, p. 481, no. 691.

10. There is only one pastel firmly attributed to Rotari; see Fiocco Drei, p. 30.

11. Versions of the reclining woman attributed to Rotari include an oil painting from a series in the Schloss Pilnitz on the Elbe (the Herbert M. Gutmann collection, sale, Paul Graupe Gallery, Berlin, 1934, no. 31) and an oil from a series at Archangelskoye near Moscow (the former Yussupov family). There is an oil once belonging to A. Seligman, New York; see Giuseppe Fiocco, "Di Pietro Rotari e di un libro che lo riguarda," *Emporium,* vol. XCVI, no. 571 (July 1942), p. 278. Another oil is found in the De Ette Holden Cummer Museum Foundation, Jacksonville, Fla. For the versions listed above, see Dauterman, Parker, and Standen, pp. 96–99, no. 16.

In addition to the Kress picture in Columbia, Mo. (inv. no. K1590), the Witt Library photographs include a work in the collection of Lady Claud Hamilton; an oil in the Mrs. J. Levy collection, Baltimore; another at the Leo Spik sale, Berlin, Oct. 12–13, 1961; an oil from a set of four female heads, Sotheby's, London, July 10, 1968, no. 77; a variation with a ruffled cap, Christie's, London, July 9, 1982; and another variation with long dark tresses and a somewhat altered pose, National Gallery of Art, Washington, D.C. (*Girl with a Flower,* from the Royal Palace of Catherine

of Russia to Prince Besborodko to Prince Kociubey, Hetman of the Ukraine, to the Samuel H. Kress Foundation). For references to other possible versions, see letters from Rouchès to the Taft Museum, June 13, 1934, and June 13, 1936.

12. For psychological realism in genre painting in northern Italy and its influence on Rotari, see Barry Hannigan, "Venice and the Veneto," in *Painting in Italy in the Eighteenth Century: Rococo to Romanticism,* exh. cat., The Art Institute of Chicago, 1970, pp. 100–101.

13. For some discussion of the strain of rococo-revival taste that runs through the nineteenth century, becoming more pronounced during the second half, see Francis Haskell, *Discoveries in Art: Some Aspects of Taste, Fashion and Collecting in England and France,* New York, 1976. It is an indication of the Taft picture's place in the rococo revival that Poletnich's print, *La Voluptueuse,* is to be found in Edmond de Rothschild's collection of works after Boucher, which was formed during the nineteenth century (see note 3 above).

14. The Taft painting's surface was perceptibly flattened when it was cleaned, lined, and revarnished in 1948 by M. Knoedler and Co.

15. See, for example, Francis Haskell, *Patrons and Painters: Art and Society in Baroque Italy,* New York, 1963, p. 261: "The Venetians cover their walls with pictures and never think their apartments properly finished until they have such as shall fill all space from top to bottom." Haskell quotes here from *Letters from Italy . . . in the Years 1770 and 1771 . . . ,* vol. III, London, 1776, p. 274.

16. Nikolenko, p. 194.

17. Poletnich's print was paired with Michel's *La Dormeuse.* See Rouchès, reporting from Isarlov to Taft Museum, 1936, museum archives.

18. See Dauterman, Parker, and Standen, pp. 95–100. I am grateful to David Cohen for identifying the secretary and generously providing this very useful reference.

Provenance Taft collection (before 1929; no invoice in Taft Museum files and not published in Taft family catalogues).

Literature *Catalogue of the Taft Museum,* Cincinnati, 1939 and 1958, no. 559.

1931.475

American Paintings and Sculpture

Diana Strazdes

1931.490

Edward Savage

Princeton, Mass. 1761–1817 Princeton, Mass.

A painter and engraver of portraits and historical subjects, Edward Savage was born and raised near Worcester, Massachusetts.[1] He began working professionally in Boston around 1785, having taught himself to paint by copying portraits by John Singleton Copley. In 1789 Savage relocated to New York and there created the first of his portraits of George Washington for which he is best known. In 1791 he went to London where he learned about stipple and mezzotint engraving, sought publishers for his prints, and perhaps studied painting under Benjamin West.

After two years Savage returned to Boston, married, and in 1795 settled in Philadelphia, where he produced portraits, historical subjects, and allegories for an engraving and print-selling business. He employed the talented English-trained engraver David Edwin and the young painter John Wesley Jarvis. In 1796 Savage also opened the Columbian Gallery, a museum that to some extent reinforced his print business: Savage hung his most ambitious portrait, a life-size group portrait of George Washington and his family (1796, Washington, D.C., National Gallery of Art), in his gallery where it no doubt spurred sales of his stipple engraving of the same image.

Around 1800 Savage moved to New York, where he took on the painter Charles Bird King as an apprentice. In 1801 he ended his association with Edwin and Jarvis and gave up printmaking in favor of museum entrepreneurship. In New York he reopened his Columbian Gallery and in 1802 added a natural-history display. Around 1812 he moved the gallery to Boston, where he resided until shortly before his death.

Savage was a competent but not particularly inspired painter whose activities — from the making of miniature portraits to history painting and print selling — typified those of American artists of his generation. Relatively well known during his lifetime, he was quickly forgotten after his death, save for the historian William Dunlap's castigation of his limited expertise and "wretched pictures."[2] It was largely the enthusiasm of the early twentieth century for historical prints and portraits from the early republic that secured for Savage a niche in the annals of American art.

1. The most complete account of Savage's career is Louisa Dresser, "Edward Savage, 1761–1817," *Art in America*, vol. XL (Autumn 1952), pp. 157–212.

2. William Dunlap, *History of the Rise and Progress of the Arts of Design in the United States*, vol. I, New York, 1834, p. 321.

After Edward Savage

George Washington

ca. 1794
Watercolor on ivory, 12.4 x 8.3 cm (4⅞ x 3¼ in.)
Inscribed on backing paper: *E. Savage pinxt. 1794*

Savage was one of some eighteen American artists who made considerable professional capital by painting a portrait of George Washington from life. Savage secured his commission by offering to donate a portrait of Washington to Harvard University if Harvard's trustees would arrange for Washington to sit for it. Three sittings, all recorded in Washington's diary, took place in New York between December 21, 1789, and January 6, 1790. The resulting oil portrait (Cambridge, Mass., Harvard University, Fogg Art Museum) is a bust-length feigned oval showing the sitter in uniform with the Order of Cincinnati threaded through his lapel.

Before delivering the promised portrait, Savage made two replicas: one for John Adams (Quincy, Mass., Adams Memorial Society) and another (unlocated), which he took to London in 1791. Savage devoted part of his two years in London to parlaying his Washington portrait into a marketable commodity. He made and published a stipple engraving of it in 1792, then painted a three-quarter-length variant (ca. 1792, The Art Institute of Chicago), which he published in mezzotint. That three-quarter-length portrait in turn became the basis of his *Washington Family* (Washington, D.C., National Gallery of Art), completed in Philadelphia in 1796. Meanwhile, the initial oval portrait of 1790 — on which the present miniature is based — enjoyed wide circulation in print form. Savage apparently gave other artists access to it as well, for the portrait was reproduced by at least twelve engravers in England and America and by one in France.[1]

This miniature was purchased in 1924 as the work of Savage. Since that time two or three similar miniatures have surfaced, all in England.[2] In each case, the artist was not Savage, but a less skilled contemporary who copied either Savage's oval portrait or one of the colored stipple engravings after it. Portraits were commonly made into miniatures by someone other than the original artist, so it is not surprising to find another hand transcribing Savage's portrait with hard contours and an oddly skewed nose and chin. Savage's own miniatures possess firmer facial structure, as can be seen in his self-portrait (ca. 1794, Worcester Art Museum) and in the miniature of Washington made for Benjamin Smith of Philadelphia (unlocated), which was engraved in London in 1794.[3]

1. See the chapters pertaining to Savage in William Spohn Baker, *The Engraved Portraits of Washington, with Notices of the Originals*, Philadelphia, 1880, and Charles Henry Hart, *Catalogue of Engraved Portraits of Washington*, New York, 1904.

2. Two — one of which is the Taft miniature — were described in John Hill Morgan and Mantle Fielding, *The Life Portraits of Washington and Their Replicas*, Philadelphia, 1931, pp. 182–83. Either the second of those two or a third was sold at Sotheby's, London, July 5, 1976, no. 38.

3. Hart, no. 226.

Provenance Admiral Sir Josias Rowley (1765–1842); descended to his great-nephew, Rowley James, Vancouver, B.C.; sale, Sotheby's, London, Dec. 10, 1923, no. 329, to Frank T. Sabin, London; [Scott and Fowles, New York, by 1924]; Taft collection, Dec. 1, 1924.

Exhibition Cincinnati Art Museum, 1934.

Literature "Questions and Answers," *Antiques*, vol. IV (Oct. 1923), p. 189; John Hill Morgan and Mantle Fielding, *The Life Portraits of Washington and Their Replicas*, Philadelphia, 1931, pp. 182–83; *Catalogue of the Taft Museum*, Cincinnati, 1939 and 1958, no. 36; Margaret Kremers, "Edward Savage's Miniature of George Washington in the Taft Museum," *Bulletin of the Cincinnati Art Museum*, vol. XI, no. 1 (Jan. 1940), p. 13, ill. p. 12.

1931.490

Frank Duveneck

Covington, Ky. 1848–1919 Cincinnati

The leading figure and guiding spirit in America's Munich School of the 1870s, Frank Duveneck was one of the most influential American expatriate painters of his generation and one of the major American realists of the nineteenth century. He was born across the Ohio River from Cincinnati in Covington, Kentucky, of Westphalian parents, who christened him Francis Decker. After his father's death and his mother's remarriage, he assumed his stepfather's surname.[1]

As a teenager Duveneck was apprenticed to a German decorator and muralist who executed paintings and plaster decoration for the interiors of churches, monasteries, and convents. Such projects became Duveneck's first professional artistic work, itinerant labor that took him as far afield as Latrobe, Pennsylvania, and Quebec. In New Jersey one of his church patrons encouraged him to go to Munich to study. Taking that advice, Duveneck enrolled at the Bavarian Royal Academy of Art in January 1870.

In Munich he became a student of the academy's young and popular professor Wilhelm von Diez and found his role models in the young painters of the city, especially Wilhelm Leibl who, like Diez, demonstrated a liking for the bold painterly quality of seventeenth-century Netherlandish realism. Duveneck's participation in Diez's class accounted for such vigorous early works as *Head of an Old Man in a Fur Cap* (1870, Cincinnati Art Museum) and *Caucasian Soldier* (1870, Boston, Museum of Fine Arts).[2] He soon developed a bold, unpretentious style based on quick brushwork, strong light and dark contrasts, and rather raw yet picturesque subject matter. He gained quick success: a medal from the academy in 1871 and his first one-person exhibition at the Munich Art Association (Kunstverein) in 1873.

In 1873 Duveneck returned to the United States. He taught for a year in Cincinnati, exhibited there in 1874, then in 1875 had an exhibition at the Boston Art Club, where his work created a sensation and won lavish praise from Henry James and William Morris Hunt. Duveneck, however, sensed greater opportunity in Europe, and, at the urging of his fellow artists, he returned to Munich two years later.

In Duveneck's second Munich period he was one of a substantial handful of young American painters, including William Merritt Chase, J. Frank Currier, John Henry Twachtman, and John White Alexander. He shared studio space and models with Chase and at this time created some of his best works: *The Turkish Page* (1876, Philadelphia, Pennsylvania Academy of the Fine Arts), *The Cobbler's Apprentice* (1877, Taft Museum), and *He Lives by His Wits* (1878, private collection). He maintained a public profile in the United States by sending his work for exhibition to Cincinnati, the Boston Mechanics' Fair, and New York's National Academy of Design and the Society of American Artists.

In 1878 Duveneck, with J. Frank Currier, began an informal summer school near Munich for English-speaking students. Established in the village of Polling, in upper Bavaria, the school attracted a following of young artists known as the Duveneck Boys. These painters — some sixty of them — kept studios in the village and shared a passion for direct painting with a bold, forthright touch. After a year, Duveneck moved his school to Italy; the "boys" rented studios in Florence during the winter and in Venice during the summer.

In Venice in 1880 Duveneck's student Otto Bacher introduced him to etching, which soon interested Duveneck greatly, and he produced etchings of Venetian scenery that quickly rivaled Whistler's in their spontaneity and tonal qualities. During his eight years in Italy, Duveneck's palette lightened as his facture became tighter and more subdued. In 1886 he married Elizabeth

Boot, one of his students; after she died in 1888, he returned to the United States.

Duveneck settled in Covington, Kentucky, took a studio in Cincinnati, and became an influential presence in the local art community. Even though his own work at this time, mostly portraits and some landscapes, did not present as strikingly personal a vision as it had previously, he continued to participate in major exhibitions throughout the country. Perhaps the greatest tribute to his reputation was a retrospective at San Francisco's 1915 Panama-Pacific International Exposition where he received the Special Gold Medal of Honor. Duveneck devoted the major part of his later life to teaching. He served on the faculty at the Art Academy of Cincinnati where he was a much respected figure until his death.

1. The chief biographies of Frank Duveneck are Norbert Heermann, *Frank Duveneck,* Boston, 1918, and Josephine W. Duveneck, *Frank Duveneck: Painter-Teacher,* San Francisco, 1970. More recent studies are Michael Quick, *An American Painter Abroad: Frank Duveneck's European Years,* exh. cat., Cincinnati Art Museum, 1987, and Robert Neuhaus, *Unsuspected Genius: The Art and Life of Frank Duveneck,* San Francisco, 1987.

2. See Quick, pp. 19–21.

Frank Duveneck

The Cobbler's Apprentice

1877
Oil on canvas, 100.3 x 70.8 cm (39½ x 27⅞ in.)
Signed, inscribed, and dated lower right: *F Duveneck. Muni[c]h. / 1877.*

The image of a boy apprentice in apron and shirtsleeves attracted Duveneck three times between 1872 and 1878. His first rendition was the so-called *Whistling Boy* (1872, Cincinnati Art Museum). Chase's similar painting of 1875, *Boy Smoking (The Apprentice)* (Hartford, Conn., Wadsworth Atheneum), may have stimulated Duveneck to repeat the theme on a larger scale in *The Cobbler's Apprentice* of 1877 and *He Lives by His Wits* (private collection) of 1878. *The Cobbler's Apprentice,* executed with exquisite care, is one of his most accomplished Munich paintings. It is also his most explicit tribute to the past schools of painting that he found inspirational.

This canvas belongs to an interval when Duveneck was energetically working to establish himself as a painter of bold sensibilities. Between 1876 and 1878 he seemed intent on producing deliberately provocative showpieces appropriate to an artist about to set himself up as a leading member of a new school. Two of these paintings, *The Turkish Page* (1876, Philadelphia, Pennsylvania Academy of the Fine Arts) and *Still Life with Watermelon* (1878, Cincinnati Art Museum), relate closely to *The Cobbler's Apprentice.*

All three paintings resist easy storytelling. In fact, the lack of a story line was a recurrent criticism of *The Turkish Page* when it was exhibited at the National Academy of Design in 1877.[1] *Still Life with Watermelon* shows a gathering of visually, but not gas-

1931.415

tronomically, compatible red foods: wine, watermelon, and tomatoes. *The Cobbler's Apprentice* similarly lacks the connective tissue that makes a narrative comprehensible. The relationship between the boots and the head of cauliflower in the basket is not evident, nor does the fence post help to identify where the boy is. Generally speaking, the artist reveals too little information and deflects too much visual attention to irrelevant details such as the boy's lips and fingernails. One can speculate that Duveneck placed his brushstrokes at a level of importance equal to the painting's narrative.

The composition of this painting is simple: a few objects are presented in a dark, shallow space. A half-length figure of a boy, dressed in a work shirt and apron, stands almost emblematically by a battered fence post. With one hand he holds a large twig basket containing a cauliflower and a pair of boots. He holds a cigar in his other hand while gently blowing smoke through his pursed lips. The head of cauliflower and the boy's head are aligned along the vertical axis of the painting; this and other verticals give the composition a steady, sure quality. Liquid brushwork defines the picture's large surfaces, while small details — the tip of the boy's nose, his lower lip, fingernails, and the ash of his cigar — are given bright, hard highlights so that one does not forget them.

Duveneck has managed a remarkably sympathetic portrayal of a youngster of low social rank. The image is dignified because of its simplicity, lack of pretension, and thinly veiled references to several seventeenth-century realists. The boy's ruddy cheeks are remarkably like those painted by Frans Hals, as is the somber but rich coloring of grays, browns, and roses against a blackened background. The gesture of blowing smoke is readily associated with Adriaen Brouwer's tavern clients, while the boy's basket recalls Spanish still-life painting. The portraitlike format in which a genre figure is shown at close range and with great specificity may be indebted to the paintings of Diego Velázquez.

This pictorial idiom, of soberly colored, strongly lit, forthright subject matter derived from seventeenth-century Dutch and Spanish *alla prima* naturalism, was adopted by progressive younger artists in Munich when Duveneck first arrived there and by the American painters who joined him during the later 1870s. To its various practitioners, the Munich style offered not just an ideology of realism but a program of painting for its own sake.

1. "Art," *The Atlantic Monthly*, vol. xxxix (May 1877), pp. 641–42; "The Academy Exhibition," *The Art Journal*, vol. iii (1877), p. 157.

Provenance The artist to Von Hessling, American vice-consul in Munich; Joseph Stransky (by 1918); purchased by Norbert Heermann for Charles P. Taft, 1918.

Exhibitions Cincinnati Art Museum, *Exhibition of the Work of Frank Duveneck*, May 23–June 21, 1936 (cat., no. 21); Cleveland Museum of Art, *American Painting from 1860 until Today*, June 23–Oct. 4, 1937 (cat., no. 51); Bloomfield Hills, Mich., Cranbrook Academy of Art, *Light and the Painter*, Sept. 5–28, 1952 (cat., no. 26); Raleigh, North Carolina Museum of Art, *Tobacco and Smoking in Art*, Oct. 14–Dec. 4, 1960 (cat. by James B. Byrnes, no. 18); Minneapolis Institute of Arts, *Four Centuries of American Art*, Nov. 27, 1963–Jan. 19, 1964; Cincinnati Art Museum (exh. organized by E. B. Crocker Art Gallery, Sacramento, Calif.), *Munich and American Realism in the Nineteenth Century*, Apr. 15–May 28, 1978 (cat. by Michael Quick, Eberhard Ruhmer, and Richard V. West, no. 24); Mobile, Ala., The Fine Arts Museum of the South, *The Ripening of American Art: Duveneck and Chase, 1876–1912*, Oct. 16–Nov. 25, 1979 (cat., no. 2); Lexington, University of Kentucky Art Museum, *The Kentucky Painter: From the Frontier Era to the Great War*, Jan. 23–Mar. 15, 1981 (cat. by Arthur F. Jones and Bruce Weber, no. 30); Cincinnati Art Museum, *An American Painter Abroad: Frank Duveneck's European Years*, Oct. 3, 1987–Jan. 3, 1988 (cat. by Michael Quick, no. 17).

Literature Norbert Heermann, *Paintings by Frank Duveneck*, Boston, 1918, p. 52; Maurice W. Brockwell, *A Catalogue of Paintings in the Collection of Mr. and Mrs. Charles P. Taft*, New York, 1920, pp. 192–93, no. 77; Walter H. Siple, "Cincinnati Honors an American Master: A Duveneck Memorial Show," *Art News* (June 13, 1936), pp. 15–16; *Catalogue of the Taft Museum*, Cincinnati, 1939 and 1958, no. 502; Josephine W. Duveneck, *Frank Duveneck: Painter-Teacher*, San Francisco, 1970, p. 65; Robert Neuhaus, *Unsuspected Genius: The Art and Life of Frank Duveneck*, San Francisco, 1987, pp. 45–48, ill. p. 44.

1931.415

John White Alexander
Allegheny City, Pa. 1856–1915 New York

In his own time John White Alexander was considered one of America's most creative expatriate painters, an artist equally at home in Paris and New York, whose style successfully bridged academic and avant-garde spheres.[1] Born and raised in what is now metropolitan Pittsburgh, he left for New York at the age of eighteen and worked as an illustrator for the Harper Brothers firm. Three years later he left to study art in Europe.

Arriving in Paris in 1877, Alexander continued on to Munich, enrolling at the Munich Royal Academy and joining the art colony in nearby Polling (the so-called Duveneck Boys), which had recently formed under Frank Duveneck and J. Frank Currier. There, Alexander practiced the style associated with the Munich School: a dark palette combined with bravura brushwork and forthright naturalism. In the fall of 1879 he accompanied the Duveneck Boys to Florence and then proceeded with the group to Venice in 1880.

Back in New York in 1881, Alexander reestablished his relationship with the Harper firm, was appointed drawing instructor at Princeton University, and gained a reputation as a portrait painter. During the next nine years he traveled widely. In the cosmopolitan ambience of London and Paris he formed friendships with a number of artists and writers, including James McNeill Whistler, who became the most important influence of his mature career.

In 1891 Alexander moved to Paris. Influenced by the atmosphere of symbolism and aestheticism, he developed his mature painting style. He presented women, posed in theatrical arabesques, in a palette that combined sharp contrasts of light and dark with shimmering pastel coloring.[2] Perhaps best exemplified by *Isabella and the Pot of Basil* (1897, Boston, Museum of Fine Arts), his painting took on the evocativeness of symbolism without the complications of private meaning.

Alexander took up mural painting in 1895 when he won a commission for six lunettes in the corridor of the Library of Congress, Washington, D.C. In 1905 he was the recipient of the largest and most lucrative mural contract ever offered to an American painter: $175,000 to decorate the central stairway for the new building of the Carnegie Institute in Pittsburgh, which opened in 1907. The work, which Alexander never completed because of ill health, was a tour de force of his elegant, tonal allegorizing.

Alexander used his considerable reputation to promote artists' causes. Elected to the National Academy of Design in 1902, he became its president in 1909 and served in that capacity until his death.

1. "John W. Alexander," *Literary Digest*, vol. l (June 19, 1915), p. 1466.

2. See the catalogues for the two most important recent exhibitions of his work: Mary Anne Goley, *John White Alexander, 1856–1915*, National Collection of Fine Arts, Washington, D.C., 1976, and Sandra Leff, *John White Alexander, 1856–1915: Fin-de-Siècle American*, Graham Gallery, New York, 1980.

John White Alexander

Profile of a Girl (Study Head of a Munich Peasant)

ca. 1879
Oil on canvas, 51.1 x 44.5 cm (20⅛ x 17½ in.)

The time Alexander spent with the American art colony in Polling lasted from June 1878 to early October 1879. Although

1931.471

Provenance The artist to Julius Rolshaven (a fellow student in Polling in 1879 and then in Florence, 1881), in 1917; Taft collection, after 1920.

Exhibition Detroit Museum of Art [also Cincinnati, Saint Louis, Colorado Springs, and Cleveland], *Memorial Exhibition of Paintings by the Late John White Alexander*, 1916–17 (cat., no. 6, as *Study Head of a Munich Peasant*).

Literature *Catalogue of the Taft Museum*, Cincinnati, 1939 and 1958, no. 551.

1931.471

John Singer Sargent
Florence 1856–1925 London

Few English-speaking painters of the turn of the century so engaged contemporary observers as did John Singer Sargent. The art critic Sadakichi Hartmann described him as one of those phenomenal individuals "who at the threshold of his career had apparently nothing more to learn."[1] By the early 1900s he was widely acknowledged — even by his detractors — to be one of the virtuosos in his field. The premier portraitist of Edwardian England, he was astoundingly successful as a producer of images that were at once casual, grand, graceful, and provocative. He was also a versatile and daring plein-air and genre painter and the most accomplished watercolorist of his generation.

Supremely cosmopolitan, Sargent was the eldest son of a Philadelphia surgeon whose wife desired to live abroad. They went to Europe in 1854, raising their family in a succession of cities on the Continent. Born in Florence, Sargent spent a peripatetic childhood in Paris, Biarritz, Rome, Florence, Venice, and Dresden. Despite his American citizenship, he spent less than eight years in the United States and was twenty years old before he saw America for the first time.

Sargent had his first contact with professional artists in Rome at the age of twelve, and then between 1870 and 1873 attended drawing classes at the Academy of Fine Arts, Florence. At age eighteen he became a student in the Paris atelier of Emile-Auguste Carolus-Duran. In 1877 he began to exhibit at the Paris Salon. During the next two years his portraits and genre scenes revealed his uncanny mastery of the subtle coloring and flashy, disciplined brushwork that were the hallmarks of the painterly faction of contemporary French academic artists.

In keeping with the tendencies of other young painters of the 1870s, Sargent developed an interest in and an allegiance to seventeenth-century realism. He traveled to Spain in 1879 and to Holland and Belgium in 1880 in search of visual stimuli and the key to a sober, probing, yet spontaneous style. The inspiration of Velázquez — strong tonal contrasts, dark coloring, and uncluttered composition — was evident in Sargent's subsequent paintings, particularly in his first major work, *The Daughters of Edward Darly Boit* (1882, Boston, Museum of Fine Arts).

Sargent began his career as a portraitist with a taste for the provocative gesture, which reached its most audacious heights in his notorious *Madame X (Madame Pierre Gautreau)* (1884, New York, The Metropolitan Museum of Art). Exhibited that year at the Paris Salon, it created a scandal that damaged

brief, it was an important interval, for it placed him in an environment of independent painters. It also provided him with his first sustained exposure to the vigorous *alla prima* painting that became a cornerstone of his later technique.[1]

In *Profile of a Girl* Alexander appropriated one of the most characteristic images of the Munich School of the 1870s. Oil sketches of heads of the Bavarian people were the Munich School's variation of the *têtes d'expression* practiced in the French and Italian art academies, but in Germany picturesque local people were substituted for studio models. These were not studies for larger works, anatomical exercises, or portraits. Instead, they are vehicles for bold brushwork and deep chiaroscuro, a distinctive and novel subgenre of picture making in which experimental rendering is practiced for its own sake.

For Alexander, the straightforwardness of a strongly lit head against a nondescript background seems to have spurred him to technical boldness. The opportunity to depict such an effect was doubtless instrumental in the creation of this profile of a peasant girl. It is similar to Duveneck's *Girl in a Black Hood* (1879, Cincinnati Art Museum) and may represent the same model. Approximately the same size, the two paintings show identically dressed young women, each wearing a veiled black cap, ruffled white blouse, and russet dress. Alexander's *Profile*, however, is more refined and delicately rendered throughout than Duveneck's figure. His feathery, thin brushwork, slightly subdued coloring, and the remoteness of his sitter's expression all prefigure the stylistic signature he eventually developed.

1. See Edwin Lockman, MS interview with Mrs. John White Alexander, Feb. 1928, John White Alexander Papers, roll 1727, Archives of American Art, Smithsonian Institution, Washington, D.C.

Sargent's portrait-painting business in Paris and, according to some reports, caused him to leave France.

By 1886 Sargent had vacated his Paris studio and relocated to London. He became a close friend of Henry James, helped found the New English Art Club, and associated with a number of American artists working in England, among them Edwin Austin Abbey and Frank D. Millet. Shortly after going to England, Sargent began experimenting with plein-air painting and soon created his most ambitious canvas in that vein, *Carnation, Lily, Lily, Rose* (1885–86, London, The Tate Gallery). He continued to paint in oils outdoors during the summers of 1887 to 1889, producing the innovative canvases that earned him a place in the annals of American impressionism.

From 1888 to 1890 Sargent worked periodically in the United States, largely in Boston and New York. Initiating this period was his first one-person show of some twenty paintings presented at the winter exhibition of Boston's St. Botolph Club. In Boston Sargent developed his strongest American roots. The first full-scale retrospective exhibition of his work was staged there in 1899, and there he won his three largest commissions: murals for the newly built Boston Public Library (1890–1919), the Museum of Fine Arts (1916–25), and Harvard University's Widener Library (1921–22).

In England Sargent's reputation as a portrait painter grew steadily through the 1890s and early 1900s. His stately full-length portraits became the contemporary counterparts to the grand manner of Van Dyck and Gainsborough and were so sought after that by 1905 he had begun to complain about the constant demand of such commissions. From the 1880s to the early 1900s Sargent executed the watercolors for which he is best known, the result of his near-constant travels, particularly summer trips across the Alps to Italy.

Sargent was elected academician by the Royal Academy, London, and the National Academy of Design, New York, in the same year: 1897. He was also made Knight of the Legion of Honor, but perhaps the most visible tributes to him were the exhibitions of his work. In the United States he participated not only in such exhibiting forums as the Society of American Artists and the National Academy but also in the major fairs, from the World's Columbian Exposition of 1893 to the 1915 Panama-Pacific International Exposition, where thirteen of his pictures were shown. In 1924 the Grand Central Art Galleries in New York opened a major retrospective of his work, only to be outdone two years later by vast memorial exhibitions at the Royal Academy and the Metropolitan Museum of Art.

1. Sadakichi Hartmann, *A History of American Art*, vol. II, New York, 1932, p. 213. The basic biographical sourcebook on Sargent is Evan Charteris, *John Sargent*, New York, 1927. The most comprehensive recent survey is Richard Ormond, *John Singer Sargent: Paintings, Drawings, Watercolors*, New York, 1970.

John Singer Sargent

Robert Louis Stevenson

1887
Oil on canvas, 51 x 61.8 cm (20⅛ x 24⅜ in.)
Signed, inscribed, and dated lower right: *John S. Sargent / Bournemouth 1887*

Robert Louis Stevenson is a portrait seemingly without artifice. Its composition does not strive to be memorable, nor is the sitter's pose particularly forceful. Stevenson sits in a wicker chair

1931.472

beside a closed cabinet in his study. Little of the area around him is visible, and his expressive hand merely holds a cigarette. Using a sober "Spanish" palette of grays and browns, Sargent kept the painting's brightest colors and busiest textures away from the sitter. In his black velvet jacket, he remains a thoroughly serene presence and in his calm simplicity becomes the painting's anchor.

Some of Sargent's most innovative and psychologically satisfying works are the informal portraits he painted of friends. Among these, *Robert Louis Stevenson and His Wife* (1885, New York, collection of Mrs. John Hay Whitney) is surely his most daring double portrait, and *Robert Louis Stevenson* is arguably his most sympathetic rendition of a male sitter. Sargent had probably been introduced to Stevenson (1850–1894) by their mutual friend Henry James. Sargent became one of the most welcome visitors to Skerryvore, Stevenson's house in Bournemouth, and the most talked-about painter to have created the writer's likeness.

The present painting was long thought to be the first of two portraits of Stevenson, begun when Sargent visited the writer in November 1884 and completed just after the new year. On January 3, 1885, Stevenson, in a postscript to a letter to the painter Will H. Low, wrote: "O, Sargent has been and painted my portrait; a very nice fellow he is, and is supposed to have done well; it is a poetical but very chicken-boned figure-head, as thus represented."[1] Sargent's first two biographers presumed this portrait to be the Taft painting, which has continued to be associated with the date 1885.[2] The signature and date of 1887 were assumed to have been added just prior to Sargent's one-person show at Copley Hall in Boston.[3]

A second portrait, of Stevenson and his wife, followed in the fall of 1885. On October 22 of that year Stevenson again wrote to Low:

Sargent was down again and painted a portrait of me walking about in my own dining-room in my own velveteen jacket, and twisting as I go my own moustache; at one corner a glimpse of my wife in an Indian dress and seated in a chair. . . . I am at one extreme corner; my wife in this wild dress, and looking like a ghost at the extreme other end.

. . . All this is touched in lovely, with that witty touch of Sargent's: but of course it looks dam [*sic*] queer as a whole.[4]

The portrait became Stevenson's and hung at Vailma, his house in Samoa.

Although Sargent's early biographers spoke of two portraits of Stevenson, in fact it appears that he made three — the Taft picture being the third, not the first. The first painting, the "poetical but very chicken-boned figure-head," must also have been given to Stevenson, for in 1908 Sargent asked Mrs. Stevenson for photographs of his two portraits. When Arnold Genthe, who had seen the double portrait in Mrs. Stevenson's home many times, asked about the other, she confided that she had destroyed it.[5]

The Taft canvas was painted during a visit by Sargent to Bournemouth in 1887, which went unrecorded by both Sargent's and Stevenson's biographers. On April 22, 1887, Fanny, Stevenson's wife, wrote to Sidney Colvin of this sitting: "Mr. Sargent came last night to do the portrait. It begins well, and the one hand that is finished expresses about all of Louis."[6] Eight days later, on April 30, Fanny wrote from Skerryvore to the playwright William Archer:

Mr. Sargent has just been here, and has painted a really good portrait of Louis. I understand that the standing figure where I play the part of an East Indian ghost is to be published by the Pall Mall. I stipulated that the ghost be left out. It seems a pity that it should not have been this new one, though for some inscrutable reason, conscientious probably, Mr. Sargent prefers the first. The last one is at Mr. Sargent's studio. . . . I should like to know your opinion of it.[7]

She asked the same question of her friend Una Taylor, who, after seeing the portrait, replied: "I liked it far away the best of any I have seen at all; it is wonderfully true and not in the least theatrical as the other standing one was. Isn't it a pity it should go off to America to this stranger lady, or is Mr. Sargent going to do a fourth and still better one soon?"[8]

This third portrait, which Mrs. Stevenson liked so much, was commissioned by Sargent's friend Charles Fairchild of Boston, whose wife, a literary hostess, was an ardent admirer of Stevenson. Fairchild was in London in May 1887 to fetch the painting, but in the meantime, William Archer suggested to Mrs. Stevenson, "Why don't you have Mr. Sargent's picture photographed? My wife and I went down to see it this afternoon (Sargent was out), and are delighted with it. It is living to the tip of the cigarette."[9] Fanny Stevenson was gathering quantities of photographs to take when she and her husband left for the South Seas, and indeed a photograph of the Stevenson portrait was among the family possessions.[10] Lacking some shading in the face and detail in the background, it could have been taken of the Taft canvas before Sargent added the final touches he usually gave his portraits.

1. Sidney Colvin, *The Letters of Robert Louis Stevenson*, vol. 1, New York, 1899, p. 393.

2. William Howe Downes, *John S. Sargent: His Life and Work*, Boston, 1925, p. 142; Evan Charteris, *John Sargent*, New York, 1927, p. 259.

3. Richard Ormond, *John Singer Sargent: Paintings, Drawings, Watercolors*, New York, 1970, pp. 244–45.

4. Colvin, pp. 428–29.

5. Arnold Genthe, *. . . As I Remember*, New York, 1937, pp. 116–17.

6. Quoted in E[dward] V[errall] Lucas, *The Colvins and Their Friends*, London, 1928, p. 164, but incorrectly dated to 1885. The original manuscript is in the Robert Louis Stevenson Papers, Beinecke Rare Book Room and Manuscript Library, Yale University (MS B3650); Richard Ormond discovered the correct date.

7. C[harles] Archer, *William Archer: Life, Work, and Friendships*, New York, 1931, pp. 149–50.

8. Letter from Una Ashworth Taylor to Fanny Stevenson, Apr. 28, [1887], Robert Lewis Stevenson Papers (MS B5874). I am grateful to Richard Ormond for also bringing this piece of correspondence to light.

9. Archer to Mrs. Stevenson, May 2, 1887, quoted in Archer, p. 151.

10. In the Austin Strong albums at the Silverado Museum, St. Helena, Calif.

Provenance Mr. and Mrs. Charles Fairchild, New York (until 1903); W. P. Paterson, London; [John Levy Galleries, New York]; [Scott and Fowles, New York, by 1922]; Taft collection, Jan. 3, 1922.

Exhibitions Boston, St. Botolph Club, *Paintings by John S. Sargent*, Jan. 28–Feb. 11, 1888; New York, Society of American Artists, *Fourteenth Annual Exhibition*, Dec. 5–25, 1892, no. 278; New York, Society of American Artists, *Twentieth Anniversary Exhibition*, Mar. 19–Apr. 23, 1898, no. 306; Philadelphia, Pennsylvania Academy of the Fine Arts, *Sixty-eighth Annual Exhibition*, Jan. 16–Feb. 25, 1899, no. 48; Boston, Copley Hall, Boston Art Students Association, *Paintings and Sketches by John S. Sargent, R.A.*, Feb. 20–Mar. 13, 1899, no. 26; Cincinnati Museum Association, *Sixth Annual Exhibition of American Art*, 1899, no. 8; New York, American Art Association, *Loan Exhibition of Portraits*, 1903, no. 208; The Art Institute of Chicago [also New York], *Sargent, Whistler, and Mary Cassatt*, Jan. 7–May 23, 1954 (cat. by Frederick A. Sweet, no. 56); Milwaukee, Marquette University, *Seventy-five Years of American Painting*, Apr. 22–May 3, 1956; Detroit, Institute of Arts [also San Francisco], *Painting in America, The Story of 450 Years*, Apr. 23– June 9, 1957, no. 125; Pittsburgh, Carnegie Institute [also Richmond, Va.], *American Classics of the Nineteenth Century*, Oct. 18, 1957–Mar. 16, 1958, no. 110; Grand Rapids Art Gallery, Mich., *The Art of Seeing*, Oct. 3–Nov. 25, 1958; Raleigh, North Carolina Museum of Art, *Tobacco and Smoking in Art*, Oct. 14–Dec. 4, 1960 (cat. by James B. Byrnes, no. 25); Washington, D.C., Corcoran Gallery of Art [also Cleveland], *The Private World of John Singer Sargent*, Apr. 18–Aug. 16, 1964 (cat. by Donelson F. Hoopes, no. 38); Columbus Gallery of Fine Arts, Ohio, *Augustus John and His Contemporaries*, Feb. 5–Mar. 14, 1971.

Literature William Howe Downes, *John S. Sargent: His Life and Work*, Boston, 1925, p. 142; Evan Charteris, *John Sargent*, New York, 1927, pp. 69, 79–80; Charles Archer, *William Archer*, London, 1931, pp. 149–51; W. G. Blaikie Murdoch, "Portraits of Robert Louis Stevenson," *The American Magazine of Art*, vol. XXIII (Aug. 1931), p. 120; *Catalogue of the Taft Museum*, Cincinnati, 1939 and 1958, no. 106 (ill.); Regina Shoolman and Charles E. Slatkin, *The Enjoyment of Art in America*, Philadelphia and New York, 1942, p. 684, pl. 653; Malcolm Elwin, *The Strange Case of Robert Louis Stevenson*, London, 1950, pp. 193–94, 226; Charles Merrill Mount, *John Singer Sargent: A Biography*, New York, 1969, pp. 96–98, 100; Richard Ormond, *John Singer Sargent: Paintings, Drawings, Watercolors*, New York, 1970, pp. 32, 244–45; Richard J. Boyle, *American Impressionism*, Boston, 1982, p. 212; Carter Ratcliff, *John Singer Sargent*, New York, 1982, pp. 93–94; Lucia Miller, "John Singer Sargent in the Diaries of Lucia Fairchild, 1890 and 1891," *Archives of American Art Journal*, vol. XXVI, no. 4 (1986), pp. 2, 6; Stanley Olson, Warren Adelson, and Richard Ormond, *Sargent at Broadway: The Impressionist Years*, exh. cat., Coe Kerr Gallery, New York, 1986, pp. 41–42; Margaret Hodges, "When Robert Louis Stevenson Was One of Us," *American Heritage*, vol. XXXIX, no. 8 (Dec. 1988), ill. p. 81; Kate F. Jennings, *John Singer Sargent*, New York, 1991, p. 41, pl. p. 42.

1931.472

Frederic van Vliet Baker

Brooklyn 1876–1964 New York

Son of the landscape and marine painter Charles Baker, Frederic van Vliet Baker began his formal art studies at the Pratt Institute in Brooklyn, where he was enrolled from 1891 to 1895. Probably in the spring of 1895 he left for Paris, attending both the Ecole des Beaux-Arts and the Colarossi Academy. He studied primarily with Gustave Courtois, then one of France's most admired academic portrait painters and one of Colarossi's most popular teachers.

During the ten years Baker spent in Paris, he worked in Courtois's studio and in 1902 assisted Courtois's good friend Pascal-Adolphe-Jean Dagnan-Bouveret on the decoration of the Sorbonne. He also traveled to Switzerland and Italy and worked as a copyist of portraits and figure paintings for socially prominent Europeans. In 1901 he became an associate of the National Society of Fine Arts, the first artist to be elected after exhibiting there just once.

Baker again exhibited at the Salon in 1902 and 1903 but also began to send his paintings to competitions in Ghent, Vienna, and several venues in the United States. His work was shown at the Art Institute of Chicago in 1903 and 1904, at the National Academy of Design in New York, and at the Saint Louis International Exposition in 1904. In Saint Louis he exhibited his most ambitious painting, *Gethsemane* (1904, unlocated), which may well have shown some influence from Dagnan-Bouveret.

Upon returning to the United States in 1905, he exhibited four of his portrait and figure paintings, including *Gethsemane*, at the Pratt Institute. He was described as one of New York's promising young artists and praised for his technical accomplishment, particularly his discipline in drawing.[1] Baker spent the rest of his career in New York. In 1906 he became a member of the Salmagundi Club and was appointed to the faculty at the Pratt Institute. He taught life drawing, painting, and composition there until 1942 but seems never again to have produced paintings with the same energy and ambition as he had in Paris. After retirement, Baker had a one-person show of pastels at the Sperling Gallery, New York.[2]

1. Unidentified newspaper review of the Pratt exhibition, registrar's files, Pratt Institute, Brooklyn, New York.

2. Howard Devree, "Among the New Exhibitions," *New York Times*, June 18, 1944, p. 7.

Frederic van Vliet Baker

Portrait of a Woman

1903
Oil on panel, 33 x 23.8 cm (13 x 9⅜ in.)
Signed, inscribed, and dated upper left: FREDERIC BAKER. / PARIS. 1903

The fashion of *japonisme*, which arose during the 1860s and lasted until about 1910, brought with it a new genre in painting: the depiction of a Caucasian studio model in oriental dress. The "*japonisme* portrait" attracted a broad range of artists from James McNeill Whistler and Claude Monet to James Tissot and Jules-Joseph Lefebvre. This tiny panel painting is a simplified version of academic costume pieces such as Lefebvre's *The Language of the Fan* (ca. 1882–83, Norfolk, Va., Chrysler Museum).

Baker's format is that of a bust-length portrait, although his image is hardly a portrait in the strict sense of the word. It is instead the base for a still life of floral motifs — in the tapestry-like backdrop, the model's kimono, and the red carnations in

1931.441

her hair. The result is an unobtrusive, orientalized decoration for a domestic interior, suitable for a patron enamored of turn-of-the-century academic tastes.

Provenance Purchased after 1920, perhaps in New York, from the artist.
Literature *Catalogue of the Taft Museum*, Cincinnati, 1939 and 1958, no. 549.

1931.441

Henry F. Farny
Ribeauvillé, Alsace 1847–1916 Cincinnati

Henry François Farny was one of the most important painter-illustrators of Native Americans during the late nineteenth century.[1] The son of an Alsatian carpenter, he arrived in the United States with his family at the age of six. His father, a Protestant and republican partisan during the Revolution of 1848, left France for religious and political reasons. The elder Farny brought his wife and three children to Warren County in northwestern Pennsylvania, where he ran a sawmill. Six years later, he moved the family to Cincinnati, where Henry attended school for two years, worked as a bookkeeper for two more, and then joined the lithography firm of Gibson and Company. When his first illustrations were published locally in 1865, he came to the attention of editors at *Harper's Weekly*. The next year he went to New York to work for the Harper Brothers firm as a wood engraver and cartoonist.

In 1867 Farny decided to go to Europe to study art, intending to become a portrait painter. His initial destination was Rome, where he arranged to study under fellow Cincinnatian Thomas Buchanan Read. Read urged Farny to study landscape and sent him to the landscape painter Hermann Herzog, who resided near Düsseldorf. By the time Farny returned to Cincinnati in late 1870, he had become familiar with the Düsseldorf landscape style, befriended the young Hungarian genre painter Mihaly Munkácsy, and spent time in Paris.

Farny once again found work in Cincinnati as a free-lance draftsman, his largest commission being the decorations (presumably illustrations of pigs) for the booth of the Cincinnati Pork-Packers' Association at the 1873 Vienna exposition. He took his drawings to Vienna, then embarked on a second European study tour lasting five months. He visited Munich, where he met Frank Duveneck and studied with Wilhelm von Diez, Duveneck's teacher at the Bavarian Royal Academy of Arts there. Along with Duveneck, John Twachtman, and Frank Dengler, Farny made a return trip to Munich in 1875, this time staying about a year.

Back in Cincinnati, Farny again turned to free-lance illustration. His first major contract, which established his stature in the field, was for seventy-two illustrations for the 1879 edition of the *McGuffy Reader* schoolbook series. Around 1880 he began painting more frequently and became interested in Native American subjects, which grew to be his specialty.

In August 1881 Farny took his first trip West, his destination the Dakota Territory. He returned to Cincinnati three months later laden with photographs, watercolor portrait sketches, and quantities of Sioux clothing and artifacts.[2] He continually used these, along with commercial photographs, to create both his magazine illustrations and his paintings. Five subsequent trips allowed Farny to add to his impressions. In 1882 he visited Washington, D.C., to see a delegation of Zuñi Indians. In 1883 he went to Montana to witness the inauguration of the Northern Pacific Railroad. He traveled down the Missouri River in 1884, to California in 1888, and to the Kiowa and Comanche settlements in Oklahoma in 1894.

Between 1883 and 1893 Farny's illustrations of Native Americans appeared in *Century Magazine, Harper's Weekly, Leslie's Illustrated Newspaper,* and *Harper's Young People.* Spontaneous and sketchlike, they presented their subjects with precision and clarity and exemplified the current standard of technical excellence in the illustrated press. They also made Farny successful enough to abandon commercial illustration in favor of painting.

In 1889 Farny began his shift away from magazine illustration and in 1893 turned to oil painting exclusively. His canvases, which he continued to produce until 1912, were consistent extensions of his illustrative style. With the easy naturalism of contemporary French academic painting, they were said to combine the fidelity of detail "of a Meissonier with the broad sweep of a Gérôme."[3] Farny had the ability to make his compositions seem immutably true, even while romanticizing his subject matter.

1931.466

His work extolled the free-ranging, noble savage at a time when that phenomenon had effectively ceased to exist.

By the 1890s Farny had become Cincinnati's most celebrated painter. He was patronized by the city's leading citizens and by such august personages as Theodore Roosevelt and Kaiser Wilhelm II. He showed work at the 1889 Universal Exposition in Paris, was a jury member at the 1893 World's Columbian Exposition in Chicago, and exhibited in the 1904 Universal Exposition in Saint Louis. However, the local demand for his paintings was sufficiently strong that he did not need to exhibit widely and chose not to. He did not make the expected affiliation with the National Academy of Design in New York and participated infrequently in national juried exhibitions. Repeatedly, art critics felt it necessary to identify him as "Henry Farny of Cincinnati."

1. The most recent investigation of Farny's art and life is Denny Carter, *Henry Farny,* New York, 1978. The Cincinnati Art Museum owns the most extensive collection of Farny's work and mounted retrospective exhibitions in 1943 and 1965.

2. "Mr. Farny among the Sioux," *Cincinnati Daily Gazette,* Nov. 8, 1881, p. 8.

3. Edward Flynn, "The Paintings of H. F. Farny," *Cincinnati Commercial Gazette,* Mar. 14, 1893.

௫♣

Henry F. Farny

The Song of the Talking Wire

1904
Oil on canvas, 56 x 101.6 cm (22⅛ x 40 in.)
Signed and dated lower right: H.F. FARNY / ☉ 1904

The scene Farny creates in *The Song of the Talking Wire* is an amalgam of his favorite visual motifs presented with the sharp delineation, subdued coloring, and restrained composition that he favored around 1900. In a winter landscape a Native American in Sioux dress presses his ear against a telegraph pole. Behind him stand his two horses, a deer carcass slung across one of them. To the left, half buried in the snow, is what may be a buffalo skull. The focus of attention is the Sioux's glowering red face, betraying the curiosity, bewilderment, and anger of one confronted with the novel paraphernalia of progress.

Farny recorded the quiet aspects of Native American life, showing his subjects either in camp or on the trail. His paintings often focus on a lone figure or a small group set against a vast horizon, frequently in snow or twilight. His Native Americans are invariably engaged in mundane tasks. Whether in camp, hunting, or gathering fuel, they are silent presences, physically and psychologically remote from the viewer. In essence Farny's was the same successful formula used in late-nineteenth-century Salon painters' depictions of Arabs, Bedhouins, and southern European peasants; only the venue is changed.

The present painting is a studio-created image using a stock backdrop. The costume of the Sioux in the foreground was assembled from the artifacts of Farny's 1881 trip to the Standing Rock Reservation in the Dakota Territory. Significantly, the image contradicts the artist's own observations, for the Sioux he saw were hardly masters of the open plain as this hunter appears to be. What he witnessed (and recorded) were Native Americans dependent on government-distributed rations, because game had long since disappeared.[1]

Such contradictions serve a symbolic purpose here. The fallen game and setting sun combine with the winter landscape to create a medley of references to death, implying that as the Native Americans' world comes to an end they do not yet understand the one taking its place. The man gives the impression that he will continue to live in isolation, remaining apart even as incursions are made into his wilderness environment. Farny's pervasive emblems add a quietly evocative note to a clearly readable image, to make this painting an example of his work at its finest.

The Song of the Talking Wire was remembered at Farny's death as one of his most widely known paintings.[2] It was his selection — at the solicitation of Kaiser Wilhelm II — for the exhibition of American paintings held in Berlin in 1910. Photographic reproductions of the work made there were widely distributed in both Europe and the United States.

Despite such recognition, Farny's work fell into critical disfavor around 1900. At a time when the aesthetics of Whistler, the Barbizon School, and impressionism became the marks of progressivism, the work of painter-illustrators, particularly of the American West, was judged deficient as art. Sadakichi Hartmann felt that Farny and his colleagues identified with subject matter that at best was only semipicturesque; Samuel Isham would have damned Farny as he did Frederic Remington: "an illustrator rather than a painter."[3]

Such judgments pertain to *The Song of the Talking Wire*, for in 1904 Farny submitted it to the Pittsburgh Annual. It was his only entry to an exhibition whose jury usually favored established artists. But Pittsburgh's was a forum that championed aestheticism, and, predictably, *The Song of the Talking Wire* was rejected. The uncertainty of Farny's reception outside his established circle of admirers may have been the reason he remained in Cincinnati near an audience that would accept his art on its own terms.

1. See *Henry Farny, 1847–1916*, exh. cat., University of Texas at Austin, Archer M. Huntington Art Gallery, 1983, p. 22.

2. [Obituary], *Cincinnati Enquirer*, Dec. 24, 1916.

3. Sadakichi Hartmann, *A History of American Art*, 1st ed., 1902, vol. I, Boston, 1932, pp. 259–60; Samuel Isham, *The History of American Painting*, 1st ed., 1905, New York, 1927, p. 501.

Provenance The artist to Charles P. Taft, ca. 1905.

Exhibitions Berlin, Royal Academy, and Munich, Art Association, *Masterpieces of American Painting*, 1910 (cat. by Christian Brinton, no. 19); Cincinnati, Rudolph Wurlitzer Gallery, *Exhibition of the Work of Henry F. Farny*, May 18–June 3, 1935; Cincinnati Art Museum, *Henry F. Farny and the American Indian*, Mar. 2–Apr. 4, 1943 (cat. by Walter H. Siple, no. 29); Art Association of Montreal, 1948; New York, Grand Central Art Galleries, *Remington to Today*, Apr. 5–30, 1955; Denver Art Museum, *Building the West*, Oct. 9–Nov. 27, 1955; Dallas Museum of Fine Arts, *Famous Paintings and Famous Painters*, Oct. 3–Nov. 2, 1958; Santa Fe, Fine Arts Museum of New Mexico, *The Artist in the American West: 1800–1900*, Oct. 6–Nov. 22, 1961; New York, IBM Gallery of Arts and Sciences, *Art of the American Frontier*, Mar. 23–Apr. 18, 1964 (brochure, no. 15); Fort Worth, Amon Carter Museum of Western Art, *Works of Henry F. Farny*, Oct. 7–Dec. 1, 1965; Washington, D.C., National Museum of American Art, Smithsonian Institution [also Cincinnati, Houston, and Denver], *Art in New Mexico, 1900–1945: Paths to Taos and Santa Fe*, May 7, 1986–Apr. 19, 1987 (cat. by Charles C. Eldridge, Julie Schimmel, and William Truettner, pp. 16, 35–36).

Literature Maurice W. Brockwell, *A Catalogue of Paintings in the Collection of Mr. and Mrs. Charles P. Taft*, New York, 1920, pp. 194–95, no. 79; *Catalogue of the Taft Museum*, Cincinnati, 1939 and 1958, no. 553; Robert Taft, "The Pictorial Record of the Old West: X. The Artists of Indian Life: Henry F. Farny," *Kansas Historical Quarterly*, vol. XVIII, no. 1 (Feb. 1950), p. 18; Peter Hassrick, *The Way West: Art of Frontier America*, New York, 1977, p. 197; Carolyn M. Appleton and Natasha S. Bartalini, *Henry Farny, 1847–1916*, exh. cat., University of Texas at Austin, Archer M. Huntington Art Gallery, 1983, p. 16; Alan Axelrod, *Art of the Golden West*, New York, 1990, p. 299, ill. p. 212; William H. Truettner, *The West as America: Reinterpreting Images of the Frontier, 1820–1920*, Washington, D.C., 1991, pp. 171–72, fig. 147; J. Gray Sweeney, *Masterpieces of Western American Art*, New York, 1991, p. 118 (color pl.).

1931.466

1988.1

❦

Henry Farny

Study for "The Song of the Talking Wire"

ca. 1904
Oil on panel, 38.1 x 26.7 cm (15 x 10½ in.)
Signed lower right (in red): H.F.F. / ⊙

In academic circles this preliminary study would have been called an *esquisse peinte*. It depicts the development of the primary thematic motif of *The Song of the Talking Wire* in its setting: a lone Sioux listening to the sound of a telegraph pole against a background of a winter landscape.

Farny, who was known for his attentiveness to details of Native American garb, gave particular attention here to the Sioux's costume. The detail, however, rather overwhelms its wearer, prompting Farny to make a number of simplifications in the final canvas. He eliminated the fur cap, subdued the vivid red-and-brown coloring of the animal-hide blanket, and made the man's stance firmer and his facial expression considerably more compelling.

The oil study was probably painted just prior to the larger canvas. It was surely not made in Sioux territory, for the painted-hide blanket, which is reproduced in the final painting, has been shown to be a girl's garment. It was one of the studio artifacts Farny brought back from his 1881 trip West, and he was probably unaware of its proper use.[1]

Three elements at the heart of the final composition are absent from this preliminary study. The study shows a clear, bright sky rather than the sunset that gives the final painting its symbolic poignancy. The skull and animal carcass are also missing, as are the curiosity and anger that mark the man's expression and set the tone of the final image.

1. Peter Hassrick, *The Way West: Art of Frontier America,* New York, 1977, p. 197.

Provenance Gift of the artist to Louis Schott, Cincinnati; anonymous gift in memory of Louis and Melba Schott, Mar. 7, 1988.

1988.1

Arthur J. Rowell, Thomas Lincoln

Miniatures of the Presidents of the United States

1914–23, 1925–28
Watercolor on ivory, each approximately 7.9 x 6.4 cm (3⅛ x 2½ in.); enclosed in gilt-metal pendant cases and mounted in a velvet-lined display frame
Signed and dated on obverse: *Rowell 1914* (Washington, Adams, Jefferson, Madison, Monroe); *Rowell 1915* (J. Q. Adams, Jackson, Van Buren, Harrison, Tyler, Polk, Taylor); *Rowell 1916* (Fillmore, Pierce, Buchanan, Lincoln, Johnson, Grant); *Rowell 1917* (Hayes, Garfield); *Rowell 1918* (Arthur, Cleveland, Harrison, McKinley, Roosevelt); *Rowell 1919* (Wilson); *Rowell 1920* (Taft); *Rowell 1928* (Harding, Hoover); *Thomas Lincoln 1925* (Coolidge)

This set of miniatures exemplifies an art form that endured in America from 1760 to 1845 but was made obsolete by the advent of daguerreotype photography. During the last two decades of the nineteenth century, however, miniature painting in the old manner — with watercolors on vellum or ivory — underwent a vigorous revival. Fueled by sentiment, a concern for lost handicrafts, and the same intense antiquarianism that also gave birth to such organizations as the Daughters of the American Revolution, the revival lasted in America for more than sixty years.

The renewed interest in miniature painting manifested itself in various ways. Histories of miniature painting included instructions on how to replicate the old techniques,[1] while the collecting of miniatures, both old and new, became fashionable. In 1899 the American Society of Miniature Painters was organized. It continued until 1956 and throughout its existence presented annual Salon-type exhibitions of its members' work.

The chief difference between revival miniatures and the originals is that the originals were private mementos intended for closed cases while the new versions were almost always meant for public display. True to this distinction, the Taft set of presidents of the United States was conceived as a display piece, even while great care was taken to give the miniatures the authentic hatchwork, coloring, and detail of old ones.

The set was painted mainly between 1914 and 1920, with individual additions made in 1925 and 1928. It reproduced the best-known images of the past presidents. Washington, Adams, Jefferson, Madison, and Monroe were copies of Gilbert Stuart's portraits; the later presidents were based on official photographs. Its creator, Arthur J. Rowell (b. 1856), sold a similar set of the presidents to Joseph G. Butler in 1919 (Youngstown, Ohio, Butler Institute of American Art).[2] A third set of presidents through Harding, signed *Rowell* and executed from 1914 to 1920, was auctioned by Sotheby-Parke Bernet in November 1977.[3]

1931.337

1931.338

1931.339

The Taft set seems initially to have been completed in 1920. Thomas Lincoln (1881–1957), who had an exhibition of his miniatures at the Hotel Sinton in Cincinnati in 1925, added Coolidge to the set, perhaps at the request of the owners. Three years later Rowell added Harding and Hoover.

1. For example, George Charles Williamson, *How to Identify Portrait Miniatures . . . with Chapters on How to Paint Miniatures by Alyn Williams*, London, 1905.

2. Butler and his son added miniatures of subsequent presidents by other artists.

3. Sotheby-Parke Bernet, New York, the American Heritage Society Auction of Americana, Nov. 17, 1977, no. 462a.

Provenance Perhaps purchased 1920, added to in 1925 and 1928.

Literature *Catalogue of the Taft Museum*, Cincinnati, 1939 and 1958, nos. 513–42.

1931.337–66

1931.340

1931.341

1931.342

1931.343

1931.344

1931.345

1931.346

1931.347

1931.348

1931.349

1931.350

1931.351

1931.352

1931.353

1931.354

1931.355

1931.356

1931.357

1931.358

1931.359

1931.360

1931.361

1931.362

1931.363

1931.364

1931.365

1931.366

Gilbert Stuart

North Kingston, R.I. 1755–1828 Boston

Few American artists have enjoyed longer-lasting admiration than Gilbert Stuart, thanks to a painting style considered elegant, natural, and devoid of pomposity. As the preeminent portraitist among American artists who came of age after the Revolutionary War, he was described, even half a decade after his death, as "one who has yet no rival" in the art of portrait painting.[1] Long after the reputations of his contemporaries had faded, he was still viewed as setting a worthy standard for American painters. Early in the twentieth century, Stuart was admired because his optical yet restrained painterliness was so compatible with the contemporary taste for Barbizon naturalism and the refined color and compositional harmonies of art-for-art's-sake aestheticism.

Raised in Newport, Rhode Island, Stuart was the son of a Scottish millwright who established the first snuff manufactory in New England. Around 1772 Cosmo Alexander, a Scot visiting Newport, gave him his first art lessons. Stuart followed his teacher to Edinburgh, where Alexander died unexpectedly, forcing the young painter to return home. In 1775 Stuart ventured again to Britain, this time to London, where he became a studio assistant to Benjamin West. While in West's employ, he was known for his flair for lifelike flesh tints, his distaste for the rigors of drawing, and his scorn for artificial formulas. "I will not follow any master. I wish to find out what nature is for myself and see her with my own eyes," he insisted.[2]

The painting that created Stuart's reputation in England was a full-length portrait of his friend William Grant ice skating (Washington, D.C., National Gallery of Art), which was exhibited to considerable acclaim at the Royal Academy in 1782. That year, Stuart set up his own portrait-painting business in which he competed successfully with Joshua Reynolds, George Romney, and Thomas Gainsborough for London's wealthy, fashionable clients. He was soon financially successful and living

lavishly, although he was eventually mired in debt. To escape his financial burdens, he moved to Dublin in late 1787, then, probably for the same reason, returned to the United States five years later.

Before settling permanently in Boston in 1805, Stuart worked in New York and in the nation's two capitals, Philadelphia and Washington, D.C., becoming the portrait painter of choice to its new ruling class. In addition to the patronage of America's wealthiest and most politically prominent citizens, he enjoyed the admiration of artists who came to him for advice and benefited from his bluntness, salty wit, and impatience with pedantry.

Stuart's most ambitious works were his state portraits of American presidents from George Washington to James Monroe. His largest legacy, however, was simple bust-lengths showing his sitters against plain backgrounds. The result of a lifelong effort to avoid "vanity and bad taste," these include some of his most memorable images.[3]

1. William Dunlap, *A History of the Rise and Progress of the Arts of Design in the United States,* 1st ed., 1834, rev. ed., vol. I, Boston, 1918, p. 192.

2. Dunlap, p. 216.

3. Dunlap, p. 257.

❧

After Gilbert Stuart

George Washington (The Vaughan Portrait)

Possibly early-twentieth-century alterations over a nineteenth-century copy
Oil on canvas, 74.9 x 62.2 cm (29½ x 24½ in.)

Before leaving Ireland for America, Stuart reportedly confided that one purpose of his trip was to paint a portrait of George Washington and make a fortune by selling replicas of it.[1] Cer-

1931.461

tainly, few portraits have enjoyed greater circulation than the two busts of Washington that Stuart painted from life, the so-called Vaughan and Atheneum heads, executed in 1795 and 1796 respectively. From virtually the beginning, they created the image most associated with Washington in the public mind.

Stuart's first life portrait of Washington was painted in Philadelphia in September 1795. It was a simple image, showing him in a black coat and white linen jabot, turned slightly to the viewer's right, against a plain dark background with a hint of red. Stuart sold the picture to the painter William Winstanley, who in turn sold it in London to the American merchant William Vaughan, from whom the portrait derived its common name.

Almost immediately, Stuart began making replicas of the Vaughan portrait. Although cataloguers of Stuart's work have counted fifteen or sixteen other versions in his hand, the artist's daughter wrote in 1876 that he had orders for thirty-nine replicas, but then allowed, "My father was not the author of all the pictures passed about the country under his name, as originals of Washington."[2] John Hill Morgan reported that perhaps some of these replicas, abraded by earlier cleaning, were so heavily touched up that "some canvases which started life from Stuart's brush now have little Stuart left." Conversely, "a good copy of a Stuart-Washington made years ago . . . may [have] . . . the varnish and some of the paint removed and Stuart's characteristic coloring . . . painted into the canvas by an 'expert,' the whole revarnished and the result is a 'Washington' sold as a recently discovered 'Stuart.'"[3]

This painting, whose heavy varnish covers an abraded and retouched surface, may belong to the category of a doctored early copy. The clothing and Venetian-red background correspond to a Vaughan replica (purchased by Richard D. Brixley of New York from Duveen Brothers in 1924) that had long been in Staffordshire, England, while the eyes resemble those in a version that has been in the Metropolitan Museum of Art since 1907.[4] This picture could be a copy of the replica from Staffordshire with some of its facial features repainted on its arrival in New York, in reference to the nearest readily available Vaughan replica.

The high price for which the painting sold in 1924 ($32,000) represents collectors' eagerness to own a Stuart bust of Washington. At that time, notable recent purchasers of Stuart's Vaughan portraits were John Jacob Astor, Andrew Mellon, Thomas B. Clarke, and Henry Clay Frick.

1. John Hill Morgan and Mantle Fielding, *The Life Portraits of Washington and Their Replicas,* Philadelphia, 1931, p. 224.

2. Morgan and Fielding, pp. 225–27.

3. Morgan and Fielding, p. 235.

4. Lawrence Park, *Gilbert Stuart: An Illustrated Descriptive List of His Works,* vol. II, New York, 1926, no. 15, p. 852, and no. 2, pp. 845–46.

Provenance Rev. A. McDonnell, United States and Ireland; Dr. James McDonnell, Belfast; Helen McDonnell, Lismoyle, Cushendall County, Antrim, Ireland; [Scott and Fowles, New York, by 1924]; Taft collection, Dec. 1, 1924.

Literature John Hill Morgan and Mantle Fielding, *The Life Portraits of Washington and Their Replicas,* Philadelphia, 1931, p. 224.

1931.461

Hiram Powers
Woodstock, Vt. 1805–1873 Florence, Italy

Hiram Powers was one of the first American expatriate sculptors to settle in Italy and the first to achieve popular success for marbles carved in the neoclassical manner. Among the sculptors of his generation, he comes closest to satisfying the definition of an elusive phenomenon: the genuinely self-made artist. Of limited formal education, he always possessed great curiosity about the physical world and approached the challenges of his profession with the unpredictable ingenuity of a tinkerer. A contemporary critic called him "a sublime mechanic," which became the label most frequently used to describe him.[1]

Born and raised in Woodstock, Vermont, Powers moved with his family to Cincinnati at the age of thirteen and there found his vocation. At seventeen he went to work at the Luman Watson Clock and Organ Factory, where he first displayed his exceptional mechanical aptitude. Between 1823 and 1825 he received instruction in drawing and modeling from Frederick Eckstein and by 1825 was working for the two dime museums in town. These private emporiums of popular curiosities — Dorfeuille's Western Museum and Letton's Museum — employed him to make and repair clockwork devices for waxwork figures.

Powers also modeled portraits in wax. These came to the attention of the Cincinnati art patron Nicholas Longworth, who financed a trip for Powers to Washington, D.C., in 1834. There, he executed his first important sculpture commission, a strikingly naturalistic marble bust of Andrew Jackson in classical drapery (1835, Washington, D.C., National Museum of American Art, and New York, The Metropolitan Museum of Art), which remains one of his most admired works. Portrait commissions from other prominent Washingtonians followed, along with an offer from one patron to finance a three-year residency in Italy.

In 1837 Powers briefly visited Philadelphia and Boston before departing for Florence, where his contemporary Horatio Greenough had established himself in 1828. Powers remained in Florence for the rest of his life, although for some thirty years he considered himself only a temporary resident there.[2] In 1840 he began working on full-length, life-size marbles of classically inspired nudes. An *Eve Tempted* (1840–43, Washington, D.C., National Museum of American Art) was the first, followed by *The Fisher Boy* (1843–44, Richmond, Virginia Museum of Fine Arts) and *The Greek Slave* (1842–44), which ultimately appeared in six versions (five remain: an English private collection; the Newark Museum; Washington, D.C., Corcoran Gallery of Art; Yale University Art Gallery; and The Brooklyn Museum).

The Greek Slave created a sensation as the first life-size sculpture of a female nude by an American, and it became the icon of American neoclassicism. It depicted a shy Christian girl forcibly sold into slavery during the recent Greek War of Independence. One statue was exhibited with astounding success in London in 1845. Another was given a shrewdly marketed and spectacularly successful American tour from 1847 to 1849. The work also appeared, in a draped booth, at the London Crystal Palace Exhibition of 1851 and at the New York Crystal Palace in 1853.

The success of *The Greek Slave* prompted Powers to create four more female nudes: *California, America, La Penserosa,* and *Eve Disconsolate.* He also found a lucrative market for busts of idealized figures. These include abbreviated versions of his famous full-length statues as well as new personages such as *Proserpina, Genevra, Clytie, Faith, Hope,* and *Charity.* The ideal busts — over 190 have been recorded — constitute the largest share of his lifetime output. Portrait busts were also important, for Powers was said to have excelled even his Italian contemporaries in naturalistic representation. Consequently, his American clients (including a substantial number of Cincinnatians) plied him continually for portraits.

Powers's large studio became a center for the growing number of English-speaking visitors to Florence. His guests included such celebrities as Margaret Fuller, William Cullen Bryant, and Elizabeth Barrett Browning. Nathaniel Hawthorne was particularly fascinated by Powers and mentioned him repeatedly in his Italian notebook of 1858.[3] Admitted to Florence's Academy of Fine Arts in 1841, Powers was appointed associate professor of sculpture. Nonetheless, he remained a plainspoken man of practical bent, who, even in Italy, never lost his rural American origins; he refused to believe anything in foreign life was worth

1931.370

emulating. During the final decades of the century, Powers's reputation suffered the same decline that affected other sculptors of his generation, and the designation "sublime mechanic" became a term of disparagement.[4]

1. Henry T. Tuckerman, *Book of the Artists, American Artist Life,* New York, 1867, pp. 276–94; see also Richard P. Wunder, "The Irascible Hiram Powers," *American Art Journal,* vol. IV (Nov. 1972), pp. 10–15.

2. Donald M. Reynolds, *Hiram Powers and His Ideal Sculpture,* New York, 1977, p. 70.

3. Nathaniel Hawthorne, *Passages from the French and Italian Notebooks,* vol. X of *Complete Works of Nathaniel Hawthorne,* Boston, 1871.

4. Lorado Taft, *History of American Sculpture,* New York, 1924, pp. 56–71.

Hiram Powers

Alphonso Taft

1869
Marble, 61.8 x 41.4 x 25.4 cm (24⅜ x 16⅜ x 10 in.)
Signature chiseled into lower left side of sculpture:
H POWERS / *Sculp.*

Hiram Powers's bust of Cincinnati's eminent jurist Alphonso Taft (1810–1891) conforms to the herm type: the figure's bare chest and shoulders terminate arbitrarily in a stone shaft that forms the sculpture's base. It was Powers's simplest portrait format, which he employed as early as his *Daniel Webster* (1836–41, Boston Athenaeum). It was a solution he turned to often, for it had the virtue of a classical reference yet was technically simple and did not detract from a natural rendering of the client's head.

Taft's facial features are vividly lifelike, a quality achieved by Powers's attention to detail. He was true to Taft's heavy brow, bulbous nose, fleshy chin, the carbuncle on his forehead, and the mole on his upper lip. It would be "blasphemy to talk or think of improving upon nature," Powers said.[1] In truth, he also felt the somewhat contradictory duty to make visible the sitter's temper and nature's unseen intentions.

Comparison with a photograph taken in 1876 (Cincinnati, William Howard Taft National Historic Site) indicates that Powers strengthened Alphonso Taft's chin and slightly elongated his jaw. More importantly — particularly to someone like Powers who took phrenology seriously — he gave his sitter a higher forehead and broader temples, thereby increasing the size of the "intellectual" region of Taft's skull. He thus presented an image of Taft for the ages. Seizing upon the potential autonomy of white marble, he created not a moment in time but an enduring record of character.

In 1839, soon after he graduated from Yale Law School, the Vermont-born Alphonso Taft left for Cincinnati, eventually to become one of its most illustrious citizens. He served as a judge of the Superior Court of Ohio, as secretary of war and attorney general in Ulysses Grant's cabinet, and then as minister to Austria and Russia under Chester Arthur. The patriarch of the Cincinnati Tafts, he fathered six children and saw four of his five sons become lawyers, including Charles Phelps and William Howard Taft. This portrait was carved in 1869 while he and his wife vacationed in Europe with their children. Their tour took them from Heidelberg to Rome, a route that afforded a convenient stop in Florence.[2]

1. Henry Bellows, "Seven Sittings with Powers, the Sculptor," *Appleton's Journal of Literature, Science and Art*, vol. 1 (June 19, 1869), p. 360.

2. Ishbel Ross, *An American Family: The Tafts*, Cleveland, 1964, p. 49. The portrait is dated in Donald M. Reynolds, *Hiram Powers and His Ideal Sculpture*, New York, 1977, p. 1062.

Provenance Purchased from the artist by the sitter, 1869; Louise Torrey Taft, by bequest, 1891; Charles Phelps Taft, by bequest, 1907.

Exhibition Cincinnati Art Museum, *Paintings by Joseph Oriel Eaton and Sculpture by Hiram Powers*, Mar. 12–Apr. 8, 1934.

Literature *Catalogue of the Taft Museum*, Cincinnati, 1939 and 1958, no. 7.

1931.370

1931.371

Hiram Powers

David Sinton

1870
Marble, 60.8 x 40.8 x 25.6 cm (24 x 16⅛ x 10⅛ in.)
Inscription and signature chiseled into lower left side: DAVID SINTON *1870* / H POWERS *Sculp*

David Sinton (1808–1900) was closefisted, brusque, blunt in speech, and careless in dress.[1] His ruggedness and disdain for the artifices of polite behavior would have appealed to Hiram Powers. The latter's portrait of him shows a wry, energetic face and a large area behind the temples — the part of the skull that, to phrenologists, connoted acquisitiveness. The face has an animation and convincing naturalness worthy of the artist who claimed that he could suggest even a blush on white marble[2] and is arguably one of the most sensitive and naturalistic portraits of Powers's late career.

At the time of his death Sinton was Cincinnati's wealthiest citizen, whose estate of twenty million dollars was thought to have made him the richest man in Ohio.[3] Even so, he was one of the last Cincinnatians to indulge in the vanity of having his portrait carved by Powers. Born in Ireland, Sinton arrived in

Cincinnati at the age of eighteen. From a poor immigrant's son, he became a self-made industrialist and investor in pig iron, gas, and land development. In 1871 he purchased for himself one of Cincinnati's stateliest residences, Belmont, Nicholas Longworth's former mansion. He afterward turned to philanthropy, contributing generously to such charities as Cincinnati's Y.M.C.A. and Union Bethel. He also became a founder of the Cincinnati Art Museum and its adjoining academy, dedicated in 1886.

1. Alvin F. Harlow, *The Serene Cincinnatians,* New York, 1950, p. 392.

2. Nathaniel Hawthorne, *Passages from the French and Italian Notebooks,* vol. x of *The Complete Works of Nathaniel Hawthorne,* Cambridge, Mass., 1870, p. 285.

3. [Obituary], *The New York Times,* Sept. 1, 1900, p. 1.

Provenance Purchased by the sitter from the artist, 1870; Anna Sinton Taft, by bequest, 1900.

Exhibition Cincinnati Art Museum, *Paintings by Joseph Oriel Eaton and Sculpture by Hiram Powers,* Mar. 12–Apr. 8, 1934.

Literature *Catalogue of the Taft Museum,* Cincinnati, 1939 and 1958, no. 498; Richard P. Wunder, *Hiram Powers: Vermont Sculptor, 1805–1873,* vol. ii, Newark, Del., 1991, pp. 90–91, no. 101 (ill.).

1931.371

Hiram Powers

Anna B. Sinton

1870
Marble, 59.4 x 48.4 x 27.3 cm (23⅜ x 19⅛ x 10¾ in.)
Inscription and signature chiseled into back: ANNA B. SINTON *1870* / H POWERS *Sculp*

Hiram Powers's portrait of Anna Sinton (1852?-1931) follows a standard type, which is meant to recall the carved busts of Roman patrician women. This version shows the eighteen-year-old daughter of David Sinton (see 1931.371) dressed chastely in a loose-fitting, relatively high-necked gown and a draped overgarment. Her hair is pulled away from her face and gathered in the simple back knot that Powers felt to be the most appropriate style for women.[1]

The model presents a demure, virtuous maiden, a role that Annie Sinton seems unequivocally to have fit. She was intelligent, good-humored, generous, and the object of her father's intense devotion.[2] However, Powers's resulting image is somewhat less successful than others of its type. Annie's features and drapery seem to have been executed by rote and are a bit lifeless, suggesting that she may not have been present for the modeling of her portrait, thereby leaving Powers to his own formulas.

Annie was David Sinton's only child. Her mother died from tuberculosis the year after her birth, and her father remained a widower. She married Charles Phelps Taft on December 4, 1873, in a lavish, well-publicized wedding[3] and lived in her father's house with her husband. She eventually had four children and

1931.372

devoted herself to the support of Cincinnati's educational and cultural charities.

1. See Charles Colbert, "'Each Little Hillock Hath a Tongue': Phrenology and the Art of Hiram Powers," *Art Bulletin,* vol. lxviii (June 1986), pp. 289–91.

2. Ishbel Ross, *An American Family: The Tafts,* Cleveland, 1964, pp. 56–59.

3. *Cincinnati Enquirer,* Dec. 5, 1873.

Provenance Purchased by David Sinton from the artist, 1870; Anna Sinton Taft, by bequest, 1900.

Exhibition Cincinnati Art Museum, *Paintings by Joseph Oriel Eaton and Sculpture by Hiram Powers,* Mar. 12–Apr. 8, 1934.

Literature *Catalogue of the Taft Museum,* Cincinnati, 1939 and 1958, no. 489; "Hiram Powers and Cincinnati," *Bulletin of the Cincinnati Historical Society,* vol. xxv, no. 1 (Jan. 1967), pp. 35–36; Richard P. Wunder, *Hiram Powers: Vermont Sculptor, 1805–1873,* vol. ii, Newark, Del., 1991, p. 97, no. 110 (ill.).

1931.372

George Grey Barnard
Bellefonte, Pa. 1863–1938 New York

America's major symbolist sculptor, George Grey Barnard is remembered for the grand scale of his artistic ambitions and for the mystical vision that informed much of his work. The son of a Presbyterian minister, his avid boyhood hobbies were rock collecting and taxidermy. At seventeen, apprenticed to a jewelry en-graver, he began working his way through the School of the Art Institute of Chicago. The school's large collection of plaster casts of Michelangelo's sculpture sparked Barnard's lifelong interest in powerful, dramatic figure sculpture in the Michelangelesque idiom.

A portrait commission executed while still in art school financed Barnard's first trip to Paris. He arrived in 1883, entering the Ecole des Beaux-Arts in 1884 as a student of the sculptor Pierre-Jules Cavelier and remaining with him for three years. He opened his own studio in Paris in 1887, with his first commission (*The Boy*, a Spinario-like figure in marble) coming from the American collector Alfred Corning Clark. His second commission was a pair of Rodin-like nude figures called *Brotherly Love* for the tomb of the Norwegian philanthropist Severin Skovgaard. In 1889 he began the most important of his early works, *The Struggle of the Two Natures of Man*. When the eight-and-a-half-foot-tall marble group was completed in 1894, it was accepted at the Paris Salon, where it won effusive praise from Auguste Rodin and considerable public acclaim.

Barnard returned to New York in 1896 and during the next eight years established his American reputation. He took over Augustus Saint-Gaudens's teaching position at the Art Students League and won gold medals at the Paris Exposition of 1900, the Buffalo Pan-American Exposition of 1901, and the Saint Louis Exposition of 1904. Commissions during this interval included a gigantic languishing Pan in bronze for Columbia University and a pair of allegorical figures for the grounds of the Rockefel-ler estate.

In 1898 Barnard began his most important work, which oc-cupied him for the next twelve years: the sculptural program for the exterior of the Pennsylvania state capitol building in Harris-burg. His vision of a virtual ocean of sprawling figures was even-tually scaled down to two groups flanking the capitol's entrance. He executed the clay models and marble figures near Paris be-tween 1904 and 1910; they were installed in the winter of 1910–11 and unveiled the following October.

While in France, Barnard began to buy and sell medieval French antiquities. He developed an enduring interest in the arts of the Middle Ages, the austere symbolism of which was in ac-cord with his own aesthetic sensibilities. He also accumulated a massive personal collection, which was purchased in 1925 by John D. Rockefeller, who made it the nucleus of the Cloisters collection at Fort Tryon Park in New York.

Barnard exhibited at the Armory Show of 1913, then produced the sculptural decoration for the Fifth Avenue façade of the New York Public Library. In 1917 he produced his most controversial work: an over-life-size bronze portrait of Abraham Lincoln, pre-sented to the city of Cincinnati by Charles Phelps Taft and now located in Lytle Park. Its exaggerated ungainliness met with a storm of criticism from a public that found the work inappro-priate and offensive as a public monument.

Barnard's last project, never finished, was an epic-scale me-morial to World War I to be located on Fort Washington Point on the Hudson River. The first model was unveiled in October 1920; by 1922 the plan included an amphitheater and two marble plazas — one surrounded by a forty-two-foot-long marble wall enclosing bronze allegorical figures, a second one incorporating a bronze, gold, and enamel Tree of Peace. He continued to alter the design, which by 1936 included a one-hundred-foot-high marble triumphal arch covered with carved figures and topped by a mosaic rainbow. By the 1930s, however, many people con-sidered such visions misplaced.[1]

1. See Edward Alden Jewell, "George Grey Barnard," *The New York Times,* Apr. 21, 1935.

George Grey Barnard

Solitude (Adam and Eve)

ca. 1906
Marble, 60.4 x 27.9 cm (23¾ x 11 in.)
Signature chiseled into front face, lower right: *Geo Barnard*

This small marble relief was originally part of a frieze of similar figures that made up the pictorial program of Barnard's *Urn of Life* (ca. 1895–98, 1918, Pittsburgh, Carnegie Museum of Art), an unfinished cinerary urn for the ashes of Anton Seidl, the former assistant to the composer Richard Wagner and, until his death in 1898, conductor of the Metropolitan Opera in New York. This

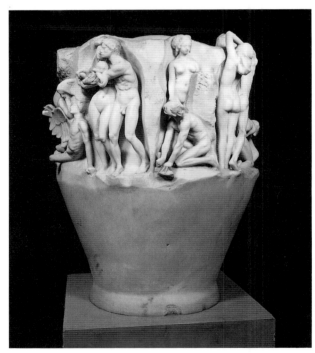

Fig. 1 George Gray Barnard, *The Urn of Life,* ca. 1895–98, reworked 1918. Marble, 96.2 x 81.9 x 76.8 cm (37⅞ x 32¼ x 30¼ in.). Pittsburgh, The Carnegie Museum of Art, purchase, 19.7.1.

1931.373

egg-shaped marble urn was encrusted with smoothly polished, symbolic figures in high relief, half-submerged in the rough stone in a manner reminiscent of Rodin's style (fig. 1).

The figures around the urn were symbolic of the cycle of birth, procreation, death, and transfiguration, each mystical vignette passing fluidly to the next. The program began with a veiled figure, symbolic of the mystery of life, then progressed through motherhood, birth, manual and spiritual labor, and, finally, death. Following the image of birth is the Taft pair, de-

scribed by the artist as "a group composed of a man and a woman expressing the thought that while they are one in love and spirit, nevertheless they are separate souls."[1]

Barnard began the piece in 1895 and worked on it until 1897 or 1898.[2] In 1902 he described it as still in progress[3] but appears not to have worked substantively on it after that. Perhaps to salvage a moribund commission, he carved separate marble reliefs of at least six vignettes encircling the urn, using his original clay models.[4] He exhibited four of these smaller marbles in his 1908 one-person show at the Museum of Fine Arts, Boston, and four at the Armory Show in 1913. Barnard made at least three reliefs of *Solitude* (other versions are owned by Vassar College Art Gallery, Poughkeepsie, N.Y., and the Chrysler Museum, Norfolk, Va.). All may have been carved shortly before his show in Boston where one, already owned by J. Randolph Coolidge, Jr., had been exhibited. Barnard may have given the present version to Charles Phelps Taft around 1917 as a token of thanks for having purchased the original bronze of Lincoln. By 1931 it was being called *Adam and Eve*, perhaps the Tafts' title for the piece.

Removed from the context of the *Urn of Life*, the Taft marble shows all the more clearly its debt to Rodin. The composition derives directly from the latter's *Orpheus and Eurydice* (1893, New York, The Metropolitan Museum of Art). Direct comparison, however, betrays a lingering hardness and reticence in Barnard's execution, for he was never completely willing to abandon the autonomy of the classical nude figure.

1. Transcription of a text provided by the artist, 1919, curatorial files, Carnegie Museum of Art, Pittsburgh.

2. 1897 was the date stated in the catalogue of the exhibition of Barnard's work held at the Museum of Fine Arts, Boston, in 1908. 1898 was the date mentioned by Alexander Twombly, "George Grey Barnard," *World's Work*, vol. XVII (1909), p. 11260.

3. Alexander Blair Thaw, "George Grey Barnard, Sculptor," *World's Work*, vol. V (1902), p. 2852.

4. Another of these marbles is *The Mystery of Life* (Washington, D.C., National Museum of American Art). One of the clay models was illustrated in Thaw, p. 2842.

Provenance The artist to Charles Phelps Taft, ca. 1917.

Exhibition Probably New York, Association of American Painters and Sculptors, Inc., *International Exhibition of Modern Art*, Feb. 17–Mar. 15, 1913, no. 998.

Literature *Catalogue of the Taft Museum*, Cincinnati, 1939 and 1958, no. 556; Maurice Rheims, *La Sculpture au XIXe siècle*, Paris, 1972, p. 142, no. 30.

1931.373

Index of Accession Numbers

Index

Page numbers in *italics* refer to illustrations.